BRYAN MALESSA was born in Chagrin Falls, Oh̶̶̶̶̶̶̶̶̶̶̶̶̶̶̶̶̶
Berkeley, where his fiction was awarded the Chancellor's and Eisner prizes. He also received a Masters of Philosophy from the Oscar Wilde Centre at Trinity College, Dublin for work based on this book.

Also by Bryan Malessa

The Flight

BRYAN MALESSA

The War Room

Based on a true story

FOURTH ESTATE • *London*

First published in Great Britain in 2011 by
Fourth Estate
An imprint of HarperCollins*Publishers*
77–85 Fulham Palace Road
London W6 8JB
www.4thestate.co.uk

Visit our authors' blog: www.fifthestate.co.uk

A catalogue record for this book is
available from the British Library

ISBN 978-0-00-724107-1

Typeset by Palimpsest Book Production Limited,
Falkirk, Stirlingshire

Printed in Great Britain by
Clays Ltd, St Ives plc

Between 1820 and 1996, 7.1 million Germans immigrated to the United States – more than from any other nation. The desire to forget an often painful past, honesty and thoroughness, a practical bent – many Germans share these qualities, and they have made absorption easier.

The New York Times, 1999

I am perfectly of your mind, that measures of great Temper are necessary with the Germans: . . . In short unless the stream of their importation could be turned from this to other colonies, as you very judiciously propose, they will soon so outnumber us, that all the advantages we have will not in My Opinion be able to preserve our language, and even our Government will become precarious.

Benjamin Franklin, 1753
(Letter to English botanist Peter Collinson)

BOOK I

Chagrin Falls

It's natural to love one's parents, and it's equally natural to love one's brothers and sisters, I thought, standing by the window again and looking down on the deserted Piazza Minerva. We therefore fail to notice that from a certain moment onward we hate them, without wanting to, just as naturally as we previously loved them, for all kinds of reasons that we become aware of only years later, often decades later.

Thomas Bernhard, *Extinction*

For me it was the opposite, I hated him from the start. But it was odd – of all his children I was the only one he beat. I never had any illusions about why he beat me. He beat me because he was angry. Because he was scared. He had hated his own childhood and resented mine. He grew quieter and quieter as each year passed, until he was finally locked as tight as a walnut sealed in its shell. He never did find a way to express himself. At least, not until I was born. And then he expressed himself through me.

I was a curious child. I asked too many questions. I wanted to know where he came from. Where my grandparents were. He responded by slapping my face. He refused to tell me anything. Then came a period in my twelfth year when he finally told me something. But that was later.

My fondest memories of childhood were those first moments when I stepped outside on a clear spring day and looked up at the blue sky after I'd been holed up in my dark room, crying because I'd been

3

punished. In that brief space, as dark seclusion gave way to the bright outside world, I sensed every living thing around me: the incessant hum of insects, leaves rustling in the breeze, countless blades of grass, colorful flower petals tracking the sun from east to west, the gurgle of the river hidden behind the trees, the damp scent of freshly turned soil. It was worth being beaten and locked in my room just for that moment of stepping out into the yard. My father loved it too. He liked to see me happy. I was the only one who seemed to care about the place he came from and couldn't talk about.

The dream, the burn and the hate formed my three earliest memories, but the dream wasn't really a dream – at least, not as I understood it then. It was as real as the pain of the burn and the embarrassment of the hate. It happened many times before anyone found out. I often woke thirsty in the middle of the night, the house dark and silent. I was too frightened to slide my feet out of the bed to the floor.

My father had once told me that an old man, visible only at night, lived under the bed. If I ever tried to sneak out he'd grab my ankles and pull me under. I had no reason to doubt him – I'd heard things sliding around under there after everyone else had fallen asleep. I kept my covers tucked under my body so that no hands could reach me.

One night I lay there for more than an hour, trying to figure out how to get a glass of water. My throat was too dry to yell for my mother – and even if she heard me, my father might come instead and hit me for waking him. Later, I felt myself levitate. I jerked awake, fell back into bed and tucked the blankets beneath my feet. Later I felt the weightless sensation again, but this time I allowed my body to rise above the bed and the old man peering from the space beneath. I knew he'd never reach me in the air.

I remained in the same place, directly above my mattress, until I felt sure I wouldn't jerk and fall again. Then I floated toward the open doorway. Outside my bedroom, I hovered long enough above the landing to be sure that no one was aware of my presence, then floated on to the bathroom, where I picked up the glass that stood on the enamel sink and filled it halfway. I never drank an entire glass at once – four half-glasses if I were thirsty, but never two full ones.

Floating required a different sense of balance and intuition from walking. Walking was clumsy and mechanical while floating was agile and fluid – more like riding a bike, a skill I'd mastered soon after my father had arrived home from work on my birthday. He'd told me to run to the car and fetch a bag of groceries he'd forgotten to carry in. I darted outside. A small bike, propped on its kickstand, stood beside the car. It was painted the shiniest metallic yellow I'd ever seen, like a ray of sun glittering on chrome.

'Go ahead, it's yours,' he said, behind me. He spent the next hour pushing me around our backyard, teaching me to trust my sense of balance, to forget my fear of falling. 'Want me to let go?' he asked.

I didn't answer. He continued holding the seat and pushing me around. We repeated this for the next few weeks. He refused to put training wheels on the bike, saying they were for sissies. One afternoon I told him to let go and glided across the grass. When I turned the handlebars I fell off.

'Not so fast,' he shouted. 'You think you're a racer or something?'

He pushed me around the yard for a little longer, letting go occasionally, then ran to grab the seat when I lost my balance. We continued in this way until I could coast the length of the yard without falling. Then, without asking, he pushed me through a gap between the bushes and out to where a steep hill fell away to the funeral home below. He pointed the bike downhill, began to run and released me.

I was terrified – I was riding five, ten times faster than I ever had before. A grove of enormous buckeye trees stood at the foot of the hill and beyond loomed the funeral home. I was racing straight toward one of the trees, going too fast to stop – I didn't know how to use the brakes because I'd never ridden beyond the flat yard.

At the last moment, I leaned to the right and bounced over the tree roots. Seconds later, I raced into the parking lot, proud and relieved that I was still upright – and slammed into a car, shattering its rear window. I flew into the air, slid across the roof and landed in a bloodied mess on the hood.

In bed at night I was shielded from the dangers of the physical world – my father's beatings, broken windows and crushed metal – secure from the daytime world where nightmares lived. My mother no longer had difficulty in putting me to bed. I went without her urging so that I could fall asleep and float later. Each night after I'd lain down, I waited patiently for her to appear. One night after we'd prayed she went out and brought back a glass of water.

'I don't need it,' I said.

'I'll put it on the floor beside the bed.'

'I don't want it.' If it were there I'd have no reason to float to the bathroom.

'Why not?'

That was when I told her how I floated out of bed every night when I was thirsty. How once I had even hovered over their bed and looked down at her and my father sleeping. How I loved to float over the landing while everyone was asleep. She started to giggle, but she was concerned too. She said it was dangerous – I might fall down the stairs if I walked around the house alone at night.

'But I'm not walking, Mom.'

'It's a dream,' she said, leaning down to kiss my forehead. 'Sometimes it's hard to know what's real and what isn't, especially when you're drifting between waking and sleeping.'

Afterward I regretted confiding in her: it became almost impossible to float. I tried nearly every night, but something had changed. Eventually one night I decided to stay awake until morning. I heard my father rise at four to leave for the bakery. I heard him go down the stairs to the kitchen, then the clink of the vodka bottle as he removed it from the freezer to take a sip before he went out. I heard the Porsche – he had bought it from another baker two years earlier – fire up in the garage, then pull out into the empty street. I had been awake all night but I hadn't succeeded in floating.

I wanted to prove to myself that the floating wasn't a dream and finally it happened again, but nothing was the same: I was excited to be floating but worried that my mother might catch me. The serenity of floating, its utter calm, was gone now that I had shared my secret. Nevertheless I crossed my bedroom and passed through the doorway. I floated above the landing and hovered, unable to go out into the empty space above the stairway. For the first time I was scared I might fall.

A window at the head of the staircase faced the backyard, and a large tree stood by the garage. I stared outside for a while. I didn't want the floating to end, but I knew it had. Slowly I let myself down onto the thick carpet, then sprinted through my bedroom door. Halfway across the room I leaped for the bed, landed on it and yanked the covers over my head, tucking them tightly around me until I was sure that every gap was sealed.

As I lay there catching my breath, I knew I'd never again try to float above the world.

My father was fascinated by technology – he had to test any tiny gizmo he could get his hands on. It had to be small and perfectly made or he'd have nothing to do with it; it also had to be practical. If he examined a product that lacked these qualities, he turned away in disgust and would not discuss its faults. 'If it's shit,' he once told me, 'any idiot can see it's shit. It doesn't need to be dissected.'

He had purchased one of the first mass-produced pocket calculators into which he had to punch a series of commands to perform simple arithmetic. It was slower than solving the problem in the usual way, but he could overlook the machine's shortcomings because it was the first of its kind. There had been other such mechanical devices – the Burroughs adding machine was one – but this was of a different order, he claimed.

My father's friends made fun of him when he tried to convince them that it signaled a turning point in evolution. When it became obsolete he displayed it in the living room to show he'd had the foresight to embrace the new technology as soon as it had become available. My mother suggested that if we planned to keep abreast of current technology we should replace our gas stove with an electric one and he agreed – but only so she wouldn't stop him buying his next electronic toy.

I was intrigued that the new stove was powered solely by electricity. My mother made stew, cabbage and a chocolate cake to celebrate its arrival. She twisted the shiny black knobs back and forth to adjust the heat. Later, when they were turned off, she carried the steaming dishes to the dining-room table, leaving me alone in the kitchen.

I ran to the stove to conduct my experiment, knowing she would be angry if she saw me playing with it. I was too short to reach the stovetop so I slid a footstool across the room, climbed onto it and laid my palm on the burner she had just turned off. The odor of burned flesh filled the air. I screamed, fell to the floor and curled up into a ball. The skin on my palm peeled away, leaving the branded imprint of the electric coil.

My mother raced in, picked me up and held my hand under the cold faucet to soothe the searing pain. 'Call the doctor,' she screamed to my father.

I felt foolish. The stove hadn't turned off instantly as I'd expected – it was like the old gas stove, which stayed hot long after my mother had turned it off. It was electric but it didn't snap on and off like a lightbulb as I'd imagined it would.

Learning about hate proved more confusing than dreaming or being burned. Each time I tried to understand it I reached a different conclusion. Unlike an electric light, it was impossible to switch on and off. It was more like a bed of coals: its embers glowed and sporadically flared.

I first became aware of it when I was watching the old black-and-white Zenith television set in the den where my father's steins lined the wall. Programs about the Second World War played incessantly, making me hate the people who could kill so many others without reason – yet it was like hating myself: nearly all of the perpetrators resembled my parents and grandparents. Worse, they wore the same uniforms as the family members in the photos my father stored in a box in the basement.

That winter when *Tora, Tora, Tora* came to the local movie theater, my father seemed happier than I had ever seen him. He knew all about airplanes. He knew about bombs, too. I sensed his excitement and understood somehow that while he watched the movie he could remember his childhood without feeling like the enemy. I had seen countless war movies with him on television, but *Tora, Tora, Tora* was the first I'd seen him watch without a dour look on his face: the enemy wasn't him.

At certain points in the movie a man sitting alone leaped to his feet and yelled, 'Kill the Japs! Kill those bastards!' It was hate, pure and simple. I could see it and feel it, much as I had when I watched television programs about what the Germans had done. But it was more than that: it was exciting, too. I could hear it in the voices of the shouting man and the other men in the theater as they egged him on. Their combined hate for the enemy on the screen was so compelling that I wanted to jump up and shout with them. It was different from the hate I felt watching television at home: that hate was balanced by shame and guilt.

When the film ended the villagers poured out onto the sidewalk. My father relished a chance to win the approval of his new country-men. He began to imitate one of the Japanese soldiers, jutting his chin and barking orders. A crowd gathered, laughing and urging him on. But I knew they were secretly laughing at him. I felt embarrassed and sad – my father was unaware that the villagers considered him as repulsive as the enemy he now imitated.

In many ways and without at first being conscious of it, I had begun to behave like my father, bullying a classmate in the school-yard. I fell into a deep depression. I even wished that I had been born to a different man – which made me feel worse; if I'd had a different father I would not exist.

I had slowly come to hate myself as much as I hated my father. I wanted to be accepted by other children, but by the time I entered kindergarten, I already knew I was different – which was confirmed

9

at the end of the year: I held the distinction of being the only child at my school who had ever flunked kindergarten. When my father learned this, he dragged me to school and screamed at the principal. In the car on the way home, he yelled, 'Are they idiots? We invented kindergarten!'

I had no idea what he meant, but he must have made his point because the next autumn I was in the first grade like everybody else. But failing kindergarten was the last thing on my mind: I had other things to worry about.

I bristled with fear whenever my father entered the room. He knew I was scared of him – and I had no choice but to respect that he was stronger. I also understood that I could survive if I planned accordingly. The flood of adrenaline I experienced whenever I heard his heavy footsteps approaching me became my first addiction. My body got ready to defend itself and my anxiety was so overwhelming that my hands trembled.

'What are you so damn nervous about?'

'Nothing.'

'What's that you're playing with?'

'Your car.' I held up the miniature toy Porsche that I had been pushing around the room.

Usually that was the end of any such exchange, which often proved our only interaction of the day since I rarely saw him in the morning and went to bed shortly after he returned at night – he often arrived home well after dark. On such days the adrenaline quickly subsided. Occasionally, when my mother wasn't in the room, he would swat the toy out of my hand and ask again, 'What did you say you were doing?'

Then he might retrieve it from where it had ricocheted off the wall and ask me to get another so that we could push them around together while he taught me the rules of the road – or he would slap my face without uttering another word.

The only consistency in my father's behavior was its inconsistency.

He was either the most charming or the cruelest man in the world –
I never knew which or when. The key to avoiding his cruelty was
to be with my siblings or mother when he appeared. That didn't
always work but at least it required him to find a plausible reason
to hit me.

One evening when he came in and pulled up his chair to the
dinner table, where we were sitting, I spilled a glass of milk as I
reached for the dumplings. Before it had run off the edge of the
table, I was dizzy from a blow to the back of my head. I had always
been clumsy, which infuriated my father and encouraged him to hit
me. But even with the beatings and the intense hatred that filled
my heart, I loved him. I believed him when he came into my room
after he'd beaten me and said, 'It hurts me more than it hurts you.'

One night when he seemed relaxed, I carried the globe from the living
room into the den where he was reading the paper and asked him to
point out where he had grown up. He told me to spin it, then jabbed
a finger at it. The globe stopped spinning; he continued reading.

'Borneo?' I asked.

He looked up and gave a short laugh. 'Borneo? Yeah, that's right.
That's where your old man's from.'

For a time I walked around the neighborhood telling the other
children my father was from Borneo and that my grandparents still
lived in the jungle, until one day an older boy told me my father
was a lying Nazi bastard – and so was I. Soon my schoolmates joined
him in taunting me. The first few times I didn't tell either parent
what they were saying, but I asked my father again where he had
come from and where my grandparents were.

Just before I turned twelve my badgering bore fruit that finally
ripened – or fell to the ground rotten. One afternoon he slapped me
so hard that he knocked me over.

'They're dead, goddammit. Stop bothering me.'

I stood up and marched back to him, silently challenging him to
hit me again.

'You're a persistent little bastard, aren't you?'

I remained silent. I could see him getting angry again, but I didn't move. I knew I was breaking him – he was talking now and I sensed his weakness. I was too inquisitive to let pain curb my curiosity.

'Nobody wants to hear this shit except you.'

I stood my ground.

Finally, he said, 'Maybe the kids at school are right. Maybe I was a little Nazi when I was no bigger than you. But everybody here seems to know everything there is to know about Nazis and what they don't know they deport you for telling. I left those stories behind long ago.' He stared at the wall, pondering, for a long time.

'How about I tell you some other things that nobody here seems interested in knowing, either – stories that won't get you deported, that have more to do with you than me?' He made me promise to memorize whatever he taught me.

The following day, he told me to come to the basement with him. He often went down there alone after dinner and I knew not to disturb him. Even my mother didn't bother him there – it was his private space. He had built a little bar at one end of the room near the giant heating-oil tank that a truck came to fill once a year. The basement walls were made from old bricks, whose moist, cool surface crumbled when you dug your fingertips into them. Small rectangular windows, a foot tall and perhaps twice as wide, lined the place where the walls met the ceiling at ground level. The ceiling formed the floor to the kitchen above, where my mother walked back and forth between the refrigerator and stove. Behind the steep stairway descending from the pantry into the basement hung the fuse box – if you stood close enough, you could hear it humming.

Beside it was the nail my father had made me hammer into the wall two years earlier, while he stood over me. On it hung one of his worn-out work belts – it was reserved for whipping me. Whenever I was to be formally punished – for getting poor marks at school, which I did every term – he'd tell me to go into the basement, take the belt off the nail and wait for him while he finished his beer. I was obedient – I always did as I was told.

For obvious reasons the basement frightened me, but that night I was happy that my father had invited me down there because it was for something other than punishment. At that point in my life all I wanted was to please him – to impress him, to make him proud. On the occasions when he dragged me away to beat me in the basement, the embarrassment of seeing him lose control in anger was worse than the pain of the beatings. I knew his outbursts embarrassed my mother also – but for me it was more than that: I felt sorry for him too.

That night in the basement, though, he had finally found somebody with whom to share his past, and for a time my anxiety melted, like an icicle in the morning sun.

Around the same time my father started taking me for long rides in the Porsche through the rolling farmland around Chagrin. Once we stopped at the beer joint he frequented in the next village. He ordered a pint for himself and a glass for me.

'He's under age,' the bartender said.

'Just get the beer, dammit. Did the Puritans take over the Midwest too?'

The bartender was German. He slunk away, fetched the drinks and set them on the counter.

'*Danke*,' my father said, sarcastically. Turning to me, he said, 'You should be more concerned about yourself than me. My past isn't important, but where you come from is. You're American. America is the most powerful country on earth.'

His face brightened when he heard his own words. It occurred to me that my being American made him feel more secure. I came to understand only much later that he was searching for his identity through me just as I had hoped to find out who I was from him.

'You're American,' he continued. 'German-American.'

Those words startled me. I didn't know what they meant. I had never heard the two words used together. The only Germans I knew outside our family were those I had seen on TV: Nazis. I knew other

13

Germans were around, but we didn't live in Milwaukee, St. Louis or Cincinnati – which, he had taught me, formed the German Triangle and were bastions of German-American culture. My father lived in silence – unless he had the chance to wave an American flag on national holidays. Few were more patriotic than Germans.

That afternoon when we got home, we slipped past my mother into the basement before dinner. He reached up to a shelf, pulled down a thick leatherbound book and set it on his desk. Some pages were dog-eared and others were marked with pieces of torn paper – much like the Bible our neighbor studied every day. On one hand I was crestfallen: I wanted to learn about where he came from, not America. On the other I was elated to be able to share an interest with him.

In a weak moment he told me he was from a village on the Samland peninsula in East Prussia. His ancestral homeland was now part of Russia. He pointed out the area, along the southeast coast of the Baltic Sea, on an old map he had thumbtacked to the hand-built bookcases lining the walls. He confessed that he had convinced my mother to name me Sam. 'I told her it was a good American name, not that we had called you after the peninsula I'm from.' A look of concern crossed his face. 'You won't tell her, either, will you?'

I said I wouldn't.

'That tiny Russian enclave, an oblast called Kaliningrad after one of Stalin's henchmen, is one of the most heavily guarded places in the world, sealed off after the war ended,' he said, with both pride and disappointment. 'No one can enter or leave. There's no past or future there, only the present. What they're waiting for, I'm not sure.'

Whatever loyalty he retained to his East Prussian peninsula had been displaced by an intense interest in all things German-American.

The next day, after he'd left for work, my mother asked what we had been doing in the basement.

'He's telling me about us.'

'About what?' she asked.

'All those books he reads.'

'Don't neglect your homework to impress your father.'

To change the subject, I asked her where babies came from. We were sitting alone on the couch in the den.

She paused. 'Two people have to be in love,' she said eventually. 'After they've been in love a long time and know they want to spend their life together, they kiss each other. When they kiss a tiny seed is planted. Over time the seed grows and turns into a baby.'

'Where does the seed come from?'

'The mother already has it inside her. She just has to find somebody she loves.'

'Can we have a baby?' I jumped up excitedly and kissed her.

It took her a moment to regain her composure. 'No, darling. You can't have a baby with your mother. You have to find somebody else. They can't be related to your family.'

'But you're perfect, Mom.' I jumped up and marched away to recover from my first broken heart.

For the first time in my life my father was doing his best to be patient instead of getting angry whenever I spoke. There was no profound transformation. He still beat me. The only difference was that the beatings seemed to create tension between my parents.

'We don't do it that way here,' I once heard my mother shout.

Since he never touched my siblings, she had already won the war. It was the battle for me that persisted. We were a fragmented family, rarely spending time together, except at the dinner table or on holidays. We didn't play together or even talk. Silence permeated the household. My older brother Carl despised my father for beating me – but I felt Carl endured worse. Physical pain dissipated. Psychological pain was more burdensome. Carl was named after my father, but the K had been replaced with a C to help him fit in better – less German, less Communist, less harsh for soft Americans, my father had once said.

Where I had succeeded in winning my father's approval by withstanding his beatings, Carl couldn't overcome the ridicule to which our father subjected him. Little by little it destroyed him, and he

frequently attacked me, called me names, blackmailed and intimidated me. I could take it because he was my brother, but I knew that
didn't make me stronger than him: my beatings paled into insignifi-
cance beside my father's behavior toward him.

One afternoon Carl grabbed me by the back of my shirt and dragged
me down the steps into the cellar. 'What's Dad teaching you now?' He
laughed. 'Big bad German.' He pushed me into the tight space between
the oil tank and the wall until I was wedged there. Then he picked up
the ax handle and started beating it against the half-empty tank. The
sound vibrated through my body and the house above.

I tried to keep calm – he'd wear himself out soon. His rage
increased. He tore a map off the wall and shoved it in my face. 'Das
Reich!' he screamed. He dropped to his knees, then stood up again
and continued banging on the tank, working himself into a frenzy.

The door to the basement flung open. From the force with which
it hit the wall at the top of the stairs, we knew it could be only one
person. Very occasionally our father came home from work early.
When the door smashed against the wall and his feet pounded down
the old wooden staircase, we knew instantly that he had heard everything my brother had said.

I was still wedged between the tank and the wall when my father
appeared and I could see my brother. He was backing up to the
furthest wall. Watching Carl now, I hated my father even more than
I usually did. Whatever my brother had done to me was forgotten. I
began to cry – tears that my father thought, mistakenly, were caused
by my brother's brutality. He grabbed my arm and yanked me out
of my prison.

Carl was silent.

My father surveyed the room. He looked at the torn map lying
on the floor near the oil tank. Then he walked over to my brother
and, without lifting a hand or saying a word, stared down at him
until Carl knelt. When he glanced up, my father said, in a low voice,
'You look at me one more fuckin' time . . .' Then he said, 'You make
your bed, you sleep in it, too.'

He grabbed my arm and marched me up the stairs, leaving my

brother behind. Carl was terrified of the dark and my father knew this. When we reached the top of the stairs, he did exactly what I had prayed he wouldn't: he flipped off the light switch.

'If you come near these stairs . . .' His booming voice echoed into the darkness below. Early winter was coming on and light bled from the sky in the late afternoon, so the basement now was as dark and dank as a cave. He shut the door, reached above its frame for the skeleton key and locked it.

That night I lay in my room listening to my brother whimpering below. My parents' bedroom door was closed. I could hear them yelling at each other inside. I knew my father had locked them in. Around one or two in the morning he must have fallen asleep.

My mother stormed out of the bedroom, ran to the cellar door, unlocked it and went down the stairs. After she had put Carl to bed, I heard her go into the den where she curled up on the couch to sleep.

For weeks after that I didn't see my brother in the house. Carl had always been more a void than a presence in our home, but now he simply vanished, spending most of his time after school by the river. My father's cruelty rarely penetrated my thickening skin, but the night he locked my brother in the basement, I cried myself to sleep. In the days that followed, knowing Carl could not feel comfortable in his own home, I cried again, sorry for him as I had previously felt sorry for my father.

About a month after the incident, I was provided with a bigger window onto my father's past. His sister arrived at our house. A decade before I was born he had sponsored her immigration to America from Bremerhaven. At the time my parents still lived in Los Angeles. They had met at a bakery on Wilshire, where my father baked in the back and my mother worked at the counter up front.

My immediate family was fragmented, but our extended family on my father's side was shattered. I had never met my aunt Leyna before her unexpected visit to Chagrin. The morning she arrived, we

17

did our best to impress her. We put on our best clothes and walked through the village to stand on the bridge near the Popcorn Shop and watch the river spilling over the two large falls. We had difficulty understanding her thick, halting accent. She wore a long wool coat that hung to her ankles and had pinned her thick, jet-black, waist-length hair into an enormous bun on the top of her head like a crown. She was also wearing high heeled black-leather boots – I had watched her zip them halfway up her calves before our walk. I couldn't take my eyes off her. Few villagers owned a coat or boots like hers and I had never seen anyone with hair so long, so black or piled so high on their head.

As we walked down the street, people stared as though Aunt Leyna had just stepped off the ship that had brought her to New York. She had saved little money from working at a deli in Marina Del Rey, but she looked like a member of the Hohenzollern dynasty arriving from the Prussian Empire to view its colonial holdings.

My father had worked hard to fit seamlessly into Chagrin Falls. His sister appeared to embarrass him. He wasn't comfortable in her presence. Every once in a while he said something to her in German when she failed to understand our questions, but I could tell he didn't like to. He didn't want anybody in town to hear him speak anything but English. He had taken trouble to learn colloquialisms to try to fit in but even these he got wrong. His favorite, 'Hey, man,' only made him seem more out of place, since few villagers used such informal language.

One evening Aunt Leyna said that as a child in Germany immediately after the war, when people were going hungry, she had been told that money grew on trees in America. She was sorely disappointed when the trees she passed on her bus journey from New York City to Los Angeles had produced only spring blooms on their branches. However, soon after that she had discovered discount stores and learned a game that many immigrants mastered.

My father had given it up years ago, but his sister, who had married a Romanian engineer, hadn't yet tired of it. One evening after visiting a local discount store and purchasing clothing for just a few dollars,

18

she raced home with my mother, excited by her savings. She held up a bright red blouse and demanded, 'How much? How much you think?'

I recognized its inferior quality but, well practiced in the game, I named a figure far higher than the article's actual value: 'Uh, thirty dollars.'

'*Nein*, stupid.'

'Forty?' I asked.

A smile appeared on her face. 'Lower.'

'Twenty-five?'

The smile widened. She shook her head.

'Ten?'

By this point my aunt could barely contain herself.

'Five dollars?' I asked.

'Less.'

'Three dollars?'

'Two for five!' she shouted triumphantly, producing a second identical blouse from the bag at her side. 'Two for five! I bet you can't believe it!'

I could.

Two days later she packed to depart. My father waited impatiently by the door to drive her back to the airport in Cleveland.

'Why is she leaving so soon?' I asked.

'She has to be back at her job in the deli.'

Secretly I wished she could stay forever. I sensed she had answers to my questions about their past.

In many ways Chagrin Falls was the most idyllic village in the world. Each May everybody gathered for the Blossom Time Festival on the riverbank beside the upper waterfall. Each Memorial Day, Carl, my father and I drove to the cemetery to stand at attention while the veterans fired live rounds from their rifles into the air – a twenty-one-gun salute to honor the dead. On Christmas Eve we gathered to sing carols at the gazebo in the village triangle.

There were peculiarities. Beyond the cemetery, only a mile or so from the center of the village, in the direction of the dump, there was a small African-American neighborhood. I had never seen its inhabitants among the crowd singing carols. Nobody who lived there attended my school. Passing the area on the way to the dump, I'd seen the crumbling roads and weathered houses of what most people called the Allotment. Others referred to it as Chagrin Falls Park, which made no sense since it was anything but a park.

When I asked my father why the African-Americans lived outside the village, he said, 'Ask your mother.'

When I did so, she told me, 'They've always lived there. Ask your grandmother.'

When I asked my grandmother, she said, 'They like to be with their own people.' Then she led me into the basement of her large home and showed me a bricked-up doorway. She claimed it was part of the Underground Railroad that had smuggled slaves north to freedom.

I still didn't understand why they didn't live closer so we could play together. 'Why don't they go to my school?'

'They have their own school,' she said. 'In the next county.'

I understood that my repeated inquiries were unwelcome, so I let the subject drop.

During the years we lived on Maple Street, the rest of my mother's family lived within a single block of us. My grandmother's home was a half-block north on Water Street, which marked the center of the extended family. My cousins lived a block east on Walnut Street, and there were more cousins behind my grandmother's house on Church Street. Each Christmas we gathered at one of our homes to celebrate with roasts, cakes, pies, stews and soups, while bowls of nuts and sweets lined tables throughout the house.

When we arrived, we removed our boots and coats and went inside. After formal greetings, drinks were served to parents and children – the women soon retreated to the kitchen to check the oven and unpack food that the others had brought.

The children raced up the front stairs, down the rear stairs, through the den, kitchen, dining room and hallways, eventually ending up in the room where the bar and pool table stood. The men gathered around the bar, while we kids attempted to play pool, soon lost interest and sprinted out again. Chaos ensued as we crashed into each other, some crying, while one cousin hammered out dissonant chords on the baby grand piano in the living room, joined by another on the trumpet. Above the din we could hear our fathers' laughter from the bar and pleas from the kitchen that they intervene to calm us.

As the night wore on, the girls disappeared into the bedrooms on the second floor, where they whispered and played house, while trying to hold the boys at bay. We would burst in on them, disrupting their games and occasionally taking a hostage. The girls' shrill screams would alert our parents, whose heavy footsteps thudded up the front stairs as we disappeared down the back flight to the pool room, grabbed cues and stood around the table as though we had been there all along.

After dinner, as our parents settled into their drinks, a large set of train tracks was brought out to occupy us. We built elaborate trestles, stretching from one room to the next, sending the train around corners, under chairs and couches, struggling through rough patches of shag carpet and flying over expanses of floor. We piled anything that would fit onto the cars behind the main engine to see how much weight it could pull. Nuts were gathered from the bowls, shoes carefully balanced, wallets from our fathers' back pockets, watches from their wrists and, once, a wedding ring that Uncle Olly agreed could do one circuit of the house. It bounced out of the car somewhere along the route, interrupting the proceedings. Every child and parent crawled on all fours, looking under chairs, in corners and along the length of the tracks. Shortly before the ensuing panic turned to hysteria, Uncle Olly's wife, Spicey Ann – named after her great-grandmother from Kentucky – produced the ring, which she had snatched from the open car when it had passed through the kitchen where she had been refilling her glass.

She handed it back to her husband with elaborate seriousness

21

and said, 'I hope we never have to deal with this problem of the ring leaving your finger again.'

We all laughed, and Uncle Olly – always one to sense the perfect dramatic moment – knelt and proclaimed, 'This ring will remain as snugly fitted around my finger as my love for you guards the doors to my heart.'

Then we returned to the den for the final family pictures of the year. Afterward we children sat quietly as our parents thanked our hosts for the party. Every picture in the family album from those years showed us smiling and happy. Never once did a frame capture a hand coming down in anger. In my own family we censored those moments from our public lives. Most people considered us exceptionally well mannered.

Winter was a time of adventure. I built my first snowman in Chagrin, tobogganed down my first hill and skated on the frozen pond in the park alongside the river. I gathered with the other kids from my block as they hurriedly assembled piles of snowballs, icing a few to cause more damage as we prepared for an imminent attack by the older boys from the next block.

Chagrin was also where I first recognized the finality of death when I peeked through the window of the building behind the funeral home where the embalmer worked. I wasn't prepared for the sight of an old lady lying serenely on her back unattended. Although I had hoped to see a dead body, I felt I had violated an unwritten law.

The following week, something happened that I interpreted as a warning not to go searching for the dead unless I wanted to join them. After an unusually heavy snowstorm, I stepped off the porch to follow Carl and my cousins into the forest. I struggled through chest-high drifts, shouting for my brother to wait. The snow engulfed the sound of my voice and the silence was more profound than I had ever experienced – it was more intense than it was when I woke alone in the middle of the night. After they disappeared, I pushed my way through the snow piled against the shrubs and tree trunks attempting to follow their tracks. I seemed to be in a narrow frozen hallway with no ceiling – a maze of sorts. Every now and then I found burrows and dens beneath the bushes bordering the yard. Except for my face, every part of my body was covered – boots, pants, coat, scarf, cap and mittens.

My fingertips tingled. Little balls of ice encrusted my mittens. I continued plowing through the snow. When my fingers went numb, I noticed that my toes were tingling and turned back. The maze had caved in, disappearing in drifts of newly fallen snow. I veered off the path and blazed a new trail, covering fifteen or twenty feet before I stopped, exhausted.

With each new effort I advanced another ten feet toward the house, and when I finally neared the steps to the back porch, they were blocked by an enormous bank of snow that had slid off the roof. It stood at least eight feet high. Each time I tried to climb over it, I slid back to the bottom. I changed direction and struggled toward the side of the house. The snow was falling so heavily that I could barely see. My legs stung where snow had slid beneath my clothing and compacted around the top of my boots, forming a seal of ice. My toes were nearly frozen.

When I reached the corner of the house, a thick cloud of steam was pouring from a vent and dissipating in the air. I plunged toward it. Even before I reached it I imagined I could feel its warmth. When I got there I held my hands in the rising cloud. It was warmer than I'd anticipated. I had always found it strange that after you returned indoors from the snow you had first to run cold water over your hands to warm them. Then, as they thawed, you slowly added hot. I pulled off my mittens and pushed my entire body into the cloud of steam, unwrapping my scarf so that it flowed around my neck.

The deep silence was now filled with the hum of the vapor pouring from the house. I thought of my mother folding laundry on the other side of the vent but I never considered calling her. I was too tired. I closed my eyes and slumped into the pocket my body had created in the snow. As sleep descended, I was yanked upward in a short, violent thrust.

23

My father was standing in front of me. He reached down and snatched my mittens and scarf from the ground. 'Are you okay?' he asked.

I nodded. My body tensed and my eyelids fluttered as I prepared to be slapped for my stupidity.

He lifted me level with his face, stared directly into my eyes, then kissed my forehead: 'You had me worried, *Dummkopf*.'

I slipped out of his hands and back into the snow. He picked me up and carried me into the house.

My warmest memories from those years weren't of the stories my father told me in the basement: he claimed that the Christmas tree, Santa Claus and carols like 'Silent Night' and 'Away in the Manger' had been brought to America by German immigrants. Instead they were of scents that reminded me of when my father had begun to treat me with a degree of respect. When he wanted to convey to me something he felt important, he'd grab one of the old, leatherbound books to prove the truth of what he was saying. A whiff of mildew filled the room from the crumbling pages, smelling like the mulch I helped my mother turn into the earth each spring when we replanted the garden. But it was more complex than that: in sharing what he knew of our country's history, he had discovered a way to express his love without beating me.

The book he pulled most often from the shelf was one of two large volumes written in the early twentieth century titled *The German Element in the United States*. He ruined one afternoon with a rant. It infuriated him to be called a WASP. 'I'm *not* Anglo-Saxon. Do I look like a fuckin' limey?' He said that British settlers had brainwashed other Americans into accepting our colonial masters and that the Irish often took credit for developing the parts where the British had failed. The Germans, who dwarfed both groups, were hardly mentioned. 'These chicken shits would rather pretend they're Anglo to get a job. They change their names from Jäger to Hunter or Schmidt to Smith instead of admitting they're a Kraut.'

Suddenly I wanted to get out of the basement. Winter would soon end and whatever warmth I had felt when he had opened the book cooled when he started yelling about WASPs. 'Can I play outside, Dad?'

He seemed disappointed but he said, 'Sure. But come with me for a spin in the car later.'

I sprinted up the steps. At the top there were two doors, one opening into the house, through the pantry to the kitchen, and the other opening directly onto the side yard. I turned the knob on the second and pulled.

'The door's stuck.'

'Pull the damn thing.'

I tried again. 'It won't open.'

I stood still, waiting for him. I wanted to go outside, look up into the sky and watch the snow falling. I heard my father climbing the stairs.

He reached over my shoulder, turned the knob and yanked it inwards. The swollen door swung open. I squinted – I hadn't expected the brightness – and darted out to the muffled sound of the door slamming behind me. Snow was falling everywhere, the ground perfectly white.

The contrast between the dank warmth of the basement and the crisp air in the snow-covered yard made the world feel more open and alive than it had before – even the air was easier to breathe. I jumped and danced around, then tripped and fell into the snow. I flipped onto my back and moved my arms and legs in wide arcs to make a snow angel.

The snow was falling so heavily that when I stood up the angel slowly disappeared. I began to make a snowman, scooping up snow and packing it together until it was the size of a softball, then rolled it around until it was as high as my chest. When it was too large and heavy to push, I started another.

As I was rolling the second snowball, my father appeared. Without speaking, he helped me until it was big enough, then picked it up and placed it on top of the first. For a moment or two we admired the truncated snowman. Then my father asked, 'Should we smash it?'

I looked up at him, dismayed.

'I'm just kidding. We need to go.'

My father drove carefully through the snowy countryside in the aging Porsche 912. It was one of the few things I ever saw him show pride in. Even though it often broke down, we were the only family who owned such an exotic vehicle, although there were many other cars in the village. My father's devotion to it stemmed from a number of factors – its sleek design, its fast engine, its representation of wealth, which indicated that he had made it in America – but also that it gave him an edge over the seemingly self-satisfied Anglo descendants, who usually dominated village affairs. 'They can dislike me as much as they want,' he had once told me. 'I don't care how much they despise me. They can pretend to be as polite and reserved as they want, but I bet every one of those pricks wishes they had this car.'

He was right. Whenever he parked it on Main Street they gathered around to admire it. Those were perhaps the only times during his years in Chagrin Falls when he was able to make the Anglo villagers the butt of a private joke, which he later shared with me. At those moments, as far as he was concerned, he had parked a German panzer on Main Street. Dr. Porsche had convinced Hitler to allow him to design the most lethal tank ever built: the Tiger, which would eventually become known as the Ferdinand – it was the doctor's first name and one of my father's middle names. The Ferdinand eventually rolled off the assembly line and into the colossal Soviet-German war. The tank, protected by some 180 tons of armor, reached the front and lumbered straight through enemy lines – only to become a sitting Goliath when Russian foot soldiers popped up from foxholes and pressed explosives to its unprotected underbelly, rendering useless the most advanced tank ever built. That part of the story held little interest for my father on the days when he saw the villagers admiring his car.

My father viewed his Porsche as an equalizer that made fools of the villagers who envied it. It also represented his private revenge for the loss of his home and his East Prussian culture on the Samland peninsula: the antlers incorporated in the manufacturer's logo on the hood were cryptically similar to the sovereign symbol of his former homeland. The villagers who stood in awe around that car were unaware that to my father it was a single unit from the once dreaded SS Das Reich Panzer Division. Some had even taken to calling him 'Porsch.' Occasionally when he walked through the village to the liquor store, someone would shout out of a car window as they passed, 'Hey, Porsch! How's it going?' This was as friendly a greeting as my father could expect, so he accepted it with rare grace and good humor.

'Couldn't be better. Yourself?'

Each year, in summer, my mother loaded us into the station wagon and took us children to a small lake near Warsaw, Indiana, where her parents had been born and owned a vacation home. I sensed that something was wrong with my parents' marriage, though I had little idea then that I was a major part of the problem.

The summer-long trips gave us a chance to recover from our father's dominance. He only took a few days off work during the summer to drive over from Ohio. One year, Carl persuaded me to canoe to a marsh on the opposite side of the lake where he hoped to find a narrow canal he'd seen the previous year. After we'd searched for more than an hour, he finally located the narrow waterway in a thick bed of cattails. Since it wasn't wide enough for the canoe to float through, we had to get out every few minutes and stand in water up to our waists to push it toward a tree that towered above us. Eventually we entered a vast stretch of bog that was hidden from the lake. Other than an occasional turtle, the only wildlife was birds. The water was too congested with roots and weeds for large fish, but the wilderness provided an impenetrable sanctuary for birds to perch, safe from predators, while they built nests and laid eggs. Hundreds of red-winged blackbirds swooped back and forth over our heads, perturbed that we had entered their fortress.

The lone tree, dead for many years, had twisted back and forth on itself as it reached into the sky.

'How did it get there?' I asked.

'A bird probably dropped a seed.'

'Maybe Moses put it there.'

'I want to climb it,' Carl said.

'Will we make it?'

'If you shut up and keep pushing. I'm tired of doing all the work.'

I helped push with my oar but stayed inside the boat. I was scared to stick my feet into the water now because of the leeches. My brother took pleasure from them: each time one attached itself to his leg, he peeled open the plastic bag of wooden matches he had meticulously wrapped in case we got stuck in the marsh and had to live there. At least that was how he had justified sneaking them out of the house. He struck a match against the side of the boat and held the flame near the head of the leech until it released its grip. Then he slung it into the water, shouting, 'I'll kill any bastard that gets near me.'

A while later, he said, 'You realize we're the first humans here?'

I had always wanted to explore uncharted territory. 'Do you think they'll name it after us?'

'Maybe. If we die.'

'Why do we have to die?'

'You can't be great unless you die.'

'But God isn't dead.'

'He doesn't count.'

'What about the President?'

'Presidents only become great when they die. That's why Mom loves Kennedy so much.'

I watched my brother near the bow, pushing off cattails with his oar. Strapped to his leg was a knife our mother had bought him at the army-surplus store. He had begged for it until she had agreed on the condition that he promised to be careful with it. He rarely took it out of its sheath. Now, though, he said that when we reached the tree he'd carve our names and the year into the trunk to prove we had been the first to explore the area.

'You have to put the year,' he said. 'Then if they find our skeletons, they'll know when we died.'

'But you said even if we got lost we'd have no problem staying alive. I thought that was why you brought the matches.'

'Don't be such a sissy.'

'I want to go home.'

'We're almost at the tree.'

We heard a loud splash.

'What's that?' I whispered.

'I don't know – maybe a beaver.'

Carl slid the knife out of the sheath and checked the compass embedded in the handle. 'It's south of us.' He gripped the blade between his teeth, its sharp edge facing outward, like he'd seen in a war movie on TV, and started paddling again.

'We should turn around.'

He removed the knife from his clenched teeth. 'It's no big deal. Would you stop worrying?'

We listened, but heard nothing else.

We resumed pushing forward. This time I tried harder to share the work. When we cleared another clump of cattails, the tree came into full view. I glanced at the desolate surroundings. The surrounding cattails looked like everywhere else we had pushed through during the previous hour.

There was a stagnant pool around the base of the tree where we were able to dock and tie the boat to a branch.

'Let's climb it,' I urged.

'In a minute.' He pointed at something shining in the cattails behind the tree. 'Sit down.' He pushed off and paddled toward the reflection. Once there he probed it with the tip of his oar, then stuck his hand in and grabbed it.

'What is it?'

Without speaking he held it up.

'A beer bottle?'

'Budweiser.'

'Is it old at least?'

'I don't think so. Look. Another one.'

He threw the bottle across the marsh. Without speaking, we paddled back to the tree. He stood up in the boat, straddled the trunk and began inching his way upward branch by branch. I waited for him to get high enough so that I could follow him, but before he attained much height, a branch snapped. He fell out of the tree and landed with a loud splash in the murky water.

He climbed back into the boat.

This time I started up the tree first, steering around the broken branches. The wide expanse of marsh surrounding us came into view. Higher still, the lake appeared. As I continued, I saw a sailboat and then, in the distance, the tall, empty flagpole in front of our house across the lake. Once we were both perched near the top I pointed out the distant flagpole. 'You ready to go home?' I asked.

'Dad's probably there already.'

'I thought he was coming tomorrow.'

'Why do you think I wanted to go out in the canoe today?'

I turned back to the empty flagpole, neither of us in any hurry to leave now.

My father arrived that afternoon for the weekend. Independence Day had been his favorite holiday since he had come to the United States more than twenty years earlier. Like many immigrants, he was more fervent in expressing his patriotism than those who had lived in America for generations. Exploding skyrockets excited him – but he had shied from lighting fireworks after a shoebox filled with them had exploded in his lap two years earlier, ignited by the hot ash from a cigar that had fallen into the box.

The same year as the fireworks accident, he had purchased an enormous flag, the largest anyone around the lake had ever seen. To display it he had cemented a metal pole into the ground near the shore. He had ordered it from a store in Maine that guaranteed the flag to be the largest and the pole the tallest produced in the world for domestic use. The order had taken nearly a year to fill because the flag – made in China – had been held up at Customs.

For my father it had been worth the wait, but it was less fun for me: when we got back from our canoe trip I had to help him raise it. After we'd anchored the cord, we stepped back for a moment to admire it.

'Help me get the boat,' he said.

The boat itself was relatively easy to drag across the grass and put in the water. The heavy outboard engine was a different matter, especially with no other men around to help. Carl had escaped to the store as soon as we'd got home to buy batteries for his flashlight.

My father and I wrestled the outboard across the yard. He knew I wasn't strong enough for the job, but he wanted to spend his first night at the lake on the motorboat, cruising over the water as he drank beer and admired his flag illuminated by a spotlight. By the time we reached the dock, my father was sweating, exhausted and frustrated. He climbed into the boat, telling me to hold the engine steady on the dock for him.

'You'll ruin it if it falls into the lake.'

He strained to pick it up. Veins bulged from his arms and neck. Another rippled across his forehead. 'Help me lift the goddamn thing.'

My hand was pinched between the engine and the dock. I screamed and pulled it away. Shaking with fatigue, my father swung the outboard over the water and slid it onto its mount in a single fluid motion. Then he straightened. He was still shaking but not with fatigue: he was enraged that I had stopped helping and watched as the outboard almost fell into the lake.

'Do you know how much I paid for that?' he screamed.

He grabbed me by the collar and threw me onto the metal floor of the boat. The oily residue along the seam smeared my face. He hooked up the fuel line and pulled the start-cord several times, choked the engine and pulled it once more. It sputtered to life. He untied the boat and raced the engine; the aluminum hull smacked each wave as we headed out past the line of seaweed that marked the drop-off, a frightening area where the shallows fell away to

31

oblivion. He set the engine to idle, then grabbed my collar and the waist of my shorts, lifted me into the air and tossed me into the lake. 'Let's see how strong you are now.' He turned the boat and gunned it toward the shore.

I was treading water as he raced away. In the distance, I watched him tie the boat to the dock and glance out at me. He had taught Carl and me to swim when we were infants by tossing us into the lake and letting us learn how to tread water on our own. When our mother joined us, he had said proudly, 'Look, they can swim.' Now he waved at me, walked across the yard and disappeared into the house.

I relaxed my breathing and swam slowly toward the shore, ignoring the small waves that slapped my face. A few minutes later I reached the drop-off, where the weeds drifted in the current a few inches below the surface. A strand brushed my leg. I stiffened and dog-paddled as close to the surface as I could to clear the plants now brushing against my belly. The unusual texture of seaweed – its slick, pliable surface, like a soggy forest rooted to the lake's floor – terrified me, which my father knew. I imagined an alien world down there, waiting for something to pass overhead. I was scared of getting tangled and being dragged down.

After passing over the weeds, I swam breaststroke, submerging my head with each stroke to move faster. The sun had dipped behind the trees in the yard and I wanted to reach the shore before dark. I kicked harder and saw Carl walking along the seawall, as he did each evening near dusk. He was holding a flashlight and net, waiting for the sun to go down so that he could find fish seeking shelter along the wall in the dark.

His method consisted of blinding the fish with the bright beam – the light temporarily paralyzed them – giving him a few seconds to slide a net into the water behind them. When the fish inched backward to escape the light and dart out into the open water, he pressed the net forward, scooping the fish out of the water and slinging it onto the grass. He'd examine its size as it drowned in the air, then repeat the process until he had enough for dinner.

He didn't look surprised when he saw me swim out of the dark and approach the wall, just yelled, 'Hurry up and get out. You're scaring the fish away.'

When we returned to Chagrin at the end of the summer, I still went for rides with my father in the Porsche and visited him in the basement, but something had changed. My parents fought more. One night I stood at the top of the stairs and listened to them argue in the den.

I heard my mother say, 'You can't treat him like that. You can't call Sam an idiot every time you see him.'

'I'll call him what I damn well please.'

'Keep calling him stupid and he'll start to believe you.'

'He is stupid.'

'That's not the point.'

'I'm his father. I'll call him what I want.'

'No, you won't. If you do, you won't be here any more.'

He laughed. 'What will you do? Nobody wants a divorced woman with children in this village.'

'You always have to say something nasty, don't you?' She started to cry and my father fell silent. I wanted to race downstairs to my mother but that would mean bumping into my father. I sneaked back into my bedroom.

I closed the door and crept back to the transistor radio I had been disassembling when they'd started fighting. I tried to figure out the schematics diagram glued to the inside of the plastic case to see where I had to reattach the diode I'd taken off. As I did so a tear fell onto the diode. It contained salt and would corrode the connection. When another tear fell, I didn't bother to wipe it away. The tears fell faster. I watched them as though they belonged to someone else. I slid the radio and its parts into a box and went out of the room again to see if they were still fighting.

Music was playing softly on the stereo. He had a stack of Bill Evans records that he put on when he was unhappy – a jazz trio: piano, bass and drums. He knew how to win back my mother when he stepped over the line. He pushed her to the limit, but he knew exactly when to stop and start reeling her in. Those were the rare moments when he knew not to blister the air with more words. Instead he let the pianist articulate his feelings.

He waited.

He waited through 'I Love You' and 'My Romance,' through 'Waltz for Debbie' and 'Peace Piece.' Through 'All of You,' 'Autumn Leaves' and 'Someday my Prince Will Come,' 'Haunted Heart,' 'Beautiful Love' and 'How Deep Is the Ocean,' all of which he had taught me as well. When necessary, he continued with 'What Is this Thing Called Love?,' 'Blue in Green' and 'Darn that Dream.' And if the fight had been particularly nasty, as it had been that night, he waited patiently through 'My Funny Valentine,' 'Stairway to the Stars,' and, finally, 'I'm Getting Sentimental over You.'

From the stairway, I imagined the movement behind the bedroom door below, my mother's gentle, almost weightless hand resting on the hidden doorknob. The key finding its way slowly around the tumbler. The bolt clicking quietly in its groove. The doorknob slowly turning. Another click as the door unlatched but stayed shut.

I imagined the events unfolding below: my mother's eye peering through the slender crack. Thick silence. Unspoken proposals. Truce. Trust. Resolution. The door cracking open wider. Light filling the room in which my father patiently waited. My mother stepping hesitantly over the threshold. My father standing. The two embracing. Tears returning. More silence. Whispers. Promises. More promises. Love.

That night I dreamed my father and I were racing in the Porsche along the Indiana Turnpike on the way to the lake. He was speeding, as usual, weaving in and out of traffic. He passed a car in the left lane, then unexpectedly swerved to the far right and brought the car to an abrupt stop on the hard shoulder in an area where it was illegal to do so.

'What are you doing?'

Without answering, he jumped out of the car, jogged a couple of hundred yards back down the turnpike, then – waving his hands in front of him and above his head like a patrolman – stepped out into the traffic and interrupted the flow. He ran toward one of the center-lines, leaned down and scooped something up, all the while holding his left hand high.

Soon he was back at the car, traffic flowing by again.

'Move your feet,' he said. 'Make room.'

Before I could ask him why, he set a turtle the size of his clenched fist on the floor at my feet. 'What are you going to do with him?'

'Save the little fellow. He nearly got crushed crossing the road.'

By that time he had already started moving out into the traffic. I tilted my head and glanced at him again. His eyes were on the road. I looked at the turtle and smiled.

Above the roar of the engine, he said, 'We'll take it over to the marina and let it out near the creek with the other turtles.'

The dream then shifted and entered another layer, fusing itself with an event from the previous summer: a flash of lightning and crash of thunder shook the lake house to its foundation. It was late at night. I lay in bed listening to the wind rip through the trees, scared the storm might swirl into the house and get me. When it subsided toward dawn, my father appeared in the doorway. 'Put on your clothes. We're going fishing.'

It was still dark outside. As we passed through the living room to go out I saw my mother's outline in bed through the door he had left open. The hinges on the front door were so dry that they creaked, no matter how carefully you opened it. I heard shuffling behind me and turned. My mother asked, 'Is that you, Karl?' My father and I went into the room and kissed her goodbye. We put the fishing rods, the tackle box and net into the boat, untied it and headed out on the lake to his favorite spot. At dawn we dropped anchor. I caught a perch on my first cast, which annoyed him. I turned away and smiled to myself. I caught another on my second.

'We came out here for pike, not perch. You trying to scare the big ones away?'

Half an hour later I spotted the largest northern pike I had ever seen resting motionless above a layer of seaweed. I didn't say anything. I let it move on without casting in its direction. In the calm after the storm the lake turned to glass. The pike appeared once more, like an angel, assuring me that everything would be okay.

When we got home my father slid the pins out of the hinges on the front door and lubricated them with the bacon grease that my mother stored in a can near the back of the stove. The door never creaked again but even though it opened smoothly and we could leave early without waking my mother something never seemed quite right. Everything was too perfect, too calm.

My father wasn't spending much time with me in the basement since it increased the tension between him and my mother, but he stayed down there on his own more often. The few times I ventured there, he was sitting at his desk, scribbling feverishly.

'What are you writing?' I asked.

'Mind your own business.'

This went on for almost three months. Every night when he got home from work, he went straight to the basement to write. He ignored me each time I asked him about it. Eventually he had a stack of paper that he took to work one morning to mimeograph. He brought it home and sat in the basement stitching the bindings of the original and the copy. He set them on the shelf beside a copy of a Martin Buber book he sometimes read on weekends, propped up on a pillow in bed. One afternoon I slipped the Buber book off the shelf. 'What's it about?' I asked.

'You better go upstairs to your mother. She doesn't want you down here.'

She didn't seem to mind, though, when he took me for rides in the car. He'd tell her he was taking me to the bakery in Cleveland and often did. I learned about boiling bagels, rolling out croissants, frying doughnuts, filling pasties, squeezing loaves of bread to test their freshness, about day-olds, pre-mixes and factory-made. He supervised the bakery, overseeing the entire operation from hiring the bakers and even helping to design labels for the products.

Even though I sometimes felt embarrassed for him I conceded that he was the only father I had and, despite his faults – for which I felt partly responsible – that it was easier to love than to hate him. And as long as I hated him I would never be comfortable in my own skin.

Driving to and from the bakery or through the countryside, he'd talk as he always did, but at least there was no one to hear him and less shame to endure. 'Two things preoccupy those who grow up in wartime and are later exiled from their homeland,' he repeated. 'Survival and preservation of memory.'

Many of our neighbors considered him frugal, stingy, cheap. When I told him so, he said, 'Who cares? Let the bastards starve when their day comes. Nobody in this village knows what hunger means. I'll stockpile money like pickled herring until the day I die – and if you're wise, you'll do the same.'

He pointed out regularly that I wouldn't exist if he hadn't survived the war. 'It's your duty,' he said, 'to retain my memories, your grandfather's memories. Life itself is duty. Nothing more.'

For years he had refused to tell me the very things that he now adamantly demanded I remember. I was no longer sure if anything he said was true.

'Germans are the largest ethnic group in America,' he said, without my prompting. 'More of us arrived here in a single year – a quarter-million in 1882 – than any other group in any other year.'

He was like a child rattling off sporting statistics, with German-Americans on a never-ending winning streak, breaking every record in the book. From time to time he insisted that knowledge should be balanced and never self-righteous. 'The year before a quarter-million Germans arrived,' he said, 'your government passed the Chinese Exclusion Act.' It was always 'my' government. He never felt at home enough to call it 'his' or 'our' government.

But I was more interested in Europe than America. When I asked him about it, he changed the subject and talked instead about how he had come here.

'I was going to join the French Foreign Legion to get out of Europe. One morning, when I was walking through the Black Forest to the bakery I worked in, a Legion truck pulled over on the side of the road. I jumped into the woods and hid behind a tree. The leader ordered everybody out, then walked up and down the line beating them for not following an order. I decided right then not to go with the French. A month later I was told I could immigrate to Canada. My cousin was already there. I couldn't stand being in Germany – most West Germans didn't care for anybody from the East and made a point of letting us know. But Canada scared me – so far north, a frozen wilderness. I imagined it was like Siberia and worried I'd spend my life in a logging camp in the Arctic. Then an East Prussian family who had known my father and made it to Los Angeles agreed to sponsor me. It was what I'd been holding out for. America.'

As he spoke we came over a rise so fast that the car was airborne for a fraction of a second and I felt myself floating. I grabbed the handle above the glove box. A tingling sensation flittered through my abdomen and traveled to my groin. The car came down hard, the metal undercarriage scraping on the road.

He slowed down and looked for a place to pull over. He wanted to see if there was any damage. Soon we came to a dirt road that ran between two pastures and disappeared into the woods. He turned off, drove up it and stopped. We climbed out and looked at the undercarriage.

'It's nothing,' he decided. He walked around to the front of the car and popped the hood to get something out of the storage compartment – the engine was at the rear. When he slammed the hood, he was holding two cans of beer. 'You want one?' he asked. He didn't wait for an answer – just tossed it to me and told me to step out into the field to open it so I didn't spill foam in the car. Next thing I knew we were both sitting in the car, with the leather bucket seats rolled back, the doors open and our legs propped on the door hinges, staring out over the green pastures, sipping Pabst Blue Ribbon.

'This place looks almost like where I grew up,' he said.

'How so?'

'The fields, the way they roll, bright green, broken up by strips of trees forming windbreaks.'

For a second I felt as if we had grown up in the same town around the same people and had always spoken the same language, until he started talking about ships.

'These fields might roll, but they don't roll anything like the sea in a storm.'

'What do you mean?'

'When I finally got papers to come here, I took the train to Hamburg and bought passage on a ship. We were at sea for a week. On the third night a storm hit. The front of the ship slammed into huge waves that were invisible in the dark. There was a moment of silence followed by a deep shudder and a horrible noise that vibrated down the length of the ship each time the propeller came out of the water. I couldn't wait to get off that ship.'

He opened another beer. This time he didn't offer me one. He told me how after he'd been in America for two years without citizenship he was drafted into the US Army. They had dressed him in an American uniform and put him on another ship sailing back to Germany. 'It was the last place on earth I wanted to go, but at least I was going as a victor instead of the defeated. The West Germans weren't so quick to piss on me that time. They were kissing my East Prussian ass.' He laughed, drained his beer, crushed the can in his hand and tossed it into the field.

'I want to give you something,' he said, 'but I don't want to talk about it other than to say my grandfather gave it to me when I was about your age, one of the last times I saw him.'

He had never mentioned his grandfather before.

'If I give it to you, you have to promise not to lose it. I didn't carry it halfway around the world for you to forget where you put it. It cost my grandfather a leg,' he said.

'You mean an arm and a leg,' I said, correcting his English.

He hit me in the face so fast and hard that I was left silent and stunned as a searing pain rose in my left cheek. I hadn't seen it coming.

'You don't know what you're talking about,' he said.

I felt sorry for the sad bastard, but not sorry enough to tell him to go fuck himself. I might have been dumb, but I wasn't dumb enough to open myself up to another sucker punch. Besides, I still wanted to see what he had.

He fumbled through the glove box and pulled out a leather purse. He unzipped it. On top of several papers – including his proof of citizenship, which he always carried with him – I saw a small tarnished Iron Cross. The letter 'W' was imprinted in the center and below that '1914.'

I waited to make sure he hadn't changed his mind, then carefully picked it up and turned it over in my fingers.

'Here's a piece of advice,' he said. 'You'd better learn to be hated. Nobody loves a German.'

With that, he slammed his door and fired up the engine. He revved it while I buckled my seatbelt and slid the Iron Cross into my pocket; then he spun the car around and headed for the main road. The wheels squealed like a stuck pig when they hit the pavement and the car fishtailed. Soon we were racing at over a hundred miles per hour toward town. I slid back in my seat and relaxed. He couldn't pull any horse shit on me while he guided the car like a missile along narrow farm roads. We both knew this and it irritated him that I had one up on him, but rather than slowing down and setting me straight, he kept 'the pedal to the metal and the hammer down,' as he loved to say. He might have thought that the sheer speed would frighten me into submission. But that never happened. If he planned on blasting us out of the universe in a cataclysmic crash that pulverized us beyond recognition, I'd welcome it.

That weekend I was out playing near the ravine down the block when I heard children screaming. I shuffled down the bank to see what was going on. I came upon five kids standing over something a level below me. Looking closer, I saw the oldest boy holding a long stick with which he was teasing a snake backed against a log. The other children were laughing nervously.

'Stop,' I said.

They looked around.

'We got ourselves a snake expert, huh?' said the tall boy holding the stick.

'I can tell if it's poisonous.'

'Nobody's stopping you,' he said, motioning in the direction of the snake.

I jumped down and landed on a pile of shale, fell backward and slid all the way to the boy's feet. I stood up and tried to brush the dirt off my back, then positioned myself beyond striking distance to examine the snake's markings. Its head was long and cylindrical, no wider than the rest of its body, unlike the triangular head of a rattler, nor was it as colorful as a corn or coral snake, the only two poisonous land snakes with slender heads that I knew of.

'It's a gardener.' I reached forward to grab it. 'I'll put it someplace safe.'

As my hand clamped on the snake's neck, the boy jabbed his stick into its body so hard that it ruptured the skin. The head slipped from my grip as the snake went into a violent spasm. He forced the stick into the snake's small head and pushed it into the dirt. It stopped moving.

The children huddled together.

'Why'd you do that?' I asked, as I stood up.

He studied me for a few seconds without speaking. Then, unprovoked, he punched me in the face. His knuckles smashed into my nose and teeth. My mouth filled with warm blood. My upper lip split. Blood ran from my nose. I wiped my mouth on my sleeve and dropped my bloody hand to my side after glancing at it.

'You're that little Nazi fuck from up the block, aren't you?' He cocked his fist again and waited for me to hit him.

I didn't move. Fighting was the last thing I wanted. Ever.

41

'What're you waiting for?' the boy challenged.

'Don't, Darin,' a young girl shouted.

I stared at him, watching his cocked arm for a few seconds, trying to figure out what to do. Then I leaned down and picked up the dead snake. I looked back at the boy. His arm remained cocked, but he didn't advance toward me.

I stepped back and walked to the bank, ignoring the entire group. The boy shouted something. When I reached the top of the bank I walked across the grass to some bushes and slid into the foliage, hidden from the kids who had started up the bank. I reached down and dug a small hole in the moist soil with my hands, placed the snake inside and carefully filled it, leaving a small mound of dirt where the hole had been a few moments earlier.

At home my mother was standing beside the picnic table at the back door. She looked up from the celery she had been slicing.

'What happened?' She dropped the knife and ran to me.

As soon as she touched me, I began crying.

'What happened?' she asked again, wiping the blood away from my mouth with a towel she had picked up from the table.

'He hit me.'

'Who?'

'A boy. He lives over there. I don't know his name.' I pointed down the street.

'You shouldn't be fighting.'

'I wasn't.'

'It doesn't matter,' she said.

My father stepped outside to see what the commotion was about.

'Fight?' He took my chin in his hand and turned my head back and forth to examine the damage. 'There's nothing wrong with you.'

'He's hurt,' my mother said. 'Look at his face.''

'He got beat. He deserved it.'

'How could he deserve it?'

'When is dinner ready?'

'I don't want you talking to the children like that.'

'Like what?'

'Don't tell him he deserved it. You don't even know what happened.'

'I don't need to know. If he can't defend himself, he deserves to get beat.'

'If you want to eat, cook the food yourself.'

'I need lunch for work tomorrow.'

'Get away from me. Get away from my child.'

'Listen—'

'You listen. I don't want to hear you right now. Get away,' she said, shielding my head in her hands. She was so angry that she let go of me, grabbed the knife and concentrated on slicing the remaining celery sticks in rapid succession, one after the other.

He stood there for a moment longer and then disappeared back into the house. I heard him descend into the basement. When he had gone she said, 'Come on, let's get you cleaned up.'

During the next two months my father cooled toward me but he still took me on drives, including an overnight trip to the Old South End in Columbus on the other side of the state – the first time we had ever been away from my mother overnight together. Despite his insistence that I learn German-American history, I was forbidden to speak a single word of German. Even though he told a co-worker when we stopped at the bakery on the way out of town that we were going to *Die Alte Sud Ende* I was prohibited from saying the same. Iowa had outlawed publicly spoken German during the First World War, a policy he supported: 'You only need to know the language of your country. Speaking multiple languages in the same place only divides people. I don't give a shit what bleeding-heart liberals say. Try introducing Chinese as the second language in Mexico. I don't think they'd be too happy.' He was eager to prove his patriotism.

Driving south, I gave him a Parker pen I'd bought with money I'd earned raking our neighbor's yard. It was for his upcoming birthday but since he didn't like celebrating it, I didn't mention that when I gave it to him. He turned to me briefly, rubbed my head with his right hand, keeping the left on the steering wheel. I looked at him, but he was concentrating on the road again. He wore dark aviator sunglasses. I sensed he knew I was looking at him but he didn't acknowledge me.

Then I saw a single tear roll down his cheek from beneath his glasses. He rubbed his face against his shoulder to hide it. He was sad about something, I dared not ask what. That night he took me to a German restaurant. We ate sauerbraten and blood sausage. Then he took me to a beer garden where we listened to an oompah band while he drank until late.

Exactly a week after we returned home my mother woke me early on Sunday morning and asked if I had heard my father leaving. At first I thought I was dreaming. I had fallen asleep with my clothes on. The night before I had watched television with him until they played the national anthem, the American flag waving in the breeze, before the station closed down and the screen went fuzzy. We flipped the dial around to the other two channels but they had gone off air until the following morning. I rubbed my eyes with my palms and heard her ask, 'Did he say anything to you?'

Her words hit me like an iced snowball in the side of my head.

I don't know how. I don't know why. But I knew.

At that second, I absolutely knew.

So did she.

I leaped out of bed, ran into their room and yanked open the drawer on his side of the bed. The zippered leather purse with his citizenship papers in it was gone. My mother opened the closet. Several shirts and slacks were missing. I darted to the basement. One of the maps – the old one of the Samland peninsula – was missing, along with some books.

At the top of the stairs my mother tried to stop me but I pushed past her and ran out to the garage. His car wasn't there. The garage stood on a slope so it was easy to put the car in neutral and roll it out silently to start in the street. I paused and took a deep breath, then sprinted out of the garage and up the street to see if he had parked around the corner or at his friend's house. He hadn't.

I raced to the opposite end of the block, dashed down the alley, came out at the other end and ran back around the block. I didn't know which way to turn. I wanted to flee, but wasn't sure what I was running from. My mother came out of the house in her robe, ran onto the sidewalk and stopped me. She took me in her arms and held my face tight against her, the robe absorbing my tears. I cried so loudly that our neighbor appeared and asked what was wrong. My mother ignored her.

That morning the house was filled with the most awkward silence I had ever experienced – like a funeral, but no one had died. He had disappeared without leaving a note or giving any explanation. My little brother Walt and little sister Rebecca were too young to understand. Carl didn't seem to care.

I was on the cusp of becoming a man, waiting anxiously for my thirteenth birthday, peering backward across my early life and ahead to the possibilities the future held. Now the ridge on which I stood had crumbled. I had lost my father. My mother and I knew – although her sisters told her otherwise – that he wasn't coming back.

I retreated to my room. My little brother and sister went to stay with our cousins. As always Carl retreated to the river. I refused to leave the house. My mother stayed with me. The first night we slept together. After that I couldn't bear to sleep in the room he had abandoned so I went back to my own bed. I heard my mother crying late at night. I curled into a ball under the blankets and prayed that he would come home. In utter exhaustion I fell asleep and dreamed that he burst through the door without knocking, yanked me up by the arm and whipped me. I wanted the pain to be real. I wanted to feel the sting of the blows he inflicted to prove he hadn't left.

Two days later, when my mother and I went for a walk in the park along the river, it wasn't the same as it had been when I'd stepped outside after I'd been locked, crying, in my room. The world no longer felt as alive, the air no longer as crisp or fresh. Nothing seemed to matter.

I felt empty inside. Like a discarded can kicked across the yard.

That day, on the way home from the park, I watched the traffic pass back and forth, wishing I had the courage to step off the curb into a truck's path when it was too close to stop. I was a coward. I had been cowed. My father had betrayed me. He would not be forgiven.

BOOK II

Going South

In my father's absence, my childhood curiosity became a burden. I often wondered if my questions had driven him away. I worried that I might get into trouble for knowing too much. My father had insisted that I be proud of my extinct East Prussian heritage and my wider culture's German-American accomplishments. Expressing it, though, was a different matter and in my enforced silence I felt my hidden pride manifest in strange and malignant ways.

My father had taught me too much and then had disappeared. For a long time I didn't speak at all. My teacher wrote to my mother, asking her to come to school for a conference. She never went. She had entered her own state of withdrawal. Where my silence was rooted in fear and hurt, hers seemed an act of decompression and recovery from nearly two decades of marriage. I had always accepted the beatings as a natural part of growing up, but it was different when my father hit my mother: parents could hit their children but not each other. Once they started fighting you knew something was wrong, and more so when only one hit the other.

My mother, once shadowed by my father's domineering presence, withdrew further into isolation. I loved her but not as much as I had initially hated my father, and the only thing by which I could measure love was its opposite. I measured life by extremes: purposely burning my hand on the stove; nearly freezing to death in the snow; questioning my father to trigger a beating. When I had eventually learned to love him, my affection for him was as great as my initial loathing had been. My love for my mother had been constant. In its consistency, its lack of variance, it seemed less. It wasn't. But in this way we came to understand one another. She didn't like overt shows of emotion and once told me not to trust people who expressed too much enthusiasm. 'If they're too happy, something's in it for themselves.'

'But what if they're in love?' I inquired.

'They'll show it gracefully.'

'What about Dad?'

'He was different when we first met. He was graceful and charming at the same time . . .' Her voice trailed off.

We were both bruised. I felt like a little boy, although I was slowly becoming a man. Without my father to guide me I felt the seam between the two worlds ripping apart. I had always watched my step for fear of reprisal. With him gone, I knew my mother would never hit me. Perhaps she should have, but it probably wouldn't have made any difference to me. We both had to forge a new path to the waterfall.

In the same way I had known instantaneously that my father had gone for good, I also knew it was only a matter of time before we would leave as well. I didn't know where my mother would take us, but I knew we were going – and so did her sisters but none of them begged her to stay. They feared that my grandmother – who perhaps wanted us gone so that my single mother couldn't ruin her family name – might dismiss them from the company my late grandfather had founded and their husbands now operated.

My father had never been invited into the family business, whose proceeds had purchased every large house that our extended family lived in, including our own. He was too foreign, unfit for the presidency, the board or even the shipping yard. He baked while they sat at desks. I once overheard my oldest uncle say to his buddy when he thought me out of earshot, 'You don't drag somebody home fresh off the boat. You let them cure a while.' I overheard another relative say that he thought my father had stopped maturing as a result of some trauma he had suffered in childhood during the war. I found this absurd. How could my father be immature? I refused to believe I had been born to a boy.

*   *   *

50

Several months passed. Our house went on the market. My mother had decided to move to Georgia. In Ohio people didn't speak highly of Kentucky, which bordered our southern state line. I could only imagine what they thought of us moving all the way down to Georgia.

'If you want anything from the basement, you'd better get it before I start throwing things away,' my mother said.

Neither of us had been down there since the morning he'd left, and I couldn't bring myself to go down that day. I lay in bed late that night, resolute that I would leave without ever going back into the basement. I awoke before dawn to the sound of glass milk jugs clinking on the front porch. I jumped out of bed and ran to the window. It was only the milkman carrying an order of milk, eggs, butter and cheese to the cooler. I returned to bed and stared up at the ceiling. I wondered if there were milkmen in Georgia. I heard the lid of the small cooler slam shut and his footsteps shuffling off our porch to his truck, idling at the curb.

A couple of hours later I woke again. The scent of bacon and eggs rose through the house, with the sound of the coffee percolator and the smell of Folgers Mountain Grown. Without leaving my bed I could taste the crisp bacon she was laying on paper towels to absorb the grease. I changed my mind about the basement. The smell of familiar food gave me confidence. I didn't want to regret leaving something behind. My father had once told me that there were no regrets in life, but I didn't believe him.

After my mother had gone to the store to buy packing materials, I went down to the basement. I felt calm – my anxiety about the basement had stemmed from my father, not the place itself. It was already apparent that my father would follow me around for a long time. I could never be sure where his thoughts ended and mine began.

Though I had little experience of life, I possessed an intuitive understanding of it. I knew my limitations. It didn't matter how kind a teacher might be, I understood my place at the back of the class. It was not for nothing that they had failed me in kindergarten. My penmanship, for example, looked like that of a three-year-old

51

compared to my classmates'. I knew what I wanted to write, but it would come out in wildly varying letter sizes, capitals and lower-case, in no apparent order, not following the lines on the paper between which I had been instructed to write. This wasn't an early act of rebellion. Math was much the same. The teacher would write formulae on the board and hand us a sheet of problems to solve. I could solve the problems correctly, but I couldn't follow her formulae. I'd watch her write them and understand to some extent, but once the problem lay before me, I would work out my own formulae to find the solution. Since only fifty percent of our grade was the result of answering correctly and the other fifty percent the result of how we solved the problems, I almost always failed the test with a fifty percent mark, unless the teacher took pity on me – as many did. One advantage of being dumb was that people were often sorry for you.

Of one thing I felt certain, and perhaps it was my slowness that allowed me to see it more clearly than others: no matter how articulate, brilliant or quick a person might be, they were far less original than they believed. While many were faster than others, spoke more clearly, wrote perfectly and solved problems exactly as instructed, this did not necessarily set them as far apart from everybody else as they or their parents were often convinced. Of all the lessons I learned from my father, the most important was the one he had not intended to teach me.

Whenever he'd held forth about a historical point he wanted to make, he'd put it in various ways to help me understand. Afterward, to prove I understood, he might ask me to recite it or write down an outline. That was the problem. While I generally understood, I could not easily articulate. If you locked me in a room, put a gun to my head and told me to scribble my recollections, then handed the result to a typist to transpose, I could probably demonstrate comprehension but, of course, the opportunity never arose. Instead I was told to recite what I had learned.

One afternoon he spent an hour telling me about the differences and similarities between Germans, Americans and German-Americans, and the finer points of hyphenation, which I found as abstract as the concept of missing variables in algebra, not to mention dull. When he asked me to recite what I had learned, I couldn't give it back to him in the clear, ordered manner he demanded, even though I'd understood most of it and even grasped the examples he had given me. I didn't want to. I wasn't interested. He had talked about it for an hour. Why did I need to repeat it?

It's difficult to describe how much this infuriated him, to say nothing about the pain of retrieving those memories. But he had insisted we remember our past, our parents' past, their parents' and so on. Were it not for my early hatred of him, which had provided a buffer at such times, I would have curled up on the floor and stayed there forever. Nothing pained me more than my father's fury about my stupidity. He failed to comprehend that children are a reflection of their parents.

Many people agree that beatings – as a form of discipline – don't work, but I'm not convinced. On that afternoon my father had flown into a rage and ordered me to get the belt from the hook near the fuse box. I decided to humor him. I stood up, shuffled over to the staircase, retrieved the belt and came back to the table, folding it in two and snapping it together on the way to warm it up.

'You think you're clever?' he asked.

'Not particularly.'

'So you admit being clever, just "not particularly"?'

'At least as smart as you.'

'Then maybe you'll learn from this.'

He took the belt and mimicked my action of folding it in two and snapping the leather against itself. For a moment I did think I was clever. I thought I had found a way to deflect his rage, in part by gaining his respect with my boldness and in part with a meeting of the minds. I was sorely disappointed to find that I had miscalculated. As odd as it sounds, I didn't mind being beaten. I was used to it. That day was different: he beat the shit out of me. When he had finished he told me to go upstairs and take a shower, then left me alone in the basement. He drove to the bakery to check on the afternoon shift workers to make sure they 'didn't fuck something up.' I lay on the cold, damp concrete floor staring up at the joists for a long time, my back absorbing the floor's chill, which relieved the swelling and pain. Eventually I limped upstairs to clean up. When I turned my back to the mirror and looked over my shoulder, I saw narrow lines of blood droplets running the length of the welts. Those were a first. But without that beating I would never have remembered this: in the years leading up to the First World War, President Theodore Roosevelt insisted that immigrants drop their hyphen and become Americans to show their patriotism. He skillfully avoided attacking Germans specifically because of their massive voting power. He had failed to grasp that politicians of the previous century, primarily Anglos, had demanded that German-speaking immigrants stop calling themselves German and stop speaking their own language. They had stopped calling themselves German in favor of German-American, but they acceded to Roosevelt's demand to drop their hyphen: they underwent a final transformation from German-American to American. Then, after living through two world wars as America's pre-eminent enemy, they became America's first post-ethnic culture: they disappeared into a generic state of tribeless white, the primary stock simmering in the melting pot, from which they never fully emerged. That day my father had also insisted that, unlike the Irish or Latin Americans in the U.S., who were primarily Catholic, or the British, who were primarily Protestant, the Germans were Catholic, Jewish and of countless Protestant sects. Within their own culture they were more divided by belief systems than any other ethnic group entering the country.

With my father gone, my life made little sense. He had given me life, taken control of my mind, then abandoned me with information I no longer wanted, as though I was a host to forward his own cultural beliefs. I wanted to overcome him. It was my only goal. I wasn't sure it was possible. The only way I could overcome him was to forget him. I had to silence my mind and erase the data with which he had so carefully programmed it. I began to see all cultures, ethnic groups, races and religions as insidious, using their children

54

to retain memories so that on reaching adulthood they could avenge something that had occurred in another lifetime. I tried to figure out a way to free my mind. It was my older brother Carl who introduced alcohol as a possibility.

As soon as Carl had learned we were moving to Georgia he went to the army's recruiter. He had wanted to leave home for years. He was only sixteen, but the recruiter's sole requirement was that my mother sign to release him from her custody into theirs. She only asked him once if it was really what he wanted. Then she signed. He would leave for boot camp before we had finished packing the house. A classmate from high school had given him a bottle of whiskey as a going-away gift. He hid it in the woods near the river. One evening, shortly before he left for the army, he asked if I wanted to drink it with him. A few days later he smuggled one of our late grandfather's rifles out of the gun cabinet in the basement of our grandmother's house and hid it among the weeds in the alley behind her house. The next morning he told our mother he was taking me out on a day's hike along the river. My mother probably thought it would be good for me. She didn't ask when we'd be back.

We left the house and walked along Church Street. Halfway down the block, Carl told me to drop back, since I was shortest and less likely to be detected, run to the alley and fetch the gun. We had worn long coats to hide it.

I walked out of the alley with a stiff leg to stop the barrel protruding. We reached Washington Street and descended into the ravine. The rushing current from the Chagrin River sounded like a small jet lifting off in the woods below. Once we were on the trail that ran deep into the woods, Carl stopped. 'Give me the gun.'

He bent over and turned down the top of his socks. A handful of bullets spilled onto the leaves that covered the ground. He pulled out a few more from his coat pocket and handed them to me. 'Carry those,' he said. 'That should be enough for you.' He pulled the bottle from beneath a bush and twisted off the cap. 'Here. You first.'

I took it and passed it under my nose. It smelled like a mixture of turpentine and lighter fluid. 'How are we going to drink this?'

He tugged a bottle of Coke out of his coat pocket.

I turned the bottle up and swallowed as much as I could without puking, then grabbed the Coke.

He followed with his own shot and chaser. Then we repeated it.

'Did you get a buzz?' he asked.

'Something like that.' It wasn't exactly a buzz, but the constant hum of anxiety that rattled in my brain had been silenced. I couldn't tell if the forest had come more alive or keeled over and died, but I liked the sensation. I didn't have to worry about anything. It was as close as I had ever come to being free.

He told me to scout the trail ahead to make sure we didn't bump into anybody. If I met someone, I was to feign a coughing fit to give Carl enough time to hide the rifle. He dropped the lever, opening the chamber. A bullet emerged from the magazine. He slammed the lever shut, forcing it into the chamber.

I disappeared up the path. Carl let a gap open between us before he started after me. We continued like that without seeing each other for a long time. I stopped when I came to a fork in the path.

When Carl caught up, I asked, 'Which way?'

Right then we heard somebody coming up the path.

Carl jumped into the brush, snapping branches. I dove in behind him and we dropped onto our bellies. From where we lay I saw a pair of ragged boots reach the fork. Through the foliage I made out a man's face – the drunk who always sat in front of the drug store near the center of town. He wore an army jacket as ragged as his boots. After a few seconds, he moved on. We remained motionless in our hiding place.

'It should be clear now,' Carl said, a while later. 'Let's hurry.'

Once out of the bushes and back at the fork, I asked again, 'Which way?'

'Left. To the Indian mounds.'

We continued along the path, stopping for another shot of whiskey. This time I took a bigger chug. So did my brother.

'When are we going to shoot the gun?' I asked.

'You want to shoot a tree? What's the point if we don't kill something?'

'We should practice first. Make sure we know how it works.'

'You pull the trigger. It fires.'

'Then let me carry it,' I said.

'You'll get your turn.'

I walked ahead to take the lead position again, feeling lightheaded. Carl dropped back. We carried on as before. An enormous boom erupted in the forest behind me. I turned and broke into a run. I found Carl still holding the rifle to his shoulder pointing into the bushes.

'What did you shoot?'

'I heard something.'

'Let's look.'

After a few minutes of rooting around and coming up empty, we got back on the trail.

'Do you think anybody heard it?'

'No – we're too far from town,' Carl said.

'Let's take another shot of whiskey.'

He pulled the bottle out and handed it to me. We both took a small drink. The sip didn't sit as well as the last had. I felt like throwing up. My brother handed me the Coke. I sat on the ground and looked up at the gun. 'Come on, give me a turn.'

He handed it to me. I cocked it and glanced around the forest. Carl had already started walking forward when I saw, less than twenty feet from the trail, a squirrel clinging to the side of a buckeye tree. Its fur blended into the bark. I raised the rifle to my shoulder, put the bead squarely on its back and squeezed the trigger. The stock slammed into my shoulder harder than I'd expected. My ears rang.

Carl spun around. 'What the hell are you doing?'

I pointed at a hole in the tree. 'I think I killed a squirrel.' I handed him the rifle and pushed through the bushes. 'Bull's eye!' I held up the dead animal.

'Bring it here.'

He pulled his knife out, the same one from our canoe trip. I threw

57

the squirrel on the ground and watched him drop to his knees. He sliced off the tail and slung the body into the woods. 'You can sell these things. Twenty for a buck. There's an ad in the back of *Boy's Life*.'

'That's it? Five cents each?'

He was already marching ahead, looking for more game. By the time I caught up with him he was passing an abandoned pump house and the chassis of a Model A Ford with a small tree growing where the engine was once bolted. The trail went over a series of pitches, short rises and falls. 'We're getting near the mounds,' he said.

As the trail briefly flattened, Carl stopped. 'You hear that?' he whispered.

'The dog?'

'It sounds like it's coming from the mounds.'

'Maybe we should go home.'

'Nobody's going home.'

He started walking again. The barking grew louder.

Within a few minutes we reached another fork in the trail. He took the left branch. I hesitated. The dog was nearby. The pitch of its bark changed so I knew it must have heard us. I ran up to Carl so I wouldn't be left behind. A few hundred yards down the path, we entered a clearing. The dog stood at the far edge, barking frantically at us. A series of mounds was partially hidden in the overgrowth. I glanced around, noticing their symmetry.

'That dog's got rabies or something.' Carl said. He lifted the rifle to his shoulder.

'He doesn't have rabies. It looks like the dog from the junkyard—'

Carl fired.

The dog yelped and fell to the ground.

I felt as if the blood had just drained from my head. Everything seemed distorted. I looked at the dog. It didn't move or make any more noise.

'Let's get out of here,' Carl yelled. He flung the rest of the whiskey into the woods, then turned and sprinted up the trail. I tried holding his pace, but he pulled away from me. Branches slapped my face as I ran after him. I didn't catch up until we reached the fork where we had hidden in the bushes from the drunk. He abruptly cut to the right and entered the thicket. I followed him. We came immediately to a small clearing, shielded on all sides by brambles. 'Let's stay here. We can't go home with alcohol on our breath.'

My brother slid down until he was lying flat on his back and closed his eyes. I did the same. Then, feeling nauseous, I opened my eyes and spread my arms. Once the ground stopped spinning, I closed my eyes again and fell into a deep sleep. Near dusk, I felt something poking me in the side. I looked up and saw Carl standing over me, nudging me with his foot.

'Get up,' he said. 'Take the rifle to Church Street, then cut over to the alley and hide it in the same place. Make sure no one sees you. I'll get it when Mom goes to sleep tonight.'

We climbed out of the hiding place and started walking along the trail. Before we reached the ravine, Carl turned off the main path.

I followed him but before I'd got very far he stopped, and said, 'Go your own way.'

I went back to the main trail. I glanced down to make sure the coat covered the barrel and started up the ravine.

Three days later Carl boarded the Greyhound bus and left for boot camp.

After the movers had carried the furniture away, I walked around inside the empty house. Each room had become an echo chamber. The rugs had been rolled up and loaded in the truck. The tables, chairs, dressers, pictures, bedding and lamps were gone. The house stood naked. My footsteps echoed down the hallways, my voice bouncing from wall to wall. The house felt larger than it had when it was furnished. The only home I had ever known felt alien, like a building I had wandered into from the street. I had taken it for granted – my home, my village, my place of birth – and now it was yanked from beneath me. The house was cold, barren, unyielding.

It would soon belong to someone else. I went down the stairs into the basement. The hook was still fixed to the wall near the fuse box, but the belt was gone. The heating-oil tank stood in the corner, but the old ax handle my father used to dip into it to measure the remaining fuel had disappeared. The maps were gone. The hand-built bookshelves remained. The books had gone, except the two on the center shelf that I had come to retrieve.

Part of me didn't want them. I had no interest in reading them, but he had left a copy of the one he had written. I worried that if I left it I'd regret it later, so I took it, with the slim volume in which I had spent two hours carving out a secret chamber for the Iron Cross my father had given me. He told me his grandfather had hidden it similarly during our trip to Columbus the week before he disappeared. Part of me didn't want the medal, either. I didn't want to leave Chagrin, but I had no choice. I carried the two books upstairs to hide in my belongings. I didn't want to upset my mother with reminders of him.

We packed the station wagon for our journey south, loading it with pillows, suitcases and a cooler stuffed with food. I kept a long, narrow space open in the back so that I could slide in and sleep while my mother drove. Once the car was loaded, my little brother, sister, mother and I climbed inside and drove away. We left town in silence. My mother crossed the entire state without saying a word. It was a silence I would come to know well over the following years. Before nightfall I already felt locked in its oppressiveness. My mother stared straight ahead as she drove. We were all scared to ask her anything. She never smiled or reached over to touch Walt or Rebecca. I sat in the back with them pointing out different makes of cars to stop them bothering her, glancing occasionally at the rear-view mirror, hoping she would acknowledge me, but she never did. Later I crawled to the very back of the car to lie in my cocoon and stared up at the clouds. I felt as if I was floating again, but instead of rising and hovering above the world, I was encased in a bubble, unable to reach out. We rolled through the southern part of the state and across the immense Ohio River and into the hills of Kentucky.

Shortly after we'd crossed the Kentucky border I crawled out of my space and over the back seat where Walt and Rebecca were now asleep and into the front beside my mother. Maybe leaving Ohio behind had freed her because for the first time that day she spoke: 'Do you want something to eat?'

'Is there any Coke left?' I asked.

She pointed at the cooler. I reached into it and pulled out a drink.

'Can you hand me one?' she asked.

It seemed to lighten her mood. She told me how, as a child, she used to drive the same route to Florida with her family. She talked about how she and her best friend used to go to Atlantic City after they'd finished high school and she mentioned a guy she had met there whom she had dated briefly before moving to Los Angeles where she had met my father. The farther away from Ohio we got, the deeper into the past her stories moved. Late that night she told me about the first boy she'd had a crush on, and as she talked I began to understand her attraction to my father.

'I was a child then, younger than you,' she said. 'My older sister and I were walking in the fields behind our farmhouse in Indiana. A set of railroad tracks ran along the back of the field. During the war, the army transported several hundred thousand POWs they had captured in Germany to camps around the country. A camp near our house held thousands of Germans. My father always warned me to be careful of the Nazis being transported on the tracks, but that only intrigued me more. One afternoon we put on the new dresses our mother had just finishing sewing and walked through the pasture. A train appeared. It was moving slower than normal. The engineer must have been waiting for an operator down the line to switch tracks because it came to a complete stop as it neared us. A group of young men in their late teens and twenties shouted at us. I got scared and turned to my sister, but she didn't move. I started to say something to her as one of the prisoners, a boy seven or eight years older than us, held up his arm and waved. I could see his face clearly. My sister was staring at the next car where another boy was waving at her.'

'Why didn't you run?' I asked.

'Something held us there. An emotion I'd never felt before. The train pulled forward again and I heard the boy yell something. At first I couldn't understand what he was saying. Then I heard him yelling, "I love you," and, again, more clearly in German, "*Ich liebe dich.*" The men in the car surrounding him laughed and began shouting other things I didn't understand but knew were vulgar. Just before the train passed from our field and into the next the boy tore at his shirt. As I stepped back he flung a small piece of fabric out of the window. We waited until the train disappeared. My sister made me look down the tracks to make sure another train wasn't approaching before she let me run over to pick it up. "Don't tell Mother where it came from." She seemed disappointed that the boy who had yelled at her hadn't tossed her anything. I took the tiny piece of cloth home and hid it in my pillowcase. I took it out every night to touch it. I'd fall asleep dreaming about marrying a German, a real German, not an American one like the boys at school. I came home from school a couple of weeks later and saw our pillowcases hanging on the line to dry. I searched everywhere for the piece of cloth but never found it. I was too scared to ask Mother if she had seen it. My father would have been angry if he knew it was from the Nazi prisoners. I never did tell your father about it. He would have been jealous. After the war I rarely heard anyone mention the German prisoners we had here, almost like it never happened. Nobody wanted to think about the war once it ended. The Germans disappeared.'

'Where did they go?'

'I guess they were sent back to Germany.'

'I wonder where the boy is now,' I said.

It was too dark to see her face, but she didn't respond. I imagined her blushing. The radio station, which had been playing softly in the background, became full of static as we entered a pass between two mountains. I twisted the dial and tuned in to a country station playing 'Behind Closed Doors,' a hit my father used to sing for my mother.

62

I reached for the dial to turn to a different station, but before I could my mother clicked the radio off. We sat in silence. I didn't know what to say. She had finally felt comfortable enough to open up and then I had ruined it by reminding her of him.

I asked, 'How long before we get to Georgia?'

She didn't answer. We were stuck again in the silence that had engulfed us crossing Ohio. Not even Tennessee saved us. All because of a stupid mistake I had made. And now I wasn't even able to drown the silence with music. It had a weight, a heaviness, that made my stomach hurt as if I'd eaten too much. It was my fault that my father had left, I was sure.

When Walt and Rebecca woke up a few hours later, my mother said, 'See if they're hungry and give them something to drink.' At least she'd said something.

I handed soft drinks to Walt and Rebecca. 'Don't bother Mom while she's driving. She has to concentrate on the road.'

They were eight and ten years old by then, but already they seemed to have withdrawn into their own private place. Our father wasn't a particularly affectionate man and our mother was reserved in an old-world-Lutheran-converted-to-new-world-Methodist kind of way: respectful, polite and well-mannered; austere, solemn and intelligent. No one could ever accuse her of not loving us, but her love seemed sterile and cold. She distrusted warmth.

In Georgia we moved into the basement of the Bon Air – a colossal, decaying white building, which jutted out, like a medieval castle, on its hill, easily seen from any location in downtown Augusta. Once a prestigious hotel that had housed such guests as Lyndon B. Johnson, it had since deteriorated into a low-income retirement home, whose owner had taken pity on my mother and allowed us to move in. We lived briefly in quiet, self-imposed exile in a basement apartment.

I complained about the damp heat for the first three weeks, begging my mother to move to the lake house in Indiana or out to the drier heat of California. The suffocating humidity rising from the Savannah River and the swamps on the southern edge of town drenched me in sweat day and night. As one month passed into the next, I abandoned my pleas to relocate as we slowly acclimatized to the spongy air.

In early November, winter arrived abruptly, much colder than we had expected after the suffocating summer. The humidity remained but now served only to pass the brittle cold through our coats, sweaters and blankets, penetrating our bones. Despite the tiny space, we kept our distance from each other by reading books or watching the small television my mother had set up in the corner of the room. It seemed to satisfy our social needs – we let it do the talking for us. Like a mute family, we lived through the characters of *Andy Griffith*, *Gilligan's Island* and *Lost in Space*. Late at night, when my mother let me, I watched *The Twilight Zone*.

After months in that dingy room, whose huge clanking radiator produced more racket than heat, my mother loaded us again into the battered station wagon. This time we crossed the border into South Carolina and drove to Edisto Beach, a tiny island on the coast she had found while perusing the road atlas, a habit she had acquired after leaving Chagrin to help her fall asleep late at night. The beach, popular by summer, was an abandoned and inexpensive place to live in the winter – long rows of uninhabited houses separated from the surf by seawalls built of timber torn from the swamplands a few miles inland. The afternoon we arrived, snow was falling on the beach. The next morning the sand had disappeared. The store owner assured us that the island hadn't seen snow in more than a decade.

Later that afternoon, scanning the desolate, razor-straight road that ran the length of the island, my mother told us it lacked the job she would need through the winter to support us. She ordered us into the station wagon and drove back to Georgia, ready to lay roots in a state and town about which she knew nothing. Still well-behaved and obedient, we sat quietly in the back as we passed through barren winter cotton, soybean and tobacco fields.

A few weeks later, we settled in an apartment on Wrightsboro Road. A letter arrived from Carl. He had just completed boot camp and had been selected to enter a second boot camp for the Special Forces – the Rangers. If he passed, he would probably be stationed in Germany – at least, that was what he had been told. I doubt he had ever considered the possibility of being sent there, but he simply stated it as fact. I could tell from the distant look in my mother's eyes that, despite the chronic depression she appeared to be sinking into, she was proud of him.

For the first time I became aware of music that was different from what I had grown up listening to at home, an aggressive sound that blasted from menacing shiny black Camaros and Firebird Trans Ams with mag wheels, wide tires and exhaust systems that rumbled when they pulled up alongside us at stoplights. They didn't have cars like those back in Chagrin. If my father's Porsche was a panzer, these were battleships. Whenever my mother went to the grocery stores – which had strange names like Winn Dixie and Piggly Wiggly – I'd stand at the magazine rack and read *Cream*, *Hit Parade* and *Rolling Stone*. When my mother noticed my interest, she bought me a portable eight-track tape player and let me pick three tapes from Home Folks, a nearby record store. I bought the ones I heard on every car stereo we passed: Lynyrd Skynyrd, the Allman Brothers Band and Molly Hatchet. I had never heard music about swamps, doing drugs, killing people, kicking ass or southern pride before. To my young mind, it was music from a foreign country. I was drawn to its aggression – compared to Charlie Rich or Bill Evans – and its sheer power. They didn't make music like that up north, at least none I'd ever heard.

My world had been stretched to the breaking point. It didn't matter that Chagrin and Augusta both had rivers at their center or that it was less than a two-day drive between the two. We might as well have crossed an ocean. I couldn't imagine my father's journey from the old world to the new being any more radical than my teenage transition from North to South. They still spoke English in Georgia, but it wasn't the same – different words, different expressions, different accents and a different attitude – and the food was different, too: hush puppies, deep-fried okra, chicken gizzards and pork rinds; even the air smelled different – humid, hot, already sticky by the first light of dawn, at least until you'd acclimatized. We were strangers in a strange land. Almost nothing was the same. Whites and blacks weren't separated from each other as they were up North. We shopped in the same stores, attended the same schools. My first teacher there was black, as were more than half of the students in my class.

After my mother finally got the money from the house we had sold in Ohio, she bought another in a section of town more like Chagrin than any other. The house was a Spanish colonial, with bars covering the windows, ivy growing up to the tiled roof and Spanish moss hanging from the limbs of the huge oak in the front yard. On our first day there, our neighbor shouted over the hedge, 'How y'all doing? Y'all from round here?'

I had no idea what he was saying, so I shrugged and walked away without answering, but I soon learned that that was not how things were done in the South. There was something called hospitality and something else called respect, but unlike the style common in the North, where you gave your neighbors plenty of space and privacy, this was a more in-your-face, stand-your-lazy-ass-up-from-that-pew-and-shout-it-loud-*and*-proud that took some adjusting to.

Another difference between my hometown and Augusta was that in Chagrin there were no private schools. In Augusta, parents who didn't want their children educated with blacks enrolled them in private preparatory schools. I attended public school but only for a few days at first, then took time off to help my mother unpack the boxes and arrange the furniture that had been delivered to our new house. After I returned to class, I was daydreaming about Ohio when I heard someone say something. I ignored it. A ruler snapped against my desktop. I jumped. The teacher, who had been calling my name with an accent that made it sound like somebody else's, was standing over my desk.

'What?' I asked.

'Don't you ever "what" me again.' She told me to come up to the front of the room. 'Where's your homework?'

'I was helping my mother move. I didn't have time.'

'Don't tell me that lie,' she said.

'What lie?'

'You say "what" one more time, I'll have you thrown out of this school.' She asked where I was from.

'Ohio.'

'They don't teach manners up North?'

I didn't know what to say so I kept my mouth shut. I had been accused of a lot of things in my life but never of being impolite. Then, in a moment of kindness – perhaps recognizing that I didn't understand what she was getting at – she told me to step out into the hallway. I heard her give the class an assignment before she came out and joined me.

'You'd better shape up,' she said, 'or you're never going to get on down here.'

She explained that whenever I was addressed, whether by man or woman, black or white, I was best responding, 'Yes, ma'am,' 'No, ma'am,' or 'Yes, sir,' 'No, sir,' but never 'What?'

'I can't believe people speak like that,' she said. 'It may not sound it to you, but you can say, "Yes, ma'am?" as a question too, instead of asking me "What?". Affirmative, confirmation, whatever. I don't want to hear you saying, "Okay," in my class, either. It sets a bad example. Apparently you've never heard of respect. You'll make a lot more friends down here if you do as I say, you understand?'

I nodded.

'I can't hear you.'

'Yes,' I said.

'I still can't hear you.'

'Yes, ma'am.'

'Now, that wasn't so hard, was it?'

'No, ma'am.'

'Don't come back to class again lying about you had to help your mother move and couldn't do your homework, you understand?'

'Yes, ma'am.'

'You can go back in the room now.'

In the months following, I automatically inserted these new phrases along with others into my vernacular. She was right: it was easier to say things the way everybody else said them. It saved time and kept you out of trouble. And even when I got in trouble, I learned that 'Yes, ma'am' and 'Yes, sir' got me out of trouble a whole lot faster. It was like learning to talk again. Despite her accusation that I had lied about helping my mother move into our new house, she was still the nicest person I had met since moving South, and the only one to pull me aside and let me know what was expected of me in this foreign place.

But even with such sound advice, it wasn't long before my world was crumbling again. The incessant hum of my father's voice droned in my head, along with the anxiety that accompanied it, recently compounded by the gnawing feeling that my mother resented my presence: my square jaw reminded her of my father and my accent, a conglomeration of northern nasal, lilting East Prussian German and a little drawling southern finding its way into the mix. Occasionally she glanced at me with a hint of the bitterness she had previously reserved for my father. I shuddered with self-revulsion whenever she did so and started to resent her in turn. As much as I wanted to put my father out of my mind, I found it impossible to do so when her eyes told me I had become him.

Once we were settled in the house, I took my father's book and the one in which I'd hidden the Iron Cross, sealed them in a plastic bag and carried them out into the backyard, where I dug a hole in the ground near the back fence in a small clump of woods. I still couldn't bring myself to read my father's book. My childhood curiosity had been crushed by his disappearance, and the love I had once briefly felt for him had turned again to hate. I had listened to him talk and he had told me hardly anything I wanted to know. If he couldn't tell it to my face, I didn't want to read it. If I ever wanted to come back for it, it would be there, but to keep my mind separate from his, I needed to bury it without letting his thoughts influence me any more than they already had.

The surges of adrenaline from my early childhood never subsided completely. I still waited for an invisible hand to knock me to the floor. My most natural state was of nervousness. It irritated me when people told me to relax – relaxing opened you up for attack. I didn't trust people who exuded calm in the same way my mother didn't trust people holding hands in public. Utter calm seemed an affectation rather than a genuine emotion.

Shortly before my fourteenth birthday, I got drunk again – shitfaced – this time for an entire week. Given what I had been through, my approaching fourteenth birthday might as well have been my twenty-first. I was old enough to drink, I convinced myself. I could take it like a man. For a week, I hardly saw my mother at all. I'd slip in late at night after hanging out alone in the woods all day. For that week booze erased my memories, but once I sobered up the distant past returned.

My mother was working as a cashier at a department store during the day and attending night school each evening. She rarely tracked my whereabouts. Walt and Rebecca learned to fend for themselves. They attended school – the bus picked them up out front in the morning and dropped them off each afternoon. They let themselves into the house with a key they wore tied with a shoestring around their necks.

A few mornings after I'd tried to cure myself with alcohol, I woke up and fried two eggs for breakfast. Minutes after I'd had the last bite, I threw up. After that, I didn't bother eating breakfast any more. I wasn't fond of puking. It was like beating yourself from the inside. I sensed that booze and I were going to have a difficult union but generations before me had stayed the course so I decided to be patient. The following week I discovered a bottle of Valium in the medicine cabinet of my neighbor's house – I'd broken in to find money for whiskey. I swallowed two five-milligram tablets. It was like finding God. Later I swallowed two more pills and I didn't throw up that night or the following morning after eating an entire omelet at Waffle House. To celebrate my discovery of pharmaceuticals, I stole a bottle of Wild Turkey. Combining Valium with alcohol was rumored to increase the effects and it did – ten-fold – but I puked my guts out so bad that I went cold turkey and stopped drinking completely. Drugs were the answer.

Even so, there were problems. Augusta wasn't Miami, with small planes buzzing in from Colombia, or El Paso, with runners coming across the Rio Grande. It was pretty much no man's land. Finding a steady stream of drugs was a puzzle. I solved it by starting a minor-league career as a cat burglar.

There were advantages to early-teen drug addiction – mainly because I was so young that nobody believed me. They naturally assumed I was lying to get attention. One afternoon, a cop saw me stumbling along the alley behind 7-Eleven, drove up behind me and asked if I was okay. The drugs acted like a truth serum: I confessed I had broken into three houses that week and stolen prescription drugs. He asked me to turn out my pockets. They were empty. He laughed and said, 'Okay, cowboy, time for you to saddle up and canter home to sleep it off. I don't want to see you stumbling around here again. Understand?'

'Yes, sir.'

With that he let me go. He didn't even take me home to my mother. After that I didn't bother confessing. I left the grown-ups to their convictions while conducting new experiments to find out if pharmaceuticals could melt my mind and the memories buried in it better than booze. I was looking for long-term relief this time, the chemical equivalent of electroshock therapy rather than alcohol-induced blackouts.

I was tickled that in my stupor I'd retained the clarity to find new substances that didn't make me sick. Apart from my dislike of vomiting, sickness would have told my mother that something was awry. She knew I was getting into trouble, but whenever I arrived home I appeared sober enough for her to ignore me. I switched drugs every four or five days to avoid physical addiction to one particular drug. In doing so I'd discovered a revolutionary way of being an addict without being addicted. I also introduced a new vice into the mix: THC, weed, ganga, mary jane, pot, dope. I loved its various names almost as much as smoking it – its pungent scent and mellow high provided the perfect balance to the other drugs, and when I did feel a little nauseous, smoking it settled my stomach. The hum of anxiety that lived inside me dissipated with each exhaled puff.

I let my mother catch me smoking cigarettes a few times, then refused to quit, so that in the future when she smelled smoke she'd assume it to be tobacco. In fact, I stopped smoking altogether once she was convinced I was a smoker and replaced cigarettes with joints. It made little sense that somebody would risk their health for a drug that barely got them high when they could smoke pot instead. I wouldn't have called myself a health nut, but I did try to strike a balance. When I got the munchies, for instance, I went for corn chips instead of candy bars. I liked drugs: I took them seriously, studied them. I identified new ones in a pharmaceutical reference book I checked out from the public library: it had a picture of each pill, the recommended dosage – for my purposes, you tripled it – and, most importantly, side effects. The ones that said 'May produce drowsiness,' 'May impair judgment' or 'Do not mix with alcohol' were keepers. I learned early on not to rely exclusively on side effects to find new highs. I spent nearly a week experiencing head rushes and hot flashes before discovering that the pills I was taking were for menopausal women and loaded with estrogen.

Regardless of the pitfalls, drugs were the tool that freed me. As with alcohol, I had to stay under the influence to remain free, which became a prison in itself, but for me it was the lesser of two evils.

Besides drugs, I'd also discovered an interest in and natural talent for robbery. When you're young and white, you can waltz through the best neighborhoods, winking at the little old ladies and waving confidently at the men, while waiting for them to turn their backs so you can climb through their windows and rob them blind. I enjoyed it. It gave me self-confidence, a sense of purpose and self-worth – all delusional, given I was under the influence of drugs. I worked in isolation and enjoyed the fruit of my labor in private. I was used to being alone. I didn't require much social interaction. I liked the challenge. I didn't feel as if I was hurting anybody. They could buy more of what I stole or go to the doctor to get their prescriptions refilled. I only targeted wealthy homes – and would return a couple of weeks later for a refill. The rich were arrogant that way. They never expected to get robbed in the first place and it was beyond their comprehension that the burglar would have the audacity to return. Sometimes I'd break into a house and take a few items, old cameras, for example, then dump them in the reservoir just so they'd go out and buy a new one that was more valuable. Rich people seemed incapable of throwing their old shit away so I did it for them. I felt untouchable. I sometimes stood outside a crime scene with the neighbors, while the police and homeowners scratched their heads, trying to figure out who could rob so many houses in broad daylight, without a single person seeing them come or go.

I'd store some of the things I stole – Nikon F4s, coin collections, an occasional handgun and dozens of bottles of prescription drugs – in the attic in our house. I'd wait until my mother left for work, then crawl up there, load a book bag and take the bus to the pawnshops downtown. I quickly learned which places didn't care how old I was as long as the goods were authentic and in working order. I wasn't allowed to walk in the front door off the street: I had to knock on the alley door and hand them the goods in a school backpack. Since they knew they had me, there wasn't much room for negotiation. They'd give me just enough to keep me coming back. They didn't buy everything, though.

The lower end of Broad Street, downtown, had been abandoned by the middle-class whites who had fled to the suburbs before I moved to Augusta, but the pawnshop owners held out, along with the old perverts who frequented the seedy bars down there. They would do just about anything for a young boy in hopes of getting into his pants, including buying stuff they had no use for at inflated prices. Some tried to talk me into living with them, claiming I'd never have to worry about anything again. I'd string them along so they wouldn't stop buying my wares. They lavished me with

72

attention, but I never let them touch me, which, in a weird way, won their respect. I found them repulsive, but they were kinder than my own father and that went a long way.

One of the old goats introduced me to speed, hoping to get me amped up enough to crawl out of my pants. I was never bashful about trying new drugs. I had sniffed coke, smoked crack and popped black beauties, but that day I snorted powder that had a pink radioactive tint. I didn't crawl out of my pants, but I definitely crawled out of my mind. After that I steered clear of amphetamines. My mind chattered enough without speed. My goal was to make it silent, not explode. Neither could I stand anything that made my hands shake. I could tell if someone was tweaked on speed a mile off and I avoided them.

On the other hand, you could never be sure whether a downer-oriented person was stoned or just plain stupid – a dichotomy that worked pretty well for me. Plus stoners had little interest in fighting or violence – drunks and speedsters loved swinging their fists if only to watch their hands moving. LSD didn't move me much, either. The hippies who sold it to me loved it, claiming they were going to save the world by making everyone drop acid at the same time and fall in love. Yet for all the clarity it supposedly invoked nobody seemed to notice that only whites liked it. Down in the ghetto there were no acid parties or love-ins. At least, not in the places I started venturing to buy my favorite mind fryer: PCP – the elusive angel dust.

The only place I could score it was in the housing projects near downtown. On PCP, you could float off the ground and hang out up there. Everything became distorted and opposites applied: falling face-first on the ground felt good. Eating was unpleasant since everything tasted of the food you hated most. But the positives far outweighed the negatives – being able to float without dreaming, getting injured without hurting. It was a miracle drug. On PCP, I rocketed into new galaxies every day. It put a bounce into my step and, for the first time ever, I was delighted to be alive.

*   *   *

73

Apparently I was a little too happy: my mother was onto me. My drug-induced psychosis forced me to spend more time away from home to continue my chemical evolution. Had we stayed in Chagrin Falls, I'm not sure I would have discovered drugs, but by then I loved the South a hundred times more than any part of my life in Ohio. When you come of age in a place it becomes part of you, no matter how hard the natives try to keep you out. One day I was buying weed from a dealer on Wrightsboro Road. He paused while measuring out an ounce to sing a few lines along with his stereo, then said to me, 'You'll never understand the "The Night They Drove Old Dixie Down," no matter how many times you listen to it, boy.'

I stared a hole through his head. 'I know you're not serious.'

'Serious as smoke rising from a fire – and what the fuck you gonna do about it?'

'Inform your pea brain that it was written by a Canadian.'

Territorial righteousness was the one aspect of the South I could have lived without. I would never be authentic in their eyes. In the North, my schoolmates called me a Nazi. Down South, they called me a Yankee. But the blacks I associated with didn't seem interested in ridiculing me.

A couple of days later the guy I bought angel dust from, down near the river, invited me to share a joint with him after completing a deal.

'Where you from?' he asked.

'California,' I lied. It was a reflex action. I had already taken too much grief for being a northerner.

'I got a cousin out there,' he said. 'He's always talking down about me staying in the South. I tell him it's home, that he ain't no freer out there. You ever seen Watts? You ever been to Oakland?'

I admitted I hadn't.

'What city you from?' he asked.

'All over. My father's from Germany,' I said, to deflect the question.

A broad grin spread across his face. 'I know you're one crazy motherfucker.'

I didn't argue with that. For once somebody had nailed it without

74

being derogatory. I thanked him for the angel dust and told him I'd be back.

Later that afternoon I was arrested for possession of a foreign substance and stolen property. The cops had staked out the area under the bridge on Broad Street, where I met one of the old goats to trade him some goods for a bag of weed. I had just climbed into his car and begun rolling a joint when the cops surrounded us. Besides the dimes of angel dust in my pocket, I was also carrying a prescription bottle of Valium with the previous owner's name and address typed on the label. My knapsack was filled with stolen camera equipment. Looking back, I don't think the cops originally had us on their radar. They had been waiting for something else to go down. But when they saw me getting into the old man's car they moved in to save me. The old man didn't have anything in his possession. He had already handed me the bag of weed and I was still holding the knapsack I had brought to trade him when they pulled us out of the car. They let him go, put me in the back of the patrol car and drove me to the station. It was the first time I had been arrested, the first time they had something that would stick.

Unfortunately, the adhesive wasn't very good. I soon learned that it rarely was with juveniles. Once I turned eighteen they could lock me up for years, but until then I would have to do something drastic to end up in jail.

I was placed on probation and assigned a probation officer, who called my mother to pressure her into making sure I attended school. I tried to attend first period, so that my name was on the attendance sheet, but by ten each morning I'd wander off campus. Otherwise, my arrest changed little. My activities slowed, but I still broke into houses. I was more cautious and selective, but I didn't stop. My drug intake increased. Each day melted into the next. I took pills to help me fall asleep and to dampen my mind so I wouldn't have any dreams. When I opened my eyes I'd do a 'wake 'n' bake': without getting out of bed, I'd pull out my pipe and take a couple of hits of weed to keep me going until I could get something stronger in my system. The key was to stay baked out of my mind as long as possible. Brainless as it sounds, it was hard work.

Unlike a drunk, I could function on drugs. They took the edge off my anxiety and allowed me to focus better. I could plan and execute a robbery with more clarity when I was stoned. I changed my methods so that nobody ever knew I had entered their house. I'd walk through a neighborhood on a reconnaissance mission and select several houses. Over the following days, I'd walk through again and steal a piece of junk mail to identify the name of a homeowner. I'd grab some junk mail from their neighbors too, which I took home and used to find their numbers in the telephone book. A few days later, I'd call the house several times to make sure no one was in and repeat this process with the neighbors.

When all was clear I walked over to the house and searched for a way to get inside without being detected. There were many ways to do this, such as forcing an old basement window off its hinges, repairing it once inside and leaving out of the rear door, locking it behind me, or I might locate an unlocked window high enough off the ground that the owners didn't imagine anyone could crawl through. There were always old boards, wheelbarrows or even ladders alongside the houses that I could use to reach the windows.

More often than not I simply used the owners' keys to unlock the house. It was amazing how stupid they were when they hid keys in case they locked themselves out – under a rock near the back door, under, or buried lightly in a flowerpot, on top of the doorframe or the entry light. If I found the key, I'd unlock the door, sneak in and search for valuables in timeworn places. If I found jewelry, I'd pick through it for a small article I figured they rarely wore, or if there were two earrings with large diamonds, I'd take only one so they'd assume they had lost whatever I stole. I was most interested in their medicine cabinet. I never took prescription bottles now: I'd pick through the drugs and if I found barbiturates or painkillers, I'd dump as many in my pocket as I figured I could take without detection. Then I'd glance at the refill date, make a mental note and place the bottle back on the shelf where I'd found it, planning to return after that date to borrow more. Then I'd slither outside, carefully locking the door and putting the key back in its hiding place.

That was my life but it was showing evidence of hairline fractures.

I sensed it one afternoon when I broke into a house and quietly climbed the stairs to the master bedroom where owners typically hid their most prized possessions. Along the staircase neatly framed pictures hung at perfect intervals. In some, the parents stood proudly with their children, hugging and holding them, laughing, but most were of the children – in a sandbox, flying a kite, skipping rope, opening a present with a huge smile. I wondered what it would be like to have a family full of love, support, nurturing and happiness. My upbringing made me distrust the images – there were photo-albums of smiling children in my house – but standing on those stairs, the sun entering a window and reflecting off the glass of the pictures, I recognized that happiness, love and trust were stronger and more powerful than the hate and constant self-doubt I knew so well.

I had felt that love during moments of my childhood. But it seemed that happiness was more difficult to achieve than depression and self-doubt. I could take a pill to relieve my anxiety but the high simply covered my sadness.

I never made it to the top of those stairs. Ashamed of my behavior for the first time, I slunk down and let myself out of the door. I hid the key beneath the rock in the garden beside the rear door and sneaked out of the yard. Over the next week, I walked past the house several times to glimpse the family. I wanted the feeling I had experienced on their stairway to return. The following weekend, I passed the bushes hiding their house from their neighbors and started to cross their driveway as they were pulling out. The father stopped the car and waved me across in front of them. I waved back, thanking him, and looked quickly into the car. The children were in the back seat laughing at something their mother had said and never noticed me. The father smiled and made sure I was clear before he pulled forward. Then they were gone and sadness swelled inside me.

*　*　*

A week or so later I met a boy from my homeroom class who briefly befriended me. I had put myself out a little more than usual, wondering what it might be like to hang out with somebody. His name was Max and he lived in a large house a few blocks from mine. His father was a banker. At school he sometimes hung out with the stoners, which was why we first talked. The students were divided between stoners, jocks and nerds, but he seemed more a loner than a stoner. When he found out I lived nearby, he said, 'Let's cut out of school early tomorrow. I have something you might be interested in. My parents are at work all day.'

The next day he unlocked his father's study with a key stored beneath a stein on the fireplace mantel. Inside his father's home office hung a calendar similar to one my father had owned. Above the month there was a picture of a rustic coastline with tall sand dunes. Beneath the picture were the words '*Das Samland*'. I stiffened when I saw it. It was the calendar that the East Prussian community in Hamburg mailed out each year to members around the world. Along the left side of the month, in vertical lettering, was printed '*Deutsches Land in Fremder Hand*,' and to the right '*Ein Stückchen Heimat Im Abonnement . . .*'

At first I said nothing. Then I noticed a picture above the desk of a man standing in front of an ancient castle. 'Who's that?'

'My grandfather. He's dead.'

'In Königsberg?' I asked. I couldn't contain myself. The castle looked exactly like one I had seen in one of my father's books, the former capital of East Prussia. I had never seen another like it. It had once been the headquarters of the Teutonic Knights.

'I knew it,' he said, as if he had caught me in a lie. 'The way you never talk to anyone at school like your shit doesn't stink. I could smell it.'

'You're East Prussian?' I asked.

'Don't tell anyone,' he said.

'Do I look like an idiot?'

'Well, actually—'

'You pig, you're an East Prussian prick.'

A huge grin spread across his face. '*Sprichst du Deutsch?*'

'No.'

He didn't push it, but he said he couldn't stand being called a Nazi at school. His parents had fled as children ahead of the Soviet troops near the end of the war. Then he asked me a peculiar question and I realized why he had befriended me. 'After being called a Nazi enough times, you ever start wondering if you are one?'

I didn't respond.

'Sometimes I worry I might start calling myself one,' he continued, 'the way some of the black kids at school call themselves niggers all the time. At least it would shut everybody up. Maybe that's why they called themselves niggers. To stop the noise.'

I had never thought about it quite like that. I attended school so little that I rarely encountered it any more. Since we'd moved south, they were more intent on calling me a Yankee. I would have thought they liked Nazis, since Nazis were white supremacists, but Max had been born in Augusta so they couldn't call him a Yankee. He didn't seem like your typical southerner: he carried himself differently and had a nasal tone similar to my own.

'Ignore it,' I said.

'You sound like my father. As if you're above it. I want to show you something else.'

We left the study, locking the door, and he led me down a long hallway to the back of the large house. In the den he opened a doorway that led to a steep flight of stairs.

'Go ahead.'

In the attic, he dug through a box until he found a videotape he had hidden there.

'Look,' he said, holding it up, '*Triumph of the Will.*'

I had never heard of it.

Noticing my blank expression, he said, 'The Nazis made it to spread their message.'

I realized at once that in an attempt to understand his parents' past, he had gotten hold of some Nazi propaganda that he was eager to share. The tape made me nervous. I was sure it was illegal. At the same time I was intrigued, for it presented part of the picture my father had refused to share with me. My old curiosity returned. I looked around the room. There was a stereo in the corner, a small television and a couple of chairs. A shelf along the edge of the room was stuffed with books on accounting and finance. 'Where'd you get it?' I asked.

'Mail order.'

'You could get arrested.'

'You never heard of the First Amendment? You could mount a swastika on your car as a hood ornament if you wanted. You sound like my father, paranoid he's going to be arrested and shipped away.'

His comments made me uncomfortable, but I tried to be polite: he had a small bag of Acapulco Gold I wanted to sample. I rolled a joint while he attached the VHS machine to the TV. The sound quality was poor but the images were clear. We watched a long opening montage before Hitler took to the stage and started a long speech I couldn't understand. I rolled another joint, this time sprinkling some angel dust on the weed, while he rewound the tape to the beginning.

'I've got a better idea,' he said. 'Let's give it a soundtrack'

He ran downstairs and grabbed a copy of a recently released album that had blown both our skulls in a way Nazi propaganda couldn't – Pink Floyd's *The Wall*. I lit the joint, took a couple of hits and passed it to him. It kicked in, and the floor rippled beneath us like a breeze blowing across a lake. I stared at the undulating carpet, then reached out to touch it, proving to myself it was solid. I took a sip from the glass of water Max had carried up the stairs. He put the record on the turntable, dropped the needle, turned up the amplifier and pressed play on the video machine.

An image of clouds appeared through the front window of the airplane, accompanied by first vocals from the new soundtrack, which seemed to be asking if we'd like to go to the show. The plane broke through the cloud cover and the roofs of the medieval city of Nuremberg emerged below, with troops marching neatly down the narrow streets.

The drone of an airplane diving out of the sky blasted from the stereo, louder and louder, then fell silent at the moment Hitler appeared from the door of the plane, which had landed in a field. Huge crowds cheered and saluted. In the next frame, as piercing cries from a baby emerged from the stereo, Hitler's limousine passed through the city streets. The film clicked to a new frame: Hitler walking in front of his troops, inspecting them, as the next cut – 'Another Brick in the Wall' – rose from the speakers. A small swastika painted on the side of a soldier's metal helmet came into view, framed against the infinite sky. Inside the stadium, lights illuminated the words 'Heil Hitler.' Crowds waved torches. The vocalist was singing something about teachers harming children. A spotlight shone against a wall, then cut to the interior of a house in which a Nazi flag hung, fluttering in the window. The stereo screamed for the teachers to leave the kids alone!

Max stood up and clicked off the TV, walked across the room and dug through another box until he found a bong. He loaded the bowl with more weed, fired it up and passed it to me. 'So, what do you think?' he asked. 'Are we Nazis or what?'

'If Nazis listen to Pink Floyd baked out of their brains maybe we are.'

He laughed. We listened to the music, too stoned to talk. He wanted to understand what had happened in our ancestral home back in Europe in a way that nobody was willing to talk to us about. We were locked in silence.

A few weeks later we cut school again to buy some pot from a dealer so that we could go back to Max's house and smoke in the attic. Azaleas were blooming on every corner, while city workers were cleaning the streets in preparation for the Masters Golf Tournament.

After we'd scored, we climbed the stairs to the attic and he dropped his school bag on the floor. His English composition book slid out. 'What are you guys reading?' I asked.

He pulled out a volume by Edgar Allen Poe and read part of a poem called 'The Raven.' 'The teacher told us Poe was a heroin addict,' he said. He took out the bag of weed and sprinkled some on a rolling paper. 'She gave us a reading list last week to pick a book to write a term paper on. I went to the library this morning and the only one left on the list was by Sylvia Plath, a poet she's crazy about. It's creepy. Grab it from the bag while I finish rolling this.'

I searched until I found a thin volume titled *Ariel*. He lit the joint and we sat in the middle of the floor facing each other, cross-legged, passing it back and forth. He reached for the book and looked through it for a poem he had read earlier that day. 'Check this out,' he said. 'It's called "Daddy."'

He picked a verse at random and read:

> It stuck in a barb wire snare.
> Ich, ich, ich, ich,
> I could hardly speak.
> I thought every German was you.
> And the language obscene.

'Are you making that up?' I asked.
Without answering, he started another verse:

> In the German tongue, in a Polish town
> Scrapped flat by the roller
> Of wars, wars, wars.

'Let me see that.' I snatched the book from his hands and scanned the entire poem. My eyes stopped on the final stanza:

> There's a stake in your fat black heart
> And the villagers never liked you.
> They are dancing and stamping on you.
> They always *knew* it was you.
> Daddy, daddy, you bastard, I'm through.

The words shook me. I closed the book and handed it back to him. Adrenaline flowed into my bloodstream. I stiffened, but before

I could speak the door at the bottom of the stairs clicked open and his father shouted, 'You up there, Max?'

Max jumped up, grabbed the bag of weed and shoved it into the closest box, then ran to the window and flung it open to toss out the joint and get rid of the smoke that hung in the air. Before he had the window fully open, his father was standing at the top of the stairs, sniffing. 'Who are you?' he asked.

'He's a friend,' Max said, answering for me.

'Get out of my house.'

I sheepishly stood up, half expecting him to hit me. His father stepped out of the way to let me pass. As I neared the bottom of the stairs, I heard his father say, 'Get over here.'

The following week, I saw Max walking home from the bus stop. He told me his parents were sending him to relatives in New York for the rest of the school year. He didn't say anything about his father catching us smoking weed and he didn't make any jokes about being German. I only saw him one other time, the day he passed in the back seat of his father's car headed for the airport. He didn't wave and neither did I. His father didn't see me. I felt as if I had lost a close friend, even though we hardly knew each other. The little bit of time we had spent together didn't matter so much as the intimate understanding we had of each other's lives. We were different but part of us was almost entirely the same.

My short-lived friendship with Max opened up a Pandora's box. Before I'd met him I had pushed most of the thoughts of my father out of my head or held them at bay with the drugs. After meeting him those thoughts re-entered my consciousness, whether I was stoned or not, and I had to work hard to keep that labyrinth of my mind sealed.

My probation officer ordered me to his office in the courthouse to tell me that he had set up a hearing to charge me with truancy. 'If you're wise maybe you'll start attending school every day so that I can tell the judge that you're trying to change.'

'What good would that do?' I asked. 'In six months I turn sixteen. I don't have to attend school then anyway.'

'I'm trying to help you, Sam. You either do it yourself or I'll see that you're sent away. After a year in lockup maybe you won't feel compelled to break into every other house on the hill.'

'Who said I've been breaking into houses?'

'Don't bullshit me, Sam. I didn't start out in life dreaming of becoming a probation officer. I took this job in hopes of being able to help people out that had been through the same things I went through as a kid. We have a saying around here, "You can't bullshit a bullshitter." Both you and I know you never stopped breaking into houses. You don't even have a job. How else are you going to buy dope?'

I didn't say anything. He knew I didn't want help and I knew he was a good-hearted person who only wanted the best for me, but it didn't change anything.

'Can I ask you something?' he said.

I raised my eyebrows. He stood up and pushed the door closed, then came back and sat down.

'What the hell is it with you? Aside from your need to steal, you seem well-mannered enough. I get kids down here that make my skin crawl and you're not one of them. You're probably smarter than half the kids at school yet you have this need to stay smashed on dope. Something about your case doesn't make sense. Am I missing something? Did something happen to you that I don't know about? Is there something you want to share?'

He really did want to help or at least understand. What could I say? I didn't want to be a smartass, but I didn't want him to leave empty-handed, either. I noticed a picture of him in uniform hanging on the wall above his filing cabinet. 'Were you in the military?' I asked.

'Vietnam. Two tours.'

'I was in the Second World War. Eastern Front.'

He absorbed my words, then asked, 'What the hell are you talking about?'

84

'Ask my mother. She was there with me.'

He sighed and didn't speak for a moment. He tapped his pen on the desk, waiting to see if I had anything else to add. 'The hearing's set for two weeks from Wednesday. If you don't show up, I'll send the police to pick you up.'

It was Monday. I had two and a half weeks to stay baked before whatever happened happened. That Friday I went out to the Pits on a rare drinking binge. The Pits was an area deep in the forest on the outskirts of town. You took Wrightsboro Road out to Belair and followed it up the hill until you came to an anonymous single-track dirt road on your left. It led deep into the woods to an area where some of the hardest partying in the history of Augusta had occurred in the late seventies and early eighties. When it rained the road turned to mush and the woods became swamps, with scattered perches from which you could see the nightlights of Augusta in the distance, providing you could still stand up once the party got going.

About a mile up the dirt road you came to a deep, treeless crater in the middle of dense forest about a quarter-mile wide, as if a small atom bomb had exploded there and left a gaping hole in the earth. I have no idea how it got there and I don't think anybody much cared beyond the common knowledge around town that it formed the perfect party spot. Every Friday night so many cars congregated there after sunset that it looked like a big church revival meeting. At the center anyone who arrived early helped build a bonfire. By midnight flames leaped twenty and thirty feet into the air, the entire pit lit up like broad daylight. The jocks with their athletic skills took it upon themselves to man the fire, racing forward to toss on another tire or a huge branch somebody had dragged out of the woods.

That night was more emotional than most. A guitarist in a local band had been killed in a car accident while driving home from a show in Atlanta. I didn't know the guy but he was a local legend, and it would be a night of mourning and hard partying. To honor the dead, the various factions – schools, neighborhoods, towns – had agreed there would be no fights. The police never interrupted the festivities.

85

Everybody in town knew about the underage drinking, free flowing drugs, fist fights, random sex and general chaos that ruled the proceedings, but apparently it was a southern rite to go into the woods every Friday night and raise holy hell just as long as you didn't kill anybody and made it home before sunrise.

The occupants of every car opened the doors wide so that everybody could hear the music they were playing. By ten the memorial was fully underway, with every car roaring its own tribute: a Ford F-150 blasted Lynyrd Skynyrd's 'Saturday Night Special'; an El Camino blared Molly Hatchet's 'Flirtin' with Disaster.' A jacked-up Blazer blared 'One Way Out' by the Allman Brothers, while a black Bonneville Supreme cranked up Black Oak Arkansas heralding 'Jim Dandy' to the rescue. A mellow idealist brought Atlanta Rhythm Section's 'Champagne Jam' into the mix. I heard some idiot, apparently new to the party, turn up the opening song on the latest Aerosmith record. I felt sure he was going to get his head bashed or the windows in his car smashed. With the exception of 'The Boys Are Back in Town' by Thin Lizzy, which had become an anthem at the Pits over the years, I doubted the southern boys would let pass a band without southern roots.

Shortly before the Midnight Ramble, as it had become known, in which everyone tried to synchronize their stereos to the same song – it never worked, but we were all too drunk to care – somebody hooked up their stereo to a loudspeaker and cut loose with 38 Special's 'Rockin into the Night.' As cheesy and kitsch as the whole affair might sound to an outsider, I sensed a primal power at work deep in the Georgia woods, with a couple of hundred people singing in unison to songs they had grown up on. As the song faded, somebody came on the loudspeaker and asked everybody to turn off the stereos and join him in a moment of silence. It's not easy getting two hundred drunken rednecks to be silent but that night the only sound during that brief pause was the crackling of the bonfire. With the stereos still off, the leader took us through an a cappella version of 'Sweet Home Alabama.' This time we achieved synchronicity, our voices echoing out through the swamps.

Then the party fired back up. Kegs of beers came out from the trunks of cars, some served only to friends, others charged per cup. A few generous souls allowed suds to flow freely to all comers. The rowdies drank Jack Daniel's, Wild Turkey, Southern Comfort and Rebel Yell from the bottle. People whooped and hollered. I wandered around selling Quaaludes – Rorer 714s – and pre-rolled joints from a Ziplock baggy. With all due respect to the dead, if there were a buck to be made I'd give it a shot. Some yahoo offered me a free line of powder he had just cut on a mirror. I guessed it to be piss-poor cocaine cut with talc and tooted it up my right nostril out of social obligation.

'You'd better sit down and wait for it to hit you, bro. I don't want to be scooping you out the fire when you start freaking out.'

'I could snort that entire baggy and still walk the line.'

'Don't say I didn't warn you.'

By the time I reached the third row of cars, my head was reeling. I began to worry that I might have snorted a line of dry battery acid from the way I was twitching. I wandered over and leaned against a Big-Foot pickup truck that had tires the size of an economy car and stood a half-mile off the ground.

'Get your paws off my truck!'

I tried to focus on the face screaming at me, but his eyeballs kept melting into his mouth, so I fixed my eyes on his baseball cap's logo: Redman Chewing Tobacco. 'You got some chew, man?' I asked.

'Yeah, chew on this, motherfucker.'

He popped me in the mouth. I fell to the ground. A group of people gathered around me and started kicking me. I assumed that the truce was now off. I curled into the fetal position, locked my fingers behind my head and protected my face with my elbows. I heard the same guy who had punched me scream, 'Get that fucker away from my truck.'

Somebody grabbed me by the collar and dragged me toward another car. I heard a girl yell, 'Leave him alone. He ain't hurt nobody.'

'If you're so in love then take this little bitch home.'

Whoever had me by the collar dropped me on the ground with

a thud. I felt someone rinsing cool water over my face to clean the blood off and opened my eyes long enough to focus on a girl with curly brown hair.

That was the last thing I remembered.

The following day I awoke deep in the woods. Swords of light from the high noon sun pierced the canopy. I guessed I had crawled for cover while I waited for the drugs to subside. My headed throbbed as if a subwoofer had been mounted on my inner ear. The money I had made the night before was missing and all the drugs I had carried with me were gone, too, except the Ziplock baggy with a single crumpled joint and a hand-scrawled note that read: 'Thanks bro. The Westside Patriots.' The name of a high school and their mascot up near the Columbia County line.

When I tried to stand up I ached all over. In the distance I heard music, but not as loud or as aggressive as the night before – mellow hangover music: the Doobie Brothers' *What Were Once Vices Are Now Habits*. I followed the fiddles and mandolins of 'Old Black Water' through the trees until I came to the top of the bank overlooking the pit below. The enormous fire from the night before was smoldering at the center of the ring. The crowd had abandoned the area, save five or six cars of hanger-ons who apparently hadn't gotten enough the night before. I hid in the bushes – was it safe to venture out into the open? – then decided that the hot sun had evaporated their fighting spirit. I staggered out of the woods and down the bank. Somebody yelled, 'What the fuck? That the creature from the Black Lagoon?'

I wandered up to the nearest car with the crumpled joint hanging out of my mouth as a peace offering. 'Gotta light?'

'What the fuck happened to you?'

'Partying like everybody else. Some of us just party a little harder.'

He struck a match and lit the joint. I took a deep hit and passed it on.

'There's some beer left in that keg,' he said, pointing to his trunk.

One of them gave me a ride back to his house and let me soak in the tub. Later, he offered fresh clothes. I was still too confused and stoned to find my way home. I had never met him before. He lived with his siblings, a sweet family of southern whites with strange names. I stayed the night partying with them – Skibo, Sister, Star, Sky and Mary, names I kept mixing up, 'Hey, Sky, pass me Star . . . I mean, tell Star to pass me Mary. Just pass the fuckin' joint, please, Bo – sorry, Skibo.'

Skibo rolled on his back laughing, 'Sambo's having trouble talking.' Then he started speaking to me as if I was his pet dog. 'Here you go, Samby,' he said, dangling the joint in front of me. 'Did Samby do a little too many drugs last night?'

I never did get their names right.

I finally made it home to my mother's house late Sunday night. When she saw my bruised face, she didn't ask what had happened – she was holding out for my court date. I never did figure out what had been in that line I snorted.

I lay in bed for the next couple of days swallowing painkillers to take the edge off, venturing from the room only long enough to go down to the kitchen to drink a glass of milk two or three times a day. My mother left me alone. I kept the door locked and shoved a towel near the bottom to cover the crack so that no scents would escape into the house and opened my window wide enough to blow smoke out whenever I needed a hit from my pipe. I put Zeppelin's *Physical Graffiti* in the eight-track and let it play in a continuous loop for twenty-four hours until the tape snapped. I spent the next hour carefully pulling it out of the stereo. Then I cleaned the drive wheel and pin with rubbing alcohol, pushed in Black Sabbath's *Master of Reality* and let it throb in the background for another twenty-four hours.

The following night at three o'clock a flickering orange glow illuminated the walls of my bedroom and a deep grumbling resonated through them. I was wedged in that space halfway between sleep and waking – that rare moment when you find yourself stuck in an unpleasant dream and do everything within your power to tear yourself from the nocturnal world but can't. I tossed my head back and forth to force my eyes open. When I succeeded I saw the fire. I heard screaming. I looked around but couldn't see anything other than a radiant orange reflecting on the bedroom wall. I listened carefully and moved my arms to prove to myself that I was awake. Then I froze.

She was in the room with me. I felt her glide across the floor, her lost life entering my realm and hovering just beyond my reach. Then I heard it again, but this time it wasn't her, it was a child screaming somewhere outside, followed by an incomprehensible force thrusting me into another zone. Then it appeared, clear as a cloudless day: the edge of a frozen pond bordered by a forest of tall trees towering into the sky, clean lines separating light from darkness, thin arms of light reaching through the trees, transmuting into seaweed and wrapping themselves around me, pulling me into the cool darkness of the forest and then downward through increasingly frigid water. I sensed life fleeing toward the surface and an odd discomforting relief at knowing both of my parents were dead, that I was free of my father's tyranny and the guilt of not treating my mother better.

I floated up to the surface. When I broke through my body became rigid and I realized it wasn't my parents but my grandparents who were dead – my father's mother was running toward me screaming. I had waited my entire life to meet her and now her presence sent a ripple of fear through me.

She stepped out of the fire and fell into my arms. I had never seen her before but we instinctively knew each other. She was crying. I hugged her, wiping away her tears and setting her gently on the bed. I stepped to the window to find out what she was running from. When I turned back, she was gone. I felt a sharp pain in my chest and looked down: my heart exploded within its cavity. I fell to the floor and jerked up in bed screaming.

There it was again – an indefinable liquid clarity. I tried to calm myself. I had to pull myself together. It was late at night. The house was silent. Not a single car passed on the street. I stood up, turned on the bedside lamp and went to the bathroom. When I returned to my room I sensed an inexplicable presence. I could no longer tell whether it was my grandmother or something else. I wanted to run out of the room but I was frightened that if I did I might trigger whatever it was to give chase and harm me. I slipped back into bed, propped myself up with my pillow and picked up a book from the nightstand. I pretended to read. At that moment I felt all the energy come together near the doorway and a shiver crept up my spine. I couldn't stop myself looking up. When I did I felt it move toward me until it was directly beside me. I was so overcome with fear that I began to shake. Then, slowly, the fear was replaced with a deeper calm than I had ever known. I wanted to get up and walk around the room but I couldn't move. I waited for a long time until the presence dissipated and waited yet longer to be sure I was alone, then slipped out of bed, crept downstairs and turned on every light.

I was too scared to go back to my bedroom, so I stayed up reading in the den until dawn as the drugs I had been using almost daily for the last two years were flushed out of my system. I relaxed on the couch and fell into a deep sleep. I woke almost eighteen hours later at midnight, according to the grandfather clock chiming in the living room. At first I thought I was still in a groggy dream, but as I regained consciousness it happened almost exactly as I had envisioned it the night before. A deep orange glow illuminated the walls of the den and a throbbing resonated as though the earth itself were speaking. It took me a few seconds to realize that the house next door was on fire and that I wasn't dreaming or hallucinating.

I leaped to my feet and ran around the house waking everyone. We gathered on the sidewalk across the street and huddled in the cold with the other neighbors and watched the roof cave in as flames engulfed its interior. The fire department assigned an engine to our house to douse it with water to stop the flames spreading.

'You didn't have anything to do with it, did you, Sam?' my mother asked.

'Why would I start a fire?'

An elderly couple who lived out of state owned the house. We stayed at a hotel for three days while workers cleaned up the debris. It felt as if we were back in the Bon Air where we had stayed for a while when we first moved to Augusta. We lived in the same room and stared at the TV to avoid interacting. When we returned home, the smell of charred wood from next door pervaded our house.

Before my mother left for work the following day, she told me she would go straight from work to night school. She didn't ask directly that I stay home to watch Walt and Rebecca, but her statement implied it. The fire had shaken her enough that she didn't want to leave them at home alone. Also, I had been sober for the three days we were at the hotel, so perhaps I had gained her trust a little.

She had been gone no longer than an hour when I started digging through the attic for a prescription bottle I might have overlooked. I didn't care what I took as long as it got me high. I found a couple of empty ones and flung them against the wall in frustration, then went on searching frantically. At the bottom of a box I found five pills. I tried to identify them. The only two I recognized were Demerol. I knew they'd give me relief, but I decided to save them for later in case the other three pills had no effect. I pocketed the Demerol and swallowed the other three as soon as I entered the kitchen. I looked in the den to check on Walt and Rebecca. They were sitting in front of the TV.

'I'll be upstairs if you need anything.' Shorthand for telling them not to bother me. They understood without replying.

I climbed the stairs and locked myself into my bedroom. I dug my water pipe out of a box in the closet and scraped the bowl for resin. There must have been some residue of angel dust in the black goop because as soon as I held a flame to the oily substance it turned bright orange with a hint of blue. It hit me immediately and I floated up off the floor. It wasn't what I'd been looking for – I'd hoped for a mellow high. I stumbled to the bathroom for a cup of cold water and went back to my bedroom, locked the door again and put on some music to try to come down a little. I have no idea how long I remained in that condition – it was probably only a couple of hours but it felt like days. Each time I stood up to walk to the window for fresh air my legs felt as if they'd buckle. Some time after dark, I decided to pop the Demerol under the false assumption that an opiate derivative would reduce the effect of the other drugs, or at least mellow them. It increased the effects three-fold and the back of my throat went completely dry. I stood up and straddled the bedpost. I needed something with sugar in it to bring me down, a soft drink, cereal or white sugar poured into a cup of water – I didn't care what it was as long as it helped counteract the drugs.

As I stood up, trying to keep my balance, an overwhelming sense of frustration and hopelessness took hold of me: I had spent the last years trying to wash my mind clean. I had used everything I could to make it blank. But nothing had worked. With the exception of robbing houses, I had failed at everything – I had even failed to fry my mind. I was too much of a coward to kill myself. I began to feel queasy.

I fumbled with the door handle. When I finally got it open, I tripped over the towel I had used to cover the crack at the bottom of the door. I pulled myself back up on the banister and hobbled to the top of the stairs. I focused on the door with a dozen window-panes at the bottom of the stairs and took hold of the handrail. As I descended the first step, my knees buckled again. I tumbled down the stairs and smashed into the front door. Shattered glass rained around me. I realized my head was sticking partially through one of the panes. I yanked it free and looked at the door to see how much damage I'd done. The smashed pane through which I had pulled my head was covered with blood. A jagged edge protruded from the frame. Most of the other panes were shattered as well. I reached up and rubbed the side of my head. A piece of glass fell to the ground.

I struggled to regain my balance, cutting my hand on the door, and stumbled into the kitchen. I thought briefly of my siblings. When I turned back toward the hallway I was startled by their presence.

They were watching me. Blood ran profusely from a cut in my

skull behind my left ear and down my shoulder, coagulating and dividing into tiny streams and creeks as it crossed my chest, ran down my legs and puddled on the floor. I tried to mop it up so my mother wouldn't see the mess when she came home. I succeeded only in smearing the pool in ever-widening arcs. I had to be careful not to fall over – it had never occurred to me how slippery one's own blood is. My little brother watched nervously from the edge of the kitchen, asking repeatedly if he could call for help. Each time he picked up the phone, I slammed it back in its cradle and ordered him to sit down. 'I'll take care of it.'

Dark red handprints were smeared across the phone, the walls, the mop handle and the refrigerator door, which I kept pressing against to keep my balance. I don't remember falling, but I do remember starting to giggle.

At some point it occurred to me that I was no longer in the kitchen. I had been placed in the back of a vehicle, like a roll of carpet tossed in a truck. The ground was passing swiftly beneath me now. I could feel it – the smooth surface, the howl of air passing between me and the ground, the rubber tires holding us safely in place, the gentle shushing sound of their fixed orbits, as we hurtled through the night. In the distance, I heard a siren whining like a cat retaining its exact distance somewhere out there in the dark – and realized I was in an ambulance.

I felt it begin its descent down the long, steep hill into town, racing toward the hospital like an airplane carefully approaching a runway. There were lights too. They were flashing. Kind of like Christmas. Everything was calm like the surface of a pond. I liked it there. I could have lived in that place forever if they hadn't jerked me awake in the emergency room.

A doctor stood above me – a pair of shears buzzing in his right hand. 'No,' I pleaded, when I realized what he was about to do. I had long hair that hung down past my shoulders – for years I'd had nightmares with people accusing me of being a skinhead. 'Please, just shave the wound.'

He shrugged and acquiesced, telling me to turn my head to the side so that my hair fell away from the bloody gash. 'You very nearly died,' he said. I had lost several pints of blood and had missed a major artery by millimeters.

BOOK III

Relativity

An emergency hearing was arranged on the day I was released from the hospital. It no longer mattered whether I was a danger to society because I was now a danger to myself. The judge declared me delinquent and a ward of the state and sentenced me to an experimental rehabilitation program. 'I'm doing you a favor,' he said. 'This is your chance to straighten up. To show that you can be somebody. From the way you're going, you're looking at a life in and out of prison when you become an adult, son.'

In the same way that Augusta sat on the Georgia-Carolina border, Columbus straddled the Georgia-Alabama border. Overnight I was thrust from one world into the next – from the unstructured life of a young drug addict into the ultra-structured environment of a treatment program. The drugs had flushed out of my system during my stay in hospital, which was good: the program required that I was clean on arrival so that they didn't have to deal with detoxification. I was driven across the state late at night as part of the initiation process in detaching me from my previous life and introducing me to a new one. I was forced to stay awake, talking to my driver from midnight until we reached the facility six hours later.

I was permitted to use the toilet only once after I'd walked through the front door, then told to sit in a chair in the hallway beside another inmate being transferred into the program that day. Prior to leaving Augusta, my probation officer had handed me a slip of paper that stated, 'Drug use and addiction is a personal disorder, not a symptom or the essence of a disordered person. Chemical detoxification is required prior to entry. The program you are entering treats disorders, not addictions. Addictions are an affiliation of the Outside. Disorders are exposed Inside.'

The staff kept us in the hallway for most of the day, part of the continuing initiation process, which we soon learned included no contact with the Outside for ninety days – no phone calls, no letters, no newspapers, no television, no nothing. This period was called Blackout. We left everything behind and entered a new life with each minute regimented from the moment we woke at six a.m., until lights out at ten p.m. Talking in the dorms after lights out was prohibited. The only downtime was an hour after lunch in which we sat in the dining room listening to music and socializing under the scrutiny of the staff who recorded our interactions in our case files.

In the hallway that first morning we were each handed a pamphlet titled *Relativity: Purpose, House Rules, Creed*. It briefly outlined the program's origin and included a long list of policies, including 'Breaking any house rule will result in immediate expulsion. Consider yourself lucky to be here. Take advantage of this opportunity to better yourself.' There was also a contract of nonviolence that we were required to sign. On the final page was a creed we were expected to memorize and recite daily. The official name for the program, like the pamphlet, was Relativity, and it was funded by the Georgia State Mental Health Department, drawing on state and federal funds, according to the pamphlet. I had no idea what they were thinking when they named it – unless it was an inside joke. Whoever was in charge of naming prisons, halfway houses and rehabilitation programs for the state of Georgia likely had a lot of time on their hands. In those years, once nonviolent offenders turned sixteen they were usually given the option of enlisting in the army to serve their time and rehabilitate – which the state preferred since it relieved them of the financial responsibility for rehabilitation – but in my case and that of my fellow inmates over sixteen, the military had classified us 4-F: 'Not qualified for service in the Armed Forces under established physical, mental or moral standards.' A history of drug abuse resulted in an automatic Class 4-F. My probation officer had

100

made this clear to me on the day I had told him I'd served in the Second World War.

Relativity was originally set up as a halfway house for inmates being released from state prisons and the penitentiary in Reidsville, where the older staff member who had handed us the pamphlet told us he had served five years. According to the pamphlet, the program had recently started admitting juveniles after statistics revealed that the age of state offenders had dropped over the previous decade. The idea was to mix young adults of eighteen and nineteen, being released from prison on parole to Relativity, with juveniles whose present behavior patterns placed them at high risk of joining the next generation of state prisoners. The program's age range was fourteen to nineteen. The intention was similar to that of the Scared Straight programs, which required young offenders to tour notorious prisons so that they would see what the future held if they continued breaking the law. Relativity took it a step further by housing us together. If someone on parole was expelled from Relativity they went back to prison. If inmates like me were expelled we were sentenced to mental hospitals or YDCs – Youth Development Centers, prisons for adolescents with individual cells and bars. For first-time offenders like me, Relativity was the halfway point to prison and our final chance to avoid being sent deeper into the system.

Inmates were called 'residents.' The state still retained a grain of hope that we could be rehabilitated, even though we were the freaks, misfits and outcasts who didn't fit easily elsewhere into the system. Unlike other young rebels, we weren't fashionably or tragically hip, shooting up heroin because it was cool. We were the broken ones with deep-seated mental issues they hoped to fix before we became lifers. In some ways, Relativity seemed more like a secular church, seeking to indoctrinate and save us from the sins that had consumed us. The creed bordered on New Age spirituality and we quickly learned that the program's administrators were serious about us memorizing and living by it.

Later that day the former prisoner who had given us the pamphlet returned and introduced himself by his nickname, Ramrod, then

101

ordered us to stand and recite the creed. When we couldn't do so without looking at the pamphlet, he said, 'You got thirty minutes to pull your act together. Otherwise – you see that door right there?' He pointed to the door we had been admitted through that morning. 'You're going out faster than you came in. You hear me, brothers?' He returned exactly twenty-nine minutes later by the clock in the hallway and told us to stand one at a time and recite the creed:

> I will hold myself responsible
> Through failure and success
> For each deed I carry out
> And never look upon another
> As more fortunate than myself.
>
> Should misfortune strike
> I will channel my grief
> Into a positive light.
>
> I will give to my fellow man
> As he has gave to me.
> I will return to society
> The good that I've withdrawn.
>
> I will not seek pity.
> I will not place blame.
> I will always seek guidance
> To support the infinite wealth within.

'Again,' he shouted. 'Louder.'

I repeated it three more times, each time louder than the last. Then he told the guy sitting beside me to do the same thing. Once we were done he congratulated us, and said, 'Nobody pulls one over on Ramrod. I'm the enforcer around here. You have a problem, you come to me. Understand?'

We nodded.

He briefly explained that the program was structured so that the inmates operated as a large family would and introduced us to each other as 'brothers.'

The guy beside me laughed when he heard that. 'Man, you're one of the palest-looking brothers I've ever seen.'

'You both best get used to it,' Ramrod said. 'Perception is the root of our actions. Right now you see yourselves as a drug addicts, hoodlums, bad asses. Other people call you worse. If you make it through Relativity, you're going to see a whole lot of things differently, so you might as well start adjusting your vision today if you plan on staying around.'

Being forced to remain sitting in the front hallway that first day was more difficult than it sounds: when I say sit I mean exactly that – we weren't permitted to stand, stretch or use the restroom. Fortunately they let us stay in the same chairs directly beside each other and allowed us to talk. They encouraged us to get to know one another. We already knew from reading the rulebook that cliques – racial, ethnic and regional – were prohibited. At the same time, we knew anyone sent into a state facility sought allies for protection. Unable to rely on people from our own background, we formed a strong bond that morning, sitting together in the front hall, unsure of what awaited us Inside. By late afternoon, before we were called in separately to record our case histories, we were joking like two long-lost brothers and our relationship never faded. We became closer. We sought each other out, spending the little recreational time after lunch together. They never pulled us apart.

His name was Tyrone. He was a voracious reader. He often carried an encyclopedia tucked under his arm, a torn piece of paper marking the page he had been reading while he finished a chore. He said he had started reading to kill time since he was first sent away at twelve. To pass time sitting in the hallway that first morning, he told me a long story about Tyrone's Rebellion in which a group of Irish chieftains had risen against the British colonialists. As he shared the history of his name with me, I realized he wanted me to know that it wasn't a stereotypical black name.

He told me that up to that point a group of northern Irish counties had been the most resistant to the British. In 1598 the Earl of Tyrone had laid siege to a fort built by the British to attack County Tyrone and destroyed the invading troops in the Battle of the Yellow Ford, but in the end the rebellion had failed. I could tell by the way he described what happened next that it was the part he identified with most closely. The British set up the Plantation of Ulster, seizing the estates of the Earl of Tyrone and his allies, then redistributed the land to Scottish and English settlers – usually poor and willing to pick fights with the Irish they had displaced in the same way, he said, that poor blacks fought with other poor blacks, and poor whites were as racist as rich ones. The plantation became the biggest in Ireland and laid the groundwork for the division of the island.

'Always the same shit,' he said. 'Pit us against each other, divide us on our own ground. It's what the slave traders did to get us here and what the government still does to keep us down.'

Less than a week after we had been admitted, he confided that he had watched the sheriff dredge a pond behind his house for his father's body. His mother had died when he was three. Before entering the juvenile system, he had lived with an uncle who rarely fed him. He was arrested the first time for stealing a loaf of bread from a corner market. He had got high from opening gas caps on cars in parking lots and sniffing fumes until he became lightheaded – it was the only free buzz he could find. He was twelve when he was arrested the second time, in a grocery-store parking lot, kneeling between two cars sniffing gas. They arrested him for robbery – he had been holding the car's gas cap.

'I got out when I was thirteen and stole what I needed after that. They were going to arrest me anyway.'

Meeting him was almost as disorienting as our first ninety days isolated from the Outside. The things he told me shifted my worldview and made me look at myself differently. By comparison I had been raised practically as royalty. I had been born in a wealthy white

104

northern village; I had known both of my parents, who were alive; I never had to steal food; I'd got high on expensive pharmaceuticals; and the police had arrested me for a crime I'd committed in rebellion, confusion or boredom, not out of need or for something I hadn't done. It was difficult to recognize his brilliance, given the way he talked, saying things like 'It be good,' and his strong southern accent – or maybe it was an African conglomeration of accents. It was Tyrone who pointed out to me that southern whites spoke more like blacks than vice versa.

'Black nannies been raising plantation owners' children forever and rich whites still hire black nannies. They picked up our accents along the way, accents they call southern instead of black. "Yeah, and my name's Biff. Pleasure to meet you,"' he said, in his best white imitation, slapping my hand and laughing as he did so.

The scars on his face, his enormous flattened nose, his pitch-black skin and his intimidating build, which he had strengthened by working out with an iron bar – he had made an inexpensive weight-lifting device by hanging cinder blocks on each end – gave him an air of meanness. But he wasn't mean. He was a smart dude, the smartest person I had ever met. He was a complex individual and had a unique way of looking at the world. Even his musical tastes were unusual compared to those of the other residents. He wasn't interested in rock, R&B or funk: he loved jazz and listened to it inside out, upside down, from modern to ragtime, and knew the names of practically every musician. He once heard me singing along with a Zeppelin song on the radio in the hallway during our cleaning shift, and said, 'Why you listening to them thieves?'

'Those guys rock.'

'They didn't invent none of that shit.' He proceeded to tell me how rock was based on blues invented by slaves. 'Don't get me wrong. I ain't no big blues fan. Too easy for whites to steal, but ain't no white ever succeeded stealing blues-based jazz. They never get it right. They stiffen it up too much and play on top of the beat.'

He could be a little arrogant, saying blues was too simplistic, a handful of repeated notes, and that rock was so limiting it drove him crazy to hear its droning beat and its white singers pretending to be black. 'I'd rather watch a blackface minstrel than Mick Jagger. At least they're up front. You got to forget all that shit, man. Jazz be the word.'

That was his favorite saying. In the months that followed he took me deeper into the world of jazz – its structure, origin, bands, musicians, instruments, songs, standards – and whenever he heard an emotional solo on a station we tuned in on Ramrod's shortwave, he applauded it, saying, 'Jazz be the word.' If the solo affected him deeply he stood up and did a quick James Brown dance move. He expressed himself gloriously with his moves. He knew I was from Augusta, James Brown's hometown, and once after executing a move, he said, 'JB's serious shit – he keeps a horn section rocking the house. Don't underestimate the Godfather of Soul.' I later learned that he occasionally applied 'Jazz be the word' to things that had nothing to do with music. It was a mantra of sorts that, for him, perhaps meant that nothing was what it appeared to be – or, more precisely, that most things were more complex than they seemed.

Thanks to the random occurrence of our being admitted on the same morning, my initiation into the program was relatively smooth. Tyrone had been in mental hospitals, locked up and shuffled around the state for years. He took me under his wing, taught me and looked out for me. He knew how to negotiate the bureaucracy. 'You be caught in the system now, white boy, like a little fly in a giant spider web.'

Other residents admitted after my arrival had it worse: they didn't have a friend like Tyrone to guide them. I was rarely concerned about violence: it got you put in isolation and taken away as soon as the police could get there. Relativity tolerated no physical aggression, not even the raising of a hand. Psychological warfare, on the other hand, was encouraged and without Tyrone I'm not sure I would have survived the first few days. Sometimes I wondered if Tyrone and I would have gotten along as well as we did if either of us had been older than fifteen or had been sent anyplace besides Relativity, with its strange amalgamation of family, New Age spirituality and confrontational therapy that we were required to study every day.

For all our differences and the little time we were permitted alone, Tyrone became the first best friend I ever had.

Each new resident was given a large binder titled *Theories of Relativity* that was several hundred pages thick with articles copied from various textbooks that the director and staff had assembled from their studies. Beyond the obvious play on the title, the theories had nothing to do with Einstein or the external world. The inner workings of the mind – motivation, behavior, trauma, therapy, addiction – formed the core of the primer on psychoanalytical theories we were expected to study. Instead of treating us only as clinical subjects, the program's visionary director Dr. Neuman had convinced the state to fund a rehabilitation program in which we underwent an intense form of confrontational therapy while simultaneously studying the basic premises behind the treatments we were subjected to. The idea was that we would emerge with the skills to be our own counselors and therapists. I arrived at Relativity in the fall of 1980. The idealistic influences of the late sixties and seventies were prevalent in the very fact that the program existed.

Dr. Neuman had been raised and educated in Philadelphia. After graduating, he had moved to Mississippi to help with the Civil Rights movement. While there he met an African-American woman who worked for the same organization. They had fallen in love and married and later settled in Columbus, where he secured funding for Relativity. In addition to its role as a mental-health and drug-rehabilitation program, it was a desegregation program of sorts, teaching us not only to live with and accept ourselves but to accept others with whom we wouldn't otherwise have socialized. The program was two-fold in that it helped rehabilitate young offenders for integration back into society while giving staff – all convicted felons either attending college or recent graduates – a meaningful job to help them become respected members of society. It was from their studies that we mostly learned. They arrived at the program after a day of classes, eager to share with us what they had learned at the university. Although the

107

reading material was beyond our comprehension, Dr. Neuman didn't consider this a hindrance – I admired that.

'Everybody starts somewhere,' he said, the first time I listened to him lead a group. 'Where you come in is less important than where you depart. It doesn't matter how disorienting the materials or foreign-sounding the terms. The longer you immerse yourselves the more thoroughly you comprehend. I expect to learn as much from you as I hope you learn from me.'

The program was self-governing in that residents were expected to organize the daily schedule, overseen by the director and staff who guided the workshops and group-therapy sessions. Everything about Relativity was a shock to my system. I had trouble concentrating and thinking, now that I was sober, having spent years under the constant influence of mind-altering substances. I could think more clearly stoned than I could sober. Stoned, I could focus like a laser and go about planning and executing a robbery. Sober, I lost my train of thought and became anxious, confused and nervous. Drugs calmed me. With sobriety, everything seemed disjointed. I suppose that was the point. While it was not explicitly stated, we were well aware that the purpose of the program was to rewrite our hard drives – to reprogram, indoctrinate and brainwash us into productive, positive, sober members of society, contributing to its well-being rather than its destruction. I argued one day with a staff member that we were a necessary element of society, that he wouldn't have a job if it weren't for people like me. He didn't appreciate my logic. We were taught that that was part of our problem: we rebelled simply to rebel, without any basis for our rebellion.

By state standards we were young enough and not yet fully conditioned enough as career criminals to be considered worth saving. The program's purpose was noble, but as I came to learn at night, away from Dr. Neuman's watchful eye, rogue staff members often oversaw group-therapy sessions that were more like feeding frenzies where we devoured each other's weaknesses. Stressing us by verbal assault and forcing us to defend ourselves without resorting to drugs or violence was considered part of the growing experience, a required element to achieve maturity and independence. But the first marathon session I attended, lasting from seven in the evening until just before midnight, went beyond any idea of therapy, as I understood from my brief readings in our workbook. It bordered on nonphysical barbarity and sadism.

It was almost as if Ramrod had planned it. Only a few nights after I had entered the program, and less than an hour after Dr. Neuman had left to go home to his wife and children, Ramrod called an Emergency Group session. 'Intervention,' he called it. I should have known from the way some residents recoiled that what followed would be more than mere therapy.

'Go to the dining room, break down the tables and put the chairs in a circle,' he barked.

Everybody jumped, hoping to avoid his ire. We scrambled down the stairs and carefully set the chairs in a perfect circle with a large empty area at the center of the room, like a circular boxing ring. Then we all sat nervously, waiting for Ramrod to appear. Nobody knew the purpose of the meeting. We were often kept in the dark, another element of initiation I learned over time. Ramrod waited upstairs creating tension in the silent room. He finally appeared and walked around the center of the ring looking at each of us individually. He circled the room three or four times without speaking, then stopped near Tyrone and me, saying to the rest of the group, 'We have two new family members here who need our help.' Then he turned to us and said, 'Would either of you like to volunteer to be on the hot seat first?'

I raised my hand, figuring it was better to get it over with. I knew vaguely from overhearing other residents that the hot seat was a chair that remained empty at the beginning of group therapy: the person undergoing therapy envisioned it as the seat in which a person who had caused them trauma sat. But Ramrod's interpretation was different. The hot seat was the place the person undergoing therapy sat while being verbally assaulted by the other residents. They even had a term for it: Verbal Haircut. I'd read about it in the workbook.

'Why are you here?' Ramrod asked.

'Because of drugs.'

'We don't want to hear about drugs. Everybody's here because of drugs. What made you do them?'

'I like getting high.'

'That's not an answer.'

'It's the truth.'

'It's a lie. There's a reason you got high. You're hiding something.'

'I'm not hiding anything. I like getting high.'

'You like getting high for a reason.'

'It makes me relax.'

'There's a reason you wanted to relax that you're not sharing with us.'

'I didn't like school.'

Ramrod laughed and looked around the room. 'Did you hear that? Our new little brother doesn't like school so he took drugs to relax.' The other residents laughed with him. 'Does anybody have anything they want to ask Sam?'

A guy I'd never spoken with on the far side of the room said, 'You're a lying piece of shit. We can see straight through you. We're the same as you. You're hiding something.'

'I've got nothing to hide,' I said. 'What good would it do to lie now? I already got sent here.'

'So you don't have to face the truth. You're weak. I can see it in your eyes. You're a liar.'

'What do I have to lie about?'

'You tell us, liar.'

Out of a group of thirty people, one after another, started repeating the same things, insulting me, raising their voices, yelling. This is how they do it, I thought. This is how they break you. I remembered reading in the workbook that it was necessary to break the subject down to reach their inner core, the root of their problems. I wasn't going to tell them anything. It didn't matter how long I was there. I was never going to tell them anything about my past.

'What are you scared of?' another screamed.

'I bet his daddy touched him,' another leered.

'Or his mommy,' somebody added.

Soon they were rising out of their seats and getting inches from my face, provoking me without touching me, trying to make me lash out physically so I'd be taken away by the police to make room for the next person they could ridicule. It was a game for them. Some of them even called it the Game. Part of their never-ending initiation. They had done it so many times that they soon fell into a routine. To remain in the program everyone was required to participate. Out of nowhere, a seemingly gentle-natured boy, who had been silent until now, rose out of his seat and said, 'You're a shitty excuse for humanity.' I saw Ramrod taking notes, making sure everyone participated.

A cacophony of voices followed.

'He's trying to keep something a secret.'

'You're a coward.'

'You're scared.'

'You can't hide it from us.'

'We know what you did.'

'We'll catch you in your lies.'

It went on for more than two hours without a break. I never said a word. They carried on attacking me, getting their energy and frustration out by verbally assaulting me in every way they could think of, continuing to get inches from me, spraying their words directly in my face. Eventually they started wearing me down, breaking me. The only thing that brought me back was when I looked up and saw Tyrone inches from my face screaming, 'You ain't worth a shit. You hear that? They ought to throw you on the street right now. You wouldn't last a minute.' He winked and sat back in his seat. He'd got into the spirit of the proceedings because he had to. Otherwise our alliance would have been revealed and they would have attacked him.

I realized I had to say something to get them to shut up or they'd carry on all night and drive me crazy. I detested violence because of my father's beatings, but sitting there being verbally assaulted for hours, I felt like physically lashing out to get them away from me. I knew that if I lifted a finger in defense, I'd immediately be thrown

111

out. I had just arrived. I didn't want to be sent away. I didn't know where they'd send me, but it wouldn't be home and it might be worse than Relativity. The constant yelling continued. I was no longer able to make out what each person was saying. Their voices blurred together and soon they were shouting in unison, 'Come out with it. Come out with it. Come out with it. Come out with it.'

I finally broke.

'He hit me,' I said.

'Who hit you?'

'My father.'

For the first time the room fell silent. The verbal assault was worse than anything I had experienced at home. I could take the short-lived pain of being beaten, but I had never had so many people screaming continuously in my face for so long. My ears rang. The room spun. The hot seat felt like it was on fire. For a brief second I thought I had their sympathy.

Then Ramrod spoke up, 'We know your daddy hit you. Don't feed us what you think we want. You want to talk about why he hit you and maybe we'll listen. You want to whine about him hitting you, then you keep on whining. You ain't getting no sympathy in this room.' He turned to the residents, who were practically foaming at the mouth. Some were literally panting, catching their breath after screaming continuously. 'Are we gonna give Sam sympathy for getting beat by his father?'

'Hell, no,' a guy sitting near me shouted. 'You want sympathy? Give me some, brother.' He ripped open his shirt. The bright white skin was stretched queerly taut across his disfigured chest. He didn't have any nipples that I could see or chest hair. 'My father threw a pot of boiling water at me. You see me crying for you? Tell us something we don't know, brother. We don't care about people getting beat in this room. We all been beat real good. Tell us something we don't know.'

Then everybody was chanting with him, 'Tell us something we don't know. Tell us something we don't know. Tell us something we don't know.'

'Shut up. Shut the fuck up,' I screamed.

'We're just getting started. We're not even warmed up.'

'Come on, scream louder,' somebody else shouted. 'We know you've got something to tell us.'

'Shout it,' another yelled. 'Come on, we're listening.'

And on and on.

Another two hours later, still screaming in my face, I broke down completely and slumped in my chair, crying in front of them, sitting submissively as they went on taunting me at the top of their lungs without a break.

Ramrod finally called it a night. 'I think Sam got a little taste of what's in store for him.'

I never did tell them anything, but for more than four hours I endured their verbal assault, the most excruciating emotional experience I had ever been through. The couple of times I had tried to say something, I was shouted down by somebody else in the group who'd had it five times worse. They all laughed in my face and barked like a pack of wild dogs. I felt like I had been lifted off the street and placed in an insane asylum.

We were the injured, the damaged, the tormented ones – a broken family of lost children placed under house arrest and forced to look at one another's scars twenty-four hours a day, seven days a week to remind us that we were unwanted, unfit for society. Everybody there was ill-adjusted for the outside world, severely abused – whether through sex, substance, violence or all three – exposing our once-shielded nerve endings. We talked too loudly, laughed too quickly and too long, sometimes hysterically when there was nothing funny. Some screamed without warning or reason. Others burst into tears if you looked at them wrong. We were hypersensitive to every slight change in the environment, every look, every sigh, forever waiting for the other shoe to drop – we were damaged goods and now one big family, trying to rebuild each other to rejoin society by breaking one another down so far that it was almost impossible to stand.

* * *

Early the following morning I woke to a radio blaring the thumping bass line of 'Another One Bites the Dust.' We filed out of the dorm and into the hallway for our morning exercise where we stood in a perfectly straight line, shoulder to shoulder, as a police officer walked one of the residents down the hallway in handcuffs.

'What happened?' I asked the guy beside me.

'Somebody saw him trying to leave the building this morning.'

'That's it? He's gone?'

'It's the second time he tried. They keep the front door unlocked so you'll hang yourself. The first time you run, they deal with you in group therapy. The second time, they report it to your probation officer and call the police to take you away.'

Once the resident was gone, the staff member who had turned up the radio clicked it off and moved into the hallway. 'Any other family members want to take a walk this morning?'

We stood silently at attention. He walked up and down the row, barking at different residents to step forward, recite the creed, then step back into line. After he had picked five or six residents at random, he signaled for the group leader to take over. He led us through push-ups, sit-ups and jumping jacks. In the middle of a push-up, our chests inches from the floor, he yelled for us to hold the position and repeat the creed.

Afterward we filed downstairs to the dining room where the group session had taken place the night before and set up the tables for breakfast. Each day different family members were assigned to kitchen duty and required to wake up earlier than the others to prepare the meal. The guy who had been taken away had been assigned to breakfast duty that morning. There was a constant rotation of new residents. The most intense period was during initiation, or Phase I, when they tried to break you to find out if you had enough perseverance to stay the course.

The program was divided between Phases I, II and III. First phasers were required to cook and clean and were kept under constant scrutiny in group therapy – hassled daily to breaking point. Most residents never made it to Phase II. Second phasers led the morning

114

exercise, picked who was responsible for cooking and cleaning and had the authority to call group sessions to interrogate a family member they suspected of breaking rules. They were the most powerful and feared family members and the most likely to abuse their power. On reaching Phase II, you were also given passes to leave the house and begin reintegrating into the Outside. At that point we were permitted to leave the program each day to attend school or work.

There were only a couple of residents who had made it to Phase III, where you weren't required to attend group meetings. They didn't interact much with the new residents. They were one step from graduating and being released. The house was their support base for any difficulties they encountered Outside, in case they needed counseling to deal with the stresses of living in an open society, and provided them with a way to save money for their release, in case they had no home, like Tyrone, to return to. In the decade since the program's founding, several thousand residents had passed through its doors but only fourteen had graduated. Despite that, the state still viewed the program favorably: it helped the staff become successful members of society – they completed their college degrees and rarely got into trouble with the law again.

In theory, we were free. There were no bars on the windows of the large brick building at the middle of an old decaying neighborhood at the center of downtown, a few blocks from the river and the Alabama border. Like many cities, those with means had fled the old city center to the newer outlying suburbs. Peering out of the windows after lunch and at night before going to sleep, I saw the homeless wander past. The windows in the dorms, where we slept fifteen to a room, were sealed shut. The staff made a point of telling us daily that there were no bars on the windows or locks on the doors and that we were free to leave at any time, but our freedom was a façade.

Second phasers were trained to watch closely for anyone showing signs of running. Whenever somebody went for the door, the second phasers sprinted after them like a pack of bloodhounds. Breakouts, as they called them, were part of the sport of living there. First phasers were often motivated to reach second phase solely so they could chase down breakouts and drag them back to the program. Whenever somebody ran for it, a shrill yell went up and the second phasers sprinted out of the door, breaking into groups to cut off the escapee. It was a beautiful sight to us first phasers: we raced to the windows to watch them spread out and disappear on the streets in pursuit. We dreamed of the freedom and power of reaching Phase II.

I was assigned to a kitchen shift less than a week in and learned the delicacies of southern institution cooking. With the exception of dinner, the food was always the same: eggs, grits, sausage and toast for breakfast, fried bologna, bread, black-eyed peas and collard greens for lunch. For more taste, I stirred the eggs, grits and sausage together on my plate into a mound of southern goulash and sprinkled salt and pepper on top, then wolfed the pile before somebody tried to steal it. The advantage to being on cooking crew was that you were able to sneak a little extra food while preparing it before everybody woke. The staff rarely came into the kitchen, leaving the second phasers to keep an eye on us. I boiled water in a large five-gallon pot, stirred in the grits and a large block of butter, while the sausage sizzled on the stovetop.

Small cockroaches often crawled out of cracks in the wall as the steaming grits warmed the cold room and walked upside down on the shelf above the stove, out over the boiling pot, as though trying to get a whiff of food. We didn't have much else to do, so we'd watch them hanging there until the gathering steam and heat made it difficult for them to cling to their positions. I tried to catch them on a small piece of cardboard when they fell but often missed and watched them plop into the grits to disappear beneath its bubbling surface.

'Stir it in, stir it in,' the second phaser watching over me shouted.

When I walked around the dining room later that morning, ladling grits onto thirty waiting plates, the second phaser stood behind me shouting, 'Twenty-five cents for extra protein.'

Cockroaches in the food, I quickly learned, were a rite-of-passage at Relativity.

* * *

When Dr. Neuman arrived each morning, he read the house log and reviewed our charts to discover whether there had been any group sessions the previous night. He often came around and asked us individually if we were doing okay or needed to talk to him. Nobody ever told Dr. Neuman of Ramrod's demented sessions out of fear that Ramrod would attack us even more brutally. I came to see Ramrod as causing more harm than good. One of the basic premises of the program was to force us to confront things we'd rather avoid under the assumption that once we understood them the perpetual anxiety that most of us lived with would eventually dissipate, allowing us to lead normal lives. We were taught that we had become addicts to avoid thinking about our past. I would never tell them any more about my father or about my German background. I knew Ramrod would say I was using them to cover something else, then lynch me in the group, screaming that my German anxieties were all in my mind, that nobody cared about my background.

Dr. Neuman was respectful and balanced in his judgment, and during the day the program was a productive, supportive learning environment that I felt fortunate to be part of, but when Ramrod was on duty without Dr. Neuman's supervision, Relativity became a perverted mental dungeon. Ramrod loved calling Emergency Group sessions and setting aggressive second phasers on weak residents. His fetish was forcing victims to talk about their sexual abuse.

'It will make you feel better to get it out,' Ramrod said, encouraging the guy on the hot seat to recount in sordid detail his painful past in front of his so-called therapeutic family. The second phasers badgered whoever was on the hot seat so relentlessly that he eventually broke down to get them to stop screaming. While it was necessary for us to confront our traumas, I felt sensitive issues were more productively explored in small groups or individual counseling sessions.

To protect myself, I paid closer attention to the lessons we were expected to study in our workbook. Most residents dismissed them as pointless academic exercises we had to do as part of the price we paid to stay out of jail. I also sought out Dr. Neuman for individual

117

counseling. Each resident was assigned to a staff member, but we were free to seek out the director and he was generous with his time. I knew I would need more than Tyrone's friendship to make it through. Dr. Neuman frequently asked me about my past, where I was born, where I had grown up, about my parents, brothers and sister, but my answers were vague in our first meetings. Slowly he won my trust. During my initiation, he never pushed me to answer his questions, but he constantly probed.

The program put us under intense pressure so that we learned how to deal with stress in a sober environment and could carry those lessons to the street. I never did tell Dr. Neuman about Ramrod's methods. In a way, Ramrod's presence taught me that the world was brutal and unfair, and that even if I had succeeded in getting him fired somebody else would have replaced him. Of course, I couldn't predict whether the new counselor would have been better or worse. Between workshops, individual and group therapy sessions, I devoted myself to the workbook in the hope of impressing Dr. Neuman. Most of the information still confused me and I doubted I'd ever fully grasp it, but the more I studied, the more I visited him to ask questions.

When I told him I still felt bad about watching the resident being taken away in handcuffs, he said, 'It doesn't do any good to sympathize. Feeling sorry for somebody accomplishes nothing. You're here to learn and separate the meanings of empathy and sympathy. By empathizing, you're able to put yourself in his shoes. Through empathy we can help others and ourselves.'

'What about that essay in the workbook by Krishnamurti?' I asked.

'He's not addressing sympathy. He's making the point that fear is accessed through thought – thinking about the past. One of the staff members included it. I'm not sure you need to worry about it right now. More importantly, be conscious that part of what we're reading and sometimes use in therapy draws on Eastern thought. For example, Buddhists believe that life is based on suffering. They don't fear suffering because they see it as an essential element of living. In the West we view suffering and depression as synonymous, which increases our pain when we fall into depression. For now, reread the excerpt from Otto Rank's *Will Therapy* on his use of the "here and now." He views emotions as grounded in the present. If you can stay in the present, in the now, you're at less risk of sinking into the depressive past. I want you to spend a few days thinking about that. Be aware, however, that we mix a lot of different concepts and theories here. Most programs concentrate only on one theory or method. It's important to live in the present to stabilize, but I also believe the past holds an important place in therapy. But for our purposes today I want you to concentrate on the present.'

We were so busy learning new material, focusing on workshops and therapy sessions, and studying in the evenings when Ramrod wasn't torturing us that the time passed quickly. We covered so much different ground that in my mind the material merged into a single psychoanalytic body. The different theorists seemed staunch on their positions and different staff members were equally staunch in defending one method as more beneficial than another. Dr. Neuman appeared to enjoy playing them off against each other in an attempt to reach something he referred to as a 'holistic consciousness.'

One staff member, for example, insisted that we focus our energy on an essay he had included in the workbook by Aaron Beck, a psychiatrist who had developed cognitive therapy. In the essay Beck said that depression was acquired from rejection, excessive criticism, the loss of a parent or growing up under a parent's negative attitude, which he defined as 'negative schemas.' Depressed people, according to him, fixated on negative or hurtful experiences in their past and in doing so created a self-fulfilling prophecy of remaining depressed. Beck sought to break such thought patterns. He viewed depression as a thinking disease. The goal of his therapy, the staff member explained, was to help us unlearn negative thought patterns and reactions and train our minds to react in new ways.

'I know some of the other staff here have different ideas, but in cognitive therapy focusing too much on the past is believed to intensify the dread that many of you experience daily. You want to move away from those memories, not focus on them.'

This was in direct contrast to Freud's belief, which Dr. Neuman lectured on a few days later, that to fully understand our present situation, we must first understand the past, specifically our childhood. Without unlocking our childhood, he said, it was impossible to unlock the present. From the little I comprehended by jumping between different theories and the more practical experience of putting those theories to the test in marathon group sessions, most of our treatment seemed rooted in a strange mixture of a misinterpreted confrontational Gestalt therapy, with bits of Beck, Freud and New Age concepts, like Otto Rank, plus elements of Buddhism and a liberal dose of something Dr. Neuman called transactional analysis.

TA, as it was called in the program, examined the ego states that we lived in and shifted between from one moment to the next – the Parent, Adult and Child egos, which were said by its founder, Eric Berne, to be acquired in childhood from watching our own parents' reactions. As I understood it, the Parent ego was the way we behaved when unconsciously imitating our parents – this formed the basis of most of our reactions. The Parent ego was shaped by reacting to events, instead of examining them objectively and arriving at well-thought-out conclusions – scolding a child, for instance, when he or she misbehaved. The Adult ego was a rational state in which different possibilities are examined unclouded by emotion. We were encouraged to develop our inner Adult. The Child ego existed in a state of naïvety, rarely thinking about end consequences and acting in accordance with parents' reactions, happy when parents praised, hurt when they scolded. There was some correlation, though I didn't fully understand it, between Freud's ego, superego and id. The staff viewed transactional analysis as easier to comprehend than Freud. Among the many books lining the shelves in the hallway that we were encouraged to read was Eric Berne's *Games People Play*. The book that interested me most, though, was on the shelf in Dr. Neuman's office. I first noticed it when I asked him to clarify the chasm between Freud's belief that our childhood should be closely examined and Beck's that it should be ignored to avoid intensifying damaging childhood memories.

'It's not an easy question to answer,' he said. 'I personally don't believe you can forget a huge part of your life simply by ignoring it. On the other hand, cognitive therapy has proved the most effective. Of course I'm simplifying here.'

As he spoke, my eyes moved to the binding of a book resting on the shelf behind him. Martin Buber's *I and Thou* – the book my father had kept in the basement. Each time I had asked him about it, he had closed it, put it back on the shelf and started telling me about some other piece of history he had uncovered. I was intrigued by the book's title and the way my father had avoided sharing its content.

'What's that book about?' I asked, pointing over Dr. Neuman's shoulder.

He craned his neck to see which I was pointing at. He started to pull a book off the shelf called *The Origins of Totalitarianism*.

'No, the other one,' I said. 'To the left. *I and Thou*.'

'Why this one?' he asked, sliding it out and setting it on his desk.

'The title. It sounds strange.'

'No other reason?'

'Do I need another reason?'

'You don't need any reason at all. But I'm interested in learning as much about you as I can.'

'What's it about?' I repeated, ignoring his inquiry.

'The relationship between two people. How one person identifies with the next. Do you remember the essay on Gestalt therapy?'

'Yeah.'

'The founders of that movement were heavily influenced by this book. They saw the I-thou relationship as the most ideal relationship between a therapist and their client.'

'But what's the book about?'

'I'm getting to that. It explores relationships between two people. Buber generally saw the I-thou relationship as one in which people identified with each other and were to some degree interconnected. Many might argue against my assessment, but the traditional therapist-client relationship is one of power over the powerless, in which the therapist objectifies his client, or what Buber called an I-it relationship. By relating to somebody through an I-thou relationship a deeper level of empathy is established, an interconnectivity that ultimately results in trust.'

'Can I read it?'

'Go ahead, but I'm not sure it'll make much sense at first. It's not the sort of book you pick up and read once to understand. It's more like philosophy or religion. You have to read it repeatedly and even then it's not completely clear. The most powerful things can't be easily understood.'

'You don't mind if I take it?'

'Of course not. Why should I keep it from you?'

In handing me the book and allowing me to leave his office with it, Dr. Neuman won my trust. He had done something my own father had refused.

When I wasn't in therapy, attending workshops or bothering Dr. Neuman, I shadowed Tyrone. We were both on a quest for knowledge but seemed to be following different paths. He was equally hungry and consumed almost everything he came across and nothing more so than a book a staff member had given him called *Black Skin, White Masks*, written by a psychiatrist named Frantz Fanon. I was curious and inquisitive, but Tyrone possessed a mental agility I lacked. He was angry at his position in life but smart enough not to let it override his capacity to absorb new ideas or end our unlikely friendship. He had had little education but he had brains and I was the recipient of his boredom. One of the things I cherished about our friendship was that he never asked me about my past, where I or my family came from. Part of me suspected that this stemmed from the assumption that most whites were alike, but in a more profound way I saw his lack of inquiry as related to the fact that he was unable to trace his own African roots. He once told me he had no idea what country, region or tribe his people had come from. Unable to access his own history, which I sensed he would have relished knowing, he refused to take an interest in anybody else's past and seemed especially to despise non-whites who used their ethnicity and ancestral histories to align themselves with black suffering to improve their social standing. Once he took this out on me.

'You'll always have it easier,' he said.

'Easier than who?'

'Me.'

'What makes you say that?'

'Same reason shit stinks – 'cause it's true.'

'I don't have it easier.'

'You will. You'll walk out of this place in a better position than me. You'll be offered a job quicker. People won't step off the sidewalk and cross the street when they see you coming. They won't use your suffering to rise and then become racist like the rest.'

'Use whose suffering?'

'The suffering of being a black man in America, a descendant of slaves.'

'I never said I suffered like blacks or came from slaves.'

'At least white racists admit blacks are fucked.'

'When did I become a racist?'

'The day you were born.'

'How's that?'

'Being liberal doesn't mean you're not racist.'

'I'm not even political.'

'You're white. Your skin is a political statement.'

'How can you say that? That makes you racist.'

'Who said I wasn't?'

'Don't get me wrong. I don't mean to accuse you of being racist.'

'I didn't say you did. What bothers me more are Mexicans, Asians, anyone with brown skin, latching on to us, saying we've suffered together and are united against our oppression by the white man. What the fuck they know about being oppressed? They're like you people coming over here, like every other immigrant that ever arrived in this country looking for work and opportunity. Wrap a chain around those motherfuckers' necks, drag them out of their country

123

against their will, choke them, erase any knowledge of where they came from, put 'em up on an auctioning block and sell them to the highest bidder and then they can claim oppression. What do they take us for? Do they really think we're that dumb? They ain't interested in helping us any more than you are. They're interested in helping themselves by using our pain and history of suffering to get what they want. At the end of the day, ain't nobody gonna help a dark-skinned nigger descended from slaves. Mark my words, brother. Nobody.'

Unprovoked, he had worked himself into a rage. I tried to change the subject.

'We should go back upstairs before they notice we're missing.'

'You're just like them, aren't you? I took you for somebody different.'

'I'm not just like anybody. I'm not claiming to have it as bad as you.'

'You best remember that. You're already a white motherfucker. That's one strike against you.'

That was the only time Tyrone blew up at me. He never apologized and I didn't expect him to. He had meant what he said. But he was a strong enough individual not to let racism spoil our friendship. He was one of the few people I ever met with enough guts to admit he was racist and still willing to make friends with people like myself. I read a section from another Fanon book, *The Wretched of the Earth*, that Tyrone consumed the following week and I started to understand the source of his rage.

It may seem too much for an Outsider to comprehend how much fifteen-year-olds in state confinement could influence one another, but we had nothing to do with our time except read and study, and we focused on those books with the same feverish energy we had once applied to drug consumption. Knowledge became our new drug. It got you high. Tyrone knew this. I knew this. I could sit around and learn as much from him in one conversation as I learned from the staff in an entire week. He had a way of altering my view. He was well aware of his power to sway, and since I was one of the few

124

people willing to fall under his spell, he shared with me everything he read and challenged me.

When a producer from *The Today Show* came to Relativity to conduct an interview for their national morning television program, Dr. Neuman selected Tyrone to represent the family. He was the fiercest and most willing to express his views. Dr. Neuman had permitted the show to come to us because he wanted to raise Relativity's profile to assure future funding.

The morning they aired the program was the only time during Blackout that I had access to the Outside. A staff member carried a television set into the front room and placed it on a table while we gathered around. Watching television proved a peculiar and unsettling experience. Listening to news from the Outside after I'd been completely cut off was overwhelming. Ronald Reagan had recently won an election over President Carter. John Lennon had been murdered. After I'd heard that, the interview with Tyrone, whose face appeared in silhouette behind a screen and whose voice had been synthesized to obscure his identity per state laws, was anticlimactic.

We congratulated Tyrone, then fell into our private worlds of dread when they clicked off the television and carried it out of the room, severing all contact with the Outside again. The following week was devoted mostly to therapy sessions helping us deal with the news. Until then, lost in our cocoon of learning, I had almost forgotten the Outside existed. Dealing with Lennon's death and Carter's defeat had thrown me into depression. Carter had grown up only an hour away from Relativity and was revered as a pacifist among the staff, in contrast to Reagan's more militaristic stance. While most residents preferred Led Zeppelin to the Beatles, Lennon's murder still came as a shock.

The news jolted me so much that the announcement in our morning meeting the following week that Tyrone and I had been approved to advance into Phase II and would soon be permitted to go Outside came as a disappointment. I wasn't sure I wanted to go Outside. I would turn sixteen next month. If I'd had my choice at that moment, I would have remained in Blackout: it was easier not knowing what was going on Outside. I had come to prefer the isolation, the insularity, the comfort and the challenge of being Inside. I wasn't sure I was ready for the confusion of being back in the world.

The core of the program emphasized setting goals, short-, medium- and long-term to provide our life with structure and a sense of purpose. Each morning, after exercise and breakfast, we entered a family meeting in which each person wrote a short-term goal – something we intended to accomplish that day, such as memorizing the definition of a word or completing a reading assignment. Each Monday we set medium-term goals, something we hoped to accomplish by the following Sunday, like completing one page each day in a journal describing our emotional state or avoiding thinking about doing drugs or killing ourselves. Privately, with our counselors, we set long-term goals – things we wanted to accomplish in a month, six months, a year, a decade or a lifetime. Long-term goals were more personal and not always shared with other residents: they might include things such as eventually confronting a person who had abused you on the Outside. Other long-term goals were graduating high school, staying sober, reuniting with a parent, getting married or finding a stable job.

I committed myself to a single long-term goal: freedom.

It frustrated Dr. Neuman. 'That's not a goal,' he said. 'It has to be something tangible, something you can be certain you accomplished.'

'It is tangible. If I make it out of here, I'll be free. If I get a job, I can live independently and I don't have to go back to my family.'

'You may be imprisoning yourself more by breaking away from your family. You'll always be on the run trying to avoid them. That's not freedom.'

'I won't be on the run. I'll be free not having to think about them and forgetting my father.'

'The only way you'll ever be truly free of your father is by confronting him and freeing yourself of the emotions that have crippled you and made you seek drugs to try to stabilize your mind.'

'How can I confront him if I don't know where he is?'

'There are other ways. If somebody close to us dies, leaving behind unresolved issues, you can go to things dear to that person to try to resolve your emotions. Did he leave you anything?'

I remembered the book he had hand-written and left in the basement for me that I had carried to Georgia and buried in a plastic bag in our backyard. I hadn't thought about it in ages. That was one of the effects of sobriety – it brought old memories back into focus. 'He left something he wrote,' I said. 'But I never bothered to read it.'

'It might be your answer. Do you still have it?'

'I haven't looked in years. It's probably there.'

'That would be the first place I'd go.'

'I can't leave here.'

'Not now. But when you finish Phase III. By then you'll have the skills you need to deal with your emotions.'

'I listened to my father talk forever. I don't want to hear what he has to say any more, not even in writing.'

'You might find the missing link. Why else would he have left it?'

'I don't care. I'm not interested in his life any more.'

'But you were, weren't you?'

'Maybe. A long time ago.'

'I think it's your only answer, especially now that you can no longer contact him directly. He's reflected in your life whether you want to admit it or not. It's better to know what parts of him you carry, instead of being ruled by emotional reactions you don't understand. In the meantime, I'd like you to set a goal of attending school. Something concrete you can accomplish that will help free you.'

'I don't want to attend school. I've had enough of it.'

'I can't legally force you, but I'd urge you to do something more than just work. You're at a stage in your life where you need to acquire skills. At the very least, enroll in a vocational program after work. Muskogee County Mental Health has a facility over near the switching yard across town.'

'What do they teach?'

'Go and talk to the counselors. Things like basic mechanics. They test your aptitude to find what you're naturally skilled at. Perhaps it's something you should start thinking about. I'm going to give you your first pass tomorrow to go outside alone.'

With a pass we could leave the program for a few hours at a time and were then required to report back and tell the staff exactly what we had done with our time. After we had built up enough trust and inner strength to avoid relapsing over the course of six weeks, we were then given permission to go out and look for a job or enroll in school.

My first day Outside was like waking up after a long dream. It had been years since I had walked down a street sober. The world seemed alien without the residue of drugs influencing my vision and providing a false sense of security. Without drugs, the street seemed like a mine-field waiting to explode. Almost everywhere I walked on Broadway, two blocks from the program, drug dealers were eyeing me. When I turned away, I saw a pervert creeping along in his car waving at me. I crossed the bridge and stopped to glance down at the rushing water of the Chattahoochee River, then walked over to the Alabama side of the river. It was worse there. The locals called it Sin City – the Mafia had settled in during the war, setting up gambling, prostitution and organized-crime rings. I scampered back to the program.

I found Dr. Neuman in his office. 'I can't take it out there.'

'You have no choice. You're here for less than a year to acquire the skills you'll need to live outside.'

'It's not safe.'

'I've lived here for years. I've never had any problems.'

'You ever walked along Broadway?'

'I drive up it every day on the way to work, pass the same people daily.'

'How do you expect me not to fall back into drugs with all those dealers so close by?'

'It doesn't matter how clean a neighborhood is. You can always find drugs if you look hard enough. It's better to learn here, where you have to face it daily and have the program to come home to for support. That's why we're here. You weren't placed here to ignore what got you sent here. You came to face up to it. You have to be able to look them in the eye and refuse, even if they offer you drugs for free.'

'I can't work on Broadway and face that every day.'

'Then take the bus out to the mall and find a job there. But the bus stop is on Broadway so you'll have to deal with it one way or the other. It's better to start dealing with it now.'

The next time they let me out I walked across town to Victory Drive near Fort Benning, a massive army base adjacent to and several times the physical size of the city. It had a population of a hundred thousand. I didn't take the bus but I was scared. Worried I was still too weak to resist temptation. Drugs soothed me. I wanted to rise to the challenge of facing the stark outside world sober. I wanted to prove to myself I could do it. I didn't want to get sent away before I'd had a chance to find out if I could live straight. I preferred walking anyway. It burned off my nervous energy. I stopped in several businesses along Victory Drive and asked whether they were hiring. Nobody took my application, but it wasn't because of my past: when I glanced at the newspaper headlines in the rack, I read that we were in the midst of the biggest recession since the Depression. Every storeowner I talked with said they hoped Reagan could turn the economy around. I watched young soldiers walking by with fresh tattoos from the parlors along Victory. I worried whether I'd be able to find a job and grew frustrated that joining the army wasn't an option to escape my present life. Working full time was my only chance to stay out of school, but like everything else in life, my entry into the working world occurred at the worst possible time.

Tyrone enrolled in the local high school so he could join their football team. He was tired of being pent up. I felt too confined by the structure of the program to spend my time Outside at another formally structured environment. I was convinced that working would give my mind a break from the program's daily structure while I concentrated on whatever physical tasks I was hired for. I hit the pavement every day, walking around town looking for a job. Finally after a month of nonstop searching, asking to talk to every manager who would listen, going into seven or eight businesses a day, every day of the week, I finally found a job at Shoney's out near the airport. The manager hired me to wash dishes and work alone occasionally at night to clean the grease out of the stoves. He locked me in after the kitchen staff and waiters had cleaned their stations and left. I felt free. There was nobody around, nobody to tell me what to do, nobody to yell at me. I turned up the stereo and worked my way through the racks of dishes stacked six feet tall, then started breaking down the grill and stoves. It was mindless work, but a relief after all the mental examination I had to face at Relativity. I usually didn't get back until two in the morning, well after lights out.

As Tyrone and I advanced through Phase II we rarely abused our power the way the others did. We didn't participate in the marathon group therapy sessions solely to destroy newly admitted residents like the second phasers before us had. We'd go along with it for a while, screaming at them, calling them names because we had to in order to advance in the program, but when it reached a breaking point we often used our seniority to guide the group session toward more productive therapy. We made no bones about verbally attacking and confronting other residents. If we didn't we would have wound up on the hot seat ourselves.

Time moved faster now that Tyrone and I were permitted to leave the program each day. I thought constantly about what I'd do once I was released. I didn't want to be bound to any one place or stuck in school. I tried to convince myself to follow Dr. Neuman's advice and acquire skills but I didn't have the patience. Sometimes returning to the program after work I became so hyperactive that I'd sprint around the large city block to exhaust myself. I worried too much, but exhausting myself through exercise had fewer negative conse-quences than doing drugs. It helped me understand Tyrone's interest in football. I didn't want to blow my chances now that I was so far along in the program.

With more free time on our hands – no longer required to follow the strict regime of the program with our outside work and school – Tyrone and I sometimes sat in the dining room late at night listening to music. One afternoon, he dropped by one of the pawnshops after school and bought a small stack of used records for twenty-five cents each to share with me. The jazz he listened to was faster and more upbeat than the Bill Evans records my father used to play. His favorite was a Miles Davis recording called *ESP* – a quintet, where many of the solos seemed understated and the musicians played at a brisk pace. Jazz was soothing in a way rock wasn't. I also liked the fact that there were no lyrics. It was easier to let my mind drift while we sat without talking, listening to the music. He was right about rock: your mind got stuck in the rut of its beat, and the lyric refrain often imprisoned you. Jazz was unexpectedly liberating. It took a while to appreciate the musicianship. He pointed out specific places in the songs and said things like, 'Listen here to the bass player. Don't listen to nobody else.' Then he waited, keeping the beat with his index finger, pointing at the speaker at a particular moment. 'You hear that? You hear the way the bass player connected up with the drummer and they both came in behind the sax player?'

A big grin spread across his face whenever he saw that I understood what he was talking about. He sensed from the look on my face when I finally started hearing the interplay between the sidemen behind the soloist. At such moments, he often tapped his finger on the table and said, 'Jazz be the word.'

Sometimes I wanted to say it with him, especially when we'd glance at each other in recognition of some new element on the recording we'd missed before, but it would have sounded stupid coming out of my mouth. I wasn't about to have him accuse me of trying to be black, but at the same time I avoided asserting my whiteness by saying, 'Dude, that rocked.' Around him I was comfortable enough in my skin. Usually I remained silent. Truth was that I knew nothing about jazz other than what he taught me, yet the more we listened the more I felt as connected to it as he did. That was the godsend of music – it transcended race, culture, social background. The beauty of the beat could never be denied.

The following week Tyrone was returning from school as I was leaving for work when he stopped me in the front hallway and asked me to sit on the front steps with him for a few minutes.

'What's going on?' I asked.

'I'm worried.'

It wasn't the sort of thing I'd expected to come out of his mouth. He always seemed so confident. 'About what?'

'You ever worry that no matter how hard you work for something that right before you accomplish it, it'll be ripped away from you?'

I wasn't sure how to respond. 'I've never really worked that hard for anything to be pulled away.'

'Well, you're working here,' he said. 'You made it through Phase I. You go to work every day. I'm sure you got some plan in your mind.'

'To make it out of here. That's all I'm really working for now.'

'That's what I'm talking about. You ever feel it could be snatched away from you?'

'I never thought about it. I'm following the rules. Long as we don't get high or steal anything we should be okay.'

'But what if something fucks up?'

'Like what?'

'I don't know. Life.'

'I don't even want to think about it.'

'Neither do I. But everything's going too smoothly. I've never had everything go this smooth. I made quarterback today, and instead of jumping up and down on the way home, I'm sitting here worried that something might fuck it up.'

'You just made quarterback and you're worried? You got to be kidding. You're kicking ass.'

He started to say something else and tried to stop me when I jumped up to run inside and announce the news that he was too shy to trumpet to the family. 'Wait a minute,' he shouted.

But I was too hyped after hearing he had just been named leader of his football team. 'We got a new quarterback out here,' I yelled into the house.

'Not now, not now,' he said. 'There's something else—'

One of the staff members appeared at the front door, followed by three family members. 'Who made quarterback?'

Within minutes, they pulled Tyrone inside and had him sit on the couch in the front room while the staff member called a spontaneous group meeting to celebrate his accomplishment. I was too excited to stop and hear what else he had to say, too proud of him. I ran around the house shouting for everyone to gather in the front room. By the time everyone finally sat down to hear Tyrone tell how he had beaten his opponent for the spot, I bowed out to make it across town so I wouldn't be late to work. The feeling of his success was infectious. I walked with a bounce in my step, sensing that if he could accomplish something so big that maybe something good lay down the road for me.

Whenever I was around the house, Dr. Neuman continued probing me to be more open about my past, but he seemed to have talked to the other staff members, because I was no longer put on the hot seat and attacked for not opening up. I think he had sensed I would close up more if attacked too much.

'Until you confront your past, the future will remain clouded,' he said. He was curious about my name. My full name was inscribed on the case folder kept on me: Sam Joachim Malessa. He asked me repeatedly about its origins. I told him I didn't know.

'It's unusual. Have you ever thought about researching it?'

'I wouldn't know where to begin.'

'Have you ever been to the library?'

'I never spent much time there.'

'Why don't you make a trip? Better yet, why don't we drive over on Friday together? I've got some things I need to look up and I can help you get started.'

I wasn't interested in looking for information I was sure I wouldn't find, but his offer interested me. He was gentler, and in a way more fatherly, than my father, so I accepted. Our first trip produced a few leads but no results.

I went back by myself a few days later. When I came up empty again, the librarian suggested I visit the library at the local college. I knew it would impress Dr. Neuman when I told him what I had done so I ended up going. The only thing I found there was a cross-reference to a book they didn't have on a person who shared my last name – a scholar of Biblical Hebrew.

I shared the news with him when he came to work the next day. He seemed genuinely proud that I'd followed through. It made me feel good, but I worried that if he found out about my father's origin he would reject me in the same way my father had.

'I'm going up to Atlanta next week,' he said. 'I'll be at Emory University for a conference. They have one of the best libraries in the state. I'd be happy to see if I can find any more information about your name if you'd like.'

I nodded. I didn't see how I could back out now. I was entering a place I wasn't sure I wanted to go, but he had cracked the door open with his persistence, reminding me in no small way of my own childhood curiosity. For that reason alone I didn't resist. As I sat in the chair in front of his desk, my sense of him as a father was replaced with the feeling that he was more a brother. I grasped for the first time that, to achieve results, therapist and client had to meet eye to eye. Dr. Neuman wasn't interested in grooming or exploiting me, only in helping me. After that I went for long walks in the city and spent time alone down at the dollar movie theater on Broadway. I didn't go back to his office for a couple of weeks and he never insisted that I come to hear any discoveries he had made at Emory. He gave me space – the only person at Relativity who understood the ramifications of silence in therapy. I needed it: if I couldn't face myself in silence I would never be able to do so in words.

*   *   *

A week later I awoke to a shakedown. They didn't happen often, but occasionally Dr. Neuman ordered the staff to lock us in the front room while they tore the house apart, searching for hidden drugs or weapons. Since the staff had all done time, they were well versed in shakedowns and seemed to take pleasure in flipping mattresses over, dumping everybody's clothes into big piles and rifling through our few possessions. None of us held it against them. They didn't find anything. We spent the rest of the morning putting the house back together, then sat in a long group meeting where we were instructed by a new staff member on the importance of thinking with our gut, not our head.

'If you think with your head, you think you know,' he said. 'If you think with your gut, you know you know. Anyone can draw a logical conclusion to justify stealing, doing drugs or whatever, but that don't make it right. They justify stealing money on Wall Street every day and they know the loopholes in the law, but that don't make it right. They're thinking with their heads, not their guts. We're all smart people. They say the smartest either end up in jail or heading corporations. We're here to find the middle ground. Life isn't logical. Mathematics is logical. You solve math problems with your head, not your gut. Use your gut on a math test and you'll flunk real quick. By the same reasoning, use your mind to find your way through life and you'll find trouble. Logic can't solve life's problems. When you feel it in your gut, you'll never go wrong.'

We were made to repeat his conclusion several times as a group in the way we had to recite the Relativity creed each day. We all repeated it enthusiastically to avoid getting written up for not participating. On one level it made sense, but if somebody became enraged enough to kill another person, that rage came more from the gut than the mind. Nobody was brave enough to raise that point.

That evening I was expected to work the graveyard shift. The manager had been tipped off that the health department would inspect the restaurant the following day. He wanted me to come in at midnight and work the entire night cleaning up to prepare for the inspectors.

It was hell. The joy of isolation – the only reason I had agreed to subject myself to working a night without sleep – was shattered by two drunk loons, relatives the manager had hired to help me strip the place down. As soon as he left, they raided the refrigerator for something to eat and knocked over a case of eggs that I spent an hour cleaning up, time I could have used to break down the kitchen. They laughed like it was the greatest joke in the world. It was the first time I had ever been stuck with two drunks while I was sober. I didn't want to be anything like them. They left me alone cleaning up their mess, went out to the grill and started frying burgers. I spent the first three hours of the shift cleaning up after them until they passed out in one of the booths up front. With them out of the way, I broke the kitchen down as fast as possible making up for lost time. By sunrise when the manager returned, I had just finished cleaning the cooking area. I hadn't even touched the prep room.

'What the hell's going on?' he asked.

I pointed to the two guys he'd hired still asleep in the booth. 'Next time let me handle this by myself.'

'Why didn't you call?'

'I did. Nobody answered.'

He went up front and told his cousins to clear out, then came back, rolled up his sleeves and helped me clean the grease traps before the morning shift arrived.

'The inspectors shouldn't be here until after lunch. We still have six hours. Can you stay on?'

'Is there an option?'

We put our heads down and ground through it. When the cooks showed up he put them on cleaning duty with me. He had the hostess turn people away at the door, saying there was an emergency. She gave out rain checks to the regulars for a free meal the next day. The managers put the waiters and waitresses to work cleaning when they showed up and pretty soon we had a full crew scrubbing and polishing the place. By the time lunch rolled around I had been going hard for twelve hours without a break and was starting to weaken. They fired up the kitchen shortly before lunch and started serving

136

customers to make it look like business as usual before the inspectors arrived. The manager asked the cook to grill me lunch to show his appreciation for my staying around.

The inspectors didn't show up until after two o'clock and spent less than thirty minutes inspecting the place. We passed with flying colors. After they left, the manager pulled out a bottle of whiskey and passed it around to celebrate. I declined and headed back to the program. Right before I left he handed me my paycheck and a small bonus. I stuffed it into my pocket.

I left the main road that I usually followed and walked along the railroad tracks, which cut directly across the city into downtown. I felt mildly high from sleep deprivation. I was exhausted and I squinted in the bright sun. When I'd been walking for forty-five minutes, I stopped and leaned against a tree to rest. I liked working hard. I liked exhaustion. It freed me from having to think too much. I thought briefly about Dr. Neuman's suggestion that I enroll in school. I knew there was no way I could confine myself like that right then. The hum of anxiety that I often felt sober was slowly starting to lift. I was finally beginning to appreciate living free of drugs and of the paranoia that accompanied stealing to support my habit. I walked the few blocks back to the program and let myself in.

I pulled the door shut behind me and turned around. Tyrone was sitting in one of the chairs in the front hallway where we had first met. 'Quarterback's in the house,' I shouted.

He didn't look up. I walked over and dropped into the chair beside him. 'What are you doing out here?' I asked.

He still didn't look up. I had expected him to shake hands or slap me on the back. I glanced down at his hands in his lap. That was when I saw the cuffs he was trying to hide. Handcuffs welded together at the center without a chain to reduce range of motion, the kind used to transport prisoners. His hands were clasped. I reached down and grabbed them to see if it was a joke. It wasn't. I panicked. 'What happened?'

He pulled away. 'Ain't nobody's business now.'

'What are you talking about?'

'They're dragging me away just like I worried they would.'

'What happened, Tyrone? I haven't been around since this time yesterday. Maybe I can help.'

'Too late now. It's done.'

'What's done?'

'I'm done.'

I stood up and darted over to the administration office. A man I had never seen before was sitting in the back office with a staff member. Tyrone's probation officer, I assumed. When I walked toward them, the staff member stood up, slammed the door and locked it.

I went back out to the hallway and sat down beside him. Tyrone stared at the floor, resigned.

'Please tell me what's going on.'

He looked at me for the first time. 'I popped a kid at school in the face.'

'You hurt him?'

'Broke his nose.'

'How did it start?'

'He called me a nigger.'

'And you popped him?'

'Yeah, I popped him. You think I'm going to let some rich punk get away with that? I hope that motherfucker's ugly for the rest of his life.'

'What are they going to do?'

'What do you think? They're holding me accountable for that nonviolence contract we signed.'

'You were defending yourself. There's got to be something we can do.'

'Nothing's gonna change their mind.'

The door opened in the office and the man who had been sitting inside appeared in the hallway. 'You ready?' he asked Tyrone.

'Where are you going?' I asked.

Tyrone looked at his probation officer. 'Ask him.'

I turned to the man standing above us. 'Where are you taking him?'

138

He didn't acknowledge my question or presence.

'Let's go,' he said to Tyrone.

Tyrone shifted in his chair and stood up. He looked directly at me. 'Forget it, man.'

I reached down and grabbed his hands again. The probation officer didn't interfere. I pulled them up and held them. He responded by tightening his grip. I started to tell him to keep his head up and realized the words were meaningless. I looked down the hallway. Other than the probation officer, nobody else was around.

'You opened my brain, brother.'

We locked eyes briefly. He didn't know how to respond, but I could see he was touched. We stood there for a couple of seconds longer and then he loosened his grip. His hands dropped back in front of him. His PO opened the front door and held it for Tyrone to walk through. Right before stepping through the threshold, he turned back and said, 'Jazz be the word.'

Between the shock of watching Tyrone taken away in handcuffs and the exhaustion of not sleeping, my body trembled. I went into the dorm, lay in bed and started to cry. I'm not sure how long I was in there, but it must have been three or four hours because it had already started to get dark outside when Ramrod came into the room and demanded to know what I was doing there. The house rules stipulated that we did not enter the dorm alone outside sleeping hours without staff permission.

'Give me a minute,' I said.

He left. I lay there for a while longer, trying to get my thoughts together. When I came out into the hallway, he was standing there.

'They're waiting for you,' he said.

'Who?'

'The family.'

'Not now,' I said. 'I can't deal with group right now.'

'You'd best check your head if you know what's wise and go down to the dining room, unless you want to go the same way as Tyrone.'

I looked at the front door, then glanced toward Dr. Neuman's office to see if he was still in. It was dark. My mind was everywhere at once, unable to articulate a thought or come up with a good excuse why I couldn't attend group therapy right then. I looked back toward the front door and then at the stairs leading down to the dining room where I knew the residents were sitting in a circle, waiting. I couldn't say I had to leave for work. He knew my schedule. I knew he had checked. He knew I knew. He chuckled when he saw the look on my face confirm it.

'After you,' he said, waving his hand at the stairs.

I was too tired to resist. It was better to get it over with. Who cares how much they yell at me? I could take it. I knew the game. I could play along.

I had hardly sat down when they started slamming me. They all knew about Tyrone. Information in the program spread like wildfire. Now they wanted to know about me. As usual, Ramrod started it off. 'I just found Sam up in the dorm lying in bed. His eyes were red like he'd been crying. What do you have to cry about?' he asked, glaring at me. 'You miss your boyfriend already?'

He pressed the wrong button. I became livid. 'What the fuck are you talking about? You going to twist this too? We just lost a brother. One fight at school and he's gone.'

'You know the rules. No violence. If you can't live by the rules you go real quick.' He looked at the residents gathered in the circle. 'They all know the rules. Only you and Tyrone seem to have a problem with them.'

'I was out all night, working. I'm tired. If you're going to send me away for being in the dorm, go ahead.'

'We don't want to hear your excuses. We want to know what you're hiding.'

Then they were back at it again, same shit as always when Ramrod was left in charge at night. I sat there and endured their insults for thirty minutes before I started boiling. By then he had the family charged up, all yelling at once.

'Why you and Tyrone spend so much time together?'

'It's not the first time somebody had a boyfriend in juvi hall.'

'Don't hide it. Man enough to blow it but not man enough to show it?'

My fuse blew. I became enraged that Ramrod even considered taking the group in that direction. He had reduced the one resident I had built a solid friendship with to a sexual encounter that didn't exist. I let the group carry on for a short while longer, then turned to Ramrod and looked him squarely in the eyes. 'You're one sick motherfucker. One day you'll choke on your own fat dick.'

The group, including Ramrod, sat in silent shock. Nobody had ever confronted him so directly or brutally. Not more than three or four seconds ticked by. I slipped out of my chair and sprinted up the stairs, out of the front door and into the street – an instinctive, survival reaction. If I had given them a few more seconds, he would have had the five biggest guys jump on me and restrain me. I was barely on the street when I heard them file out of the door after me.

I ran up the street, came to a set of railroad tracks, turned right and raced three blocks to an overpass. I slipped over the railing, gripping it tightly, and hung outward over the swooshing traffic racing past below before they were able to grab me and wrestle me to the ground. Hanging above the traffic, I turned and glared at them.

'Come a step closer and I'll let go. Try me. You want to see me die?'

I meant every word. They stood feet from my hands clinging to the steel bar, my wide eyes confronting their own. They were peering at me like a pack of trained hyenas. Their pathetic faces flinched under the pressure – they were unsure what to do. I knew they'd soon turn and leave – abiding by the rules they had been taught: 'You must return to the program if the situation threatens to escalate into violence or if you cannot immediately recapture the escapee.' The biggest guy stepped back first, foot crunching in the gravel strewn between railroad ties, and the others followed, taking a single step back and then two before turning and fading into the darkness, leaving me hanging above the world.

I waited to be sure they were gone before I climbed back over the railing and jogged along the tracks to where the bridge met earth.

141

I slid down a steep hill to the roadway below and began walking, sharp, deliberate steps. I wanted to get as far from the overpass as possible before the police showed up. I was almost free. I knew where I was going.

You didn't have to spend any great amount of time on the street or be a genius to understand it – you just had to be young. Some things in life change, but for a young man the street never changes. I had only walked four city blocks when a car driven by a middle-aged man pulled to the curb; the driver leaned over, rolled down the passenger window and asked if I needed a ride. I preferred walking but I had to get beyond the city limit as fast as possible. I knew the police wouldn't look for me beyond their jurisdiction. I wasn't a danger to anyone other than myself. I glanced into the vehicle – he was old, maybe forty, thin arms and a vague smile. I climbed in.

As he pulled into the flow of traffic, he asked where I was going. 'Macon.'

'Kinda far to reach on foot, don't you think?'

I watched the road ahead, red taillights brightening and dimming. We came to a wide bend. I squinted at the headlights flashing across my face. I didn't respond.

'You need a place to stay?'

I brushed his hand from my thigh and continued staring up the road, hypnotized by the small yellow reflectors at the center and the seemingly infinite trail of lights. Ahead an airplane lifted off a runway and rose into the night sky. It continued in our direction, passing overhead. As we passed the airport, the stores and billboards diminished. I pointed to an empty parking lot, then asked him to pull over and let me out. When the car had stopped, he asked again, 'You sure you don't need a place to rest for the night?' I stepped out without responding, walked into an open area and stood, waiting for him to pull away. He leaned out of the window and said something into the night air. I was no longer watching him or listening. I wanted him to disappear. He remained parked there behind me, doing what he was compelled to do. Then the car lurched forward. The tires bit the pavement and barked into the darkness, leaving me behind in silence. I stood in the abandoned parking lot on the edge of the city.

I was no longer tired. My lack of sleep now fueled me.

As I started across the parking lot another small plane lifted off the runway and climbed into the dark night. My eyes followed its inclining path, its twin engines roaring and then diminishing until it was no louder than the passing cars. When I looked up again it had vanished into the clouds. I walked eastward. As the lights of the city disappeared behind me, an orchestra of frogs inhabiting the bog along the road's edge came to life. I walked for more than an hour in the darkness before, oddly, a street lamp appeared, emitting a hollow bluish light in the woods ahead. Hoping to find drinking water, I increased my pace.

Ahead I saw a tall chain-link fence surrounding a single-story brick building. When I neared it, I read the sign in front: Muscogee County Morgue. The thought of dead bodies resting inside it startled me. There was no evidence of life nearby other than the frogs and thick foliage threatening the narrow two-lane country road. I quickened my stride to distance myself from the lone building. A half-mile away I reached a slight rise in the road, went over the top and down the other side. The more I walked, the more tired I became until it was clear that I wouldn't even reach the next town if I didn't stop and rest. I was thirsty and exhausted. Not a single car had passed me since I'd left the city behind. I breathed a sigh of relief. I didn't want anyone appearing in the middle of the night so far out in the countryside. I walked off the edge of the roadway into the tall grass and found a soft area to lie down. I fell asleep as soon as I hit the ground and didn't wake until the sun was high overhead.

I brushed myself off and walked back to the road. It was as empty as it had been the night before. A mile or so on I came to a creek and scrambled down its bank for a drink of water. Back on the road, I continued walking eastward, acknowledging for the first time that my destination was too far for me to walk. When I heard a car coming around a long curve, I stopped and put out my thumb before it came

143

into view. Then I saw the lights on top of the car. It was too late to act like I wasn't hitchhiking. I kept my thumb up, hoping it would pass. Instead he stopped in the middle of the road and asked where I was headed.

'Augusta.'

'You gonna walk all the way there?'

'No, sir. Just want to get to the next town to catch the bus.'

'I can take you up to Talbotton.'

I reached out to open the door and noticed the emblem affixed to it: Talbot County Sheriff. He answered a call on the radio. I sat silently, staring up the road as we passed through the countryside. After a while, he said, 'You ain't wanted for anything, are you, kid?'

'No, sir,' I said nervously.

'Calm down, boy. I'm joking. I'm stopping for lunch up here. If you're hungry, I'll buy before taking you into town.'

'I could use a lunch, sir.'

We sat at a table near the edge of the room. He joked with the waitress, telling her he had just picked me up for armed robbery and was feeding me before he took me to jail.

'My, my, they're getting younger every day, aren't they?'

'Damn straight,' he said. 'But you ain't. When are you gonna go out on that date with me?'

'Stop it now. Can't you see I'm busy working?'

'I can see those yellow panties through your skirt. I'm going to have to take you in for indecent exposure if you don't cover up.'

Afterward we drove into town. The place looked almost abandoned, built in a bygone era – an old courthouse in the square and a few stores lining the street. He parked in front of the courthouse. I glanced at the clock on his dash: 4:25. He turned to me and asked, 'Where did you say you're going again, son?'

'Augusta, sir. To see my mother.'

'You already missed the bus. Greyhound comes through here once a day at ten in the morning. Stops right here in front of the courthouse.'

'I'll head on to Macon, then.'

144

'You got another seventy miles to reach Macon. I don't think you're gonna make it there tonight walking, and I don't suggest you hitch-hike out here late at night. You see that building across the street?' He turned in his seat and pointed to the opposite end of the town, a few blocks away. 'One of my deputies is serving dinner there at seven. You can sleep out back on the grass if you want or you can tell him I said you're welcome to the empty cell across from his office. The cot's got a comfortable mattress. You can sleep with the door open. Nobody's going to lock you up. I'd much prefer you go spend the night there. I don't want to be called out to write a report tomorrow morning if something goes wrong on your walk to Macon tonight.'

'Yes, sir. I'll go over and take a look.'

He didn't seem interested in where I came from. I assumed he had enough problems in his own county to worry about. I thanked him, walked across the street and checked in with the deputy. Before dinner he put me to work, mopping the lobby and his office. All the cells in the jailhouse were empty, except one. I sat in the cafeteria with the deputy and the prisoner, eating dinner, before going in and falling asleep on the cot. The next morning the deputy walked over to the bank with me to help me cash my paycheck. I got on the bus at exactly ten and rode out of town. We picked up people in dozens of small towns along the way, then stopped in Macon for an hour.

After the layover, we spent the rest of the day making our way across the eastern part of the state, stopping at almost every cross-roads and town to pick up and drop off people – Milledgeville, Sparta, Warrenton, Boneville, Dearing. When the bus pulled into the Greene Street station in downtown Augusta, I walked over to Broad Street and down to where the pawnshops stood. I felt like an old man returning to a place he had lived as a child that had changed him. Free of the program, I had only myself to watch over me. I wanted to prove that I could stay sober. I had no desire to do drugs, but that wasn't enough. Habit was stronger than desire and would pull me back into its orbit if I wasn't careful. I walked across town and up Central Avenue toward my mother's house. I knew Relativity or my probation officer had called her by now. I wanted to see her but I was too scared to knock on the door – frightened she would reject me for running from the program. I knew she wouldn't be happy if I showed up. I had already caused too much trouble, but I had to go there anyway. Even if she wouldn't let me in, I'd still see her and finish what I'd come to town to do.

I stopped at a shop on Central Avenue and bought a heavy wool blanket, then went into the hardware store next door and bought some candles and a box of matches. There was a patch of woods up near the reservoir by my mother's house where I used to hang out and get stoned. I hiked up there and found a place to hide in case my probation officer had the police looking for me in my old neighborhood. I rolled out my blanket behind a clump of bushes and lay down to wait until midnight after the traffic had died down and everyone was asleep. Then I walked to my mother's house and slipped into the backyard. I saw the glow of television illuminating the den. I sneaked over to the high windows above the bookcases, pulled myself up and looked in. My mother was lying on the couch sleeping. I let myself down and walked around to the window closest to her and stood outside peering in. I placed my hand on the window near her head, flattening my palm and stood there for a long time, breathing calmly for the first time since leaving Columbus two nights before. After a while I started to worry that I'd scare her if she woke up. I didn't want her to be frightened that she was being stalked, so I disappeared into a small section of woods in the backyard where the ground was covered with ivy and searched until I found the place near the largest tree where I had buried the books.

I took a candle out of my pocket, lit it and stuck it in the ground. I pulled the ivy away in the area I had buried them and started digging in the moist soil. It didn't take long. The package was exactly where I remembered burying it, three feet out from the tree, less than a foot below the surface. The hand-bound mimeographed book fell out. I flipped through it. It had some moisture damage, but it was still readable. As I flipped through its pages, peeling apart those that were stuck together, the sweet scent of mildew emerged, the same pungent smell of freshly turned earth that I remembered as a child in the basement whenever my father opened an old leather-bound book to share a piece of long-lost history. I reached down and picked up the other book that I had hollowed out. The tarnished Iron Cross fell out onto the ground. I reached down and turned it in my hand. It was small, half the size of my palm, but heavier than I remembered. I thought back to the day my father had given it to me, sitting in his Porsche on a narrow farm road between two rolling fields. I held its edge up to the flame and then pulled it away. Part of me wanted to fling it out into the woods but another part didn't feel it was mine to fling. My father had given it to me, but it had belonged to his grandfather. It seemed too old, too much of a relic, to toss away in a fit of rage. Maybe that's why he had given it to me, aware of the dilemma it might cause. It was too much to think about right then, with my father's book resting on my thigh. I placed the cross back inside the book, closed its cover, put it back into the hole and filled it in, patting down the dirt and covering it with leaves and sticks.

I looked around to see if I had disturbed anything else, then blew out the candle and sat in the dark woods, staring at my mother's house on the other side of the yard. The glow from the television no longer illuminated the porch. A chill went up my spine as I wondered if she was standing in the dark house staring out of a second-floor window at the spot where I was sitting, where the candle had been lit moments earlier. I remained motionless, watching the house. There was no movement. I got up, grabbed the book, hopped the back fence into the neighbor's yard and worked my way up the block through the yards until I came out on the street at the end. From there, I climbed back up to the reservoir and my hidden encampment where I fell into a deep sleep.

When I woke up, I rolled over and grabbed the book lying at my side. Without Dr. Neuman's persistence I doubt I would have come back for it, but the more he had prodded me about my past, the more it had brewed in my mind and the more essential it had become to return, even if I hadn't been conscious of it until Tyrone's removal. I was still upset that they had taken him away for a high-school fight. Everybody I became close to disappeared. More than ever the world seemed unfair. I was angry that Ramrod twisted every psychological issue into a sexual question and wondered what secrets he had buried in his own past.

The morning sun glanced across my arm, warming it. I listened to the traffic passing on the street below and the birds talking to each other in the tree above my encampment. The reservoir was composed of two large, open ponds. Combined, they were maybe a half-mile wide, lined with concrete to supply water to the neighborhood where my mother lived. The waterworks plant was at the base of the reservoir. I climbed out from beneath the blanket, stood near the chain-link fence and looked out over the houses and businesses below, then across the shopping center to Daniel Field – a small airplane lifted off the runway and circled back, flying directly overhead.

I went back to my blanket, sat down and opened the book. It was slender, a hundred or so pages written in my father's neat, tiny, circular script. At first I thought it was a journal, but as I started to read I discovered he had written in the third person. He hadn't changed his own or his parents' names, Ida and Paul, but it read more like a story than a journal. Twenty or so pages in I realized it was the history I had begged him for years to tell me. As I read, I wondered if he would have written it if I hadn't pushed.

Had he written it for me? If he had, why had he left?

It took me deep into his life in East Prussia before the war, then entered the war that had torn his family apart, and came out the other side. I read it in a single sitting. Each time I turned a page a knot tightened in my stomach. It wasn't the story I had wanted to hear. It wasn't the history I wanted to descend from. I understood why he had disguised himself in the third person. He didn't want Immigration or anyone else to be able to use it against him to deport or hold him accountable for crimes. I had begged to hear it, but now

148

I didn't want to know everything that had happened during the war. I didn't want to know exactly what he had done. It was too much and confirmed that which I had always been scared was true: he had been a Nazi, raised as a child in a regime that had shaped his early life and the way he had treated me. Instead of helping me to understand him, it made me hate him more. The full force of my early hate turned to rage. By birth, by descent, by history, I was directly connected to his actions. If he had been a Nazi, I could be associated with that. My schoolmates had accused me of it. The places were too vivid, the details of the journey too clearly remembered for it to be anything but the truth. He had known what he was doing. He had been aware of the effect it would have on me if I read it. I slammed it shut and looked at the title page with his inscription in bold letters: THE FLIGHT. In a fit of rage, I ripped it in two, threw it out into the reservoir and watched it float. Eventually, when its pages had absorbed enough water, it sank.

All these years later, he was still fucking with me. Why had I been burdened with it? I wished I had never been curious. I wanted him permanently out of my mind. I wanted to be free of the shackles of family, culture, race, religion, lineage, history and ethnic identity. I wanted to sever all ties. I hated pride. It formed the root of conflict. As long as pride existed, so would war. As long as war existed, I feared history would repeat itself in a downward spiral. The goal I had set after arriving at Relativity resurfaced stronger than ever: freedom. Complete unfettered freedom. I didn't want to be affiliated. I wanted to be left alone.

But I was thrown into deeper turmoil by the desire to see my mother. Maybe she alone had the key to free me. I wanted to be free but I didn't want to let go of her. The story had a strange effect on me. For several days after reading it I felt as though I were watching myself through a video camera.

After three or four days the worst had passed and I felt vaguely attached to the world again, but the emptiness and anger remained. I thought about jumping into the reservoir and drowning myself. I knew I was going crazy, that I had to get out of there. I wanted to go back to Relativity. I wanted to go back to Dr. Neuman. He had pushed me to go back to my past. All it had done was bring back the basement and my father.

I didn't want to get caught by the police. I didn't want to go to the state mental hospital in Milledgeville. I could deal with confinement in Relativity, but I knew I'd snap anywhere else. Dr. Neuman was the only person I trusted.

Each day I walked down to the Dairy Queen near the reservoir and bought a large chocolate malt. Every night I went back to my mother's house, hid in the darkness outside and watched her through the window. One evening I stayed out in the backyard all night, waiting for my mother, brother and sister to leave for work and school. Then I climbed up onto the porch roof, opened a window and slid inside. I went through the house, from room to room. I couldn't recall being sober there. The rooms were familiar and foreign at the same time. Walt had moved into my old bedroom. I went downstairs, looked in the refrigerator for something to eat and remembered hanging onto its door to keep my balance the night I had sliced my head open.

I took a pillow out of the hall closet and pressed it to my face – it had the familiar scent of the house and of the hairspray my mother used. I rolled it up tightly, tucked it under my arm, slipped out of the house and made my way back up to the reservoir. I lay there, with my head on the pillow, for the rest of the afternoon looking up at the sky. I decided that tomorrow I would go over to the house after my mother got home from work and knock on the front door so I wouldn't scare her. I didn't want to leave without seeing her. I hoped that somehow she could help.

'What are you doing here?' she asked. She looked frightened, as if I might harm her. 'You've been in the house, haven't you?'

'I just got here,' I lied. 'I came to see you.'

'You can't stay.'

'I don't want to. I wanted to see you.'

150

'I have to call the police, Sam. Your probation officer calls every day.'

'I'll go. I just wanted to visit.'

'Why can't you behave for once in your life?'

'They pushed me, Mom. I couldn't take it.'

'You won't ever learn, will you?'

'I've been doing good. I got a job at a restaurant.'

'I'm sure they'll want you back now that you've run away,' she said sarcastically. 'I thought the program would change you.'

'It has changed me.'

She stared at me as if I was someone other than her son. We stood there locked in silence for a long time. She didn't invite me in or step out onto the porch to hold me. Eventually she looked away and I saw her eyes follow a car down the street. I turned as a cruiser passed the house. They saw me standing at the door near my mother. I waited for them to disappear up the road, but instead they slowed for the traffic to clear and did a U-turn. I looked back to my mother.

'I don't want them to take me to the hospital.'

'You can't run forever, Sam.'

I glanced back – they were approaching the house. I sprinted off the porch and along the edge of the house into the backyard, hopped the fence and wove my way up the center of the block, darting across a side street and through the backyards of another block. When I was three or four blocks away, I hid in a storage shed behind an old house with an overgrown yard and waited until dark.

Late that night I came out and walked the back streets across town toward Gordon Highway, jumping behind bushes whenever a car appeared. By the time I reached the highway, I was far enough from the neighborhood to start hitchhiking. A soldier picked me up.

'Does Greyhound stop out at the base?' I asked.

'Yeah, of course. How do you think we get around – in limos?'

He dropped me off at the place where the bus stopped each morning. I slept in the bushes near the edge of the road so the Military Police wouldn't see me and woke up early the next morning when a group of soldiers was gathering at the bus stop to go home to their families. I found a window seat near the middle of the bus and sank back in it as we started west across the state. I was confused: hurt that my mother hadn't taken me in to hide me and angrier than I had ever been with my father. I thought about Tyrone as well.

The bus pulled into Columbus late that night. I wandered around downtown and slept near the river to wait until morning when I knew Dr. Neuman would be in. I didn't want to turn myself in to anyone else.

When he saw me walk into the program the following morning, dirty and unkempt, he shook his head in disappointment. I walked down the front hallway and straight into his office where I sat in the chair before his desk and waited for him to finish his business in the staff office. He knew I wasn't going anyplace soon, so he took his time.

'I have to report you,' he said, when he slumped down in his chair behind the desk. 'You can't disappear without telling anyone where you are when you're on probation, Sam. I'm not sure what they'll do when they learn you're here.'

'You've got to help me. I don't want to go anywhere else.'

'It's out of my hands. It's between you and the judge now. They'll set up another hearing. I can request that you stay here until your hearing, but I can't guarantee they'll allow you to return afterward.'

I dropped my head into my hands. First Tyrone and now me. We had been doing so good. 'There has to be something you can do.'

'The only thing I can do is talk with you, Sam. I can try to buy you some time, but I have no control over your future. If you had come back the next morning it would have been one thing, but you crossed the state, broke into your mother's house and did who knows what else?'

'I didn't break into anybody's house.'

'That's not what she told your probation officer.'

'I went back there like you told me to.'

'I didn't tell you to go back there.'

'You told me I had to go find my past. I went. I found it. I read it.'

He perked up in his chair. 'Did you bring it with you?'

I raised my empty hands in the air. 'Does it look like I brought it?'

'Where is it?'

'At the bottom of the reservoir near my house. I should have never followed your advice. It's exactly what I didn't want to know.'

'I don't understand. What didn't you want to know?'

'The truth. I didn't want to know the truth about where my father came from and what my grandparents had been through. I didn't know it before, but I know it now.'

'Whatever you found out you had to know. You know you did. Only with that knowledge can you begin to free yourself. You can't free yourself from the unknown. Now you know exactly what you want to distance yourself from and you're already one step closer to your goal of freedom.'

'But this isn't the way it was supposed to be. Usually people get to learn about their family's history with a sense of accomplishment. The only thing I feel is guilt and shame.'

'You've achieved what you set out to do. I'm curious, but I won't pester you about what you learned. I know it's more important for you to distance yourself from it now than to relive it. But I will tell you this. I know your father came from Germany after the war. I called your mother when you were admitted to get your parents' backgrounds. I can only guess at what you learned.' He paused. 'My parents went through the war, too, Sam. They lived in Belarus. What they experienced and whatever your father went through are two different worlds, no matter how closely their paths may have crossed. But I don't hold anything against you, Sam. We all live with anger. I can dislike the Germans for what they did but still like you. I know that's hard for you to believe, but it's true. Until you understand that you'll never find the freedom you're after.'

I slid down in my chair, too embarrassed to look at him. We sat in silence for a long time.

Finally, I said, 'I don't want to leave. I don't like it Outside.'

'It's what I call the prisoner's dilemma,' he said, 'but not in the classic game theory sense where police play off two persons accused of the same crime against each other to get one conviction. You've

153

entered a mental state where you're playing off yourself against yourself to stay incarcerated. For all the strain of being institutionalized, there remains one element that is easier than being free – knowing what the next day holds, knowing where your meals are coming from, knowing what to expect, even if it's uncomfortable. If you hope to fully mature, you have to accept that the future is unknowable. It's the one variable that cannot be solved. You've always struck me as strong, Sam. If you can learn to live with knowing that you can't ever be certain what the future holds, I have no doubt that you'll succeed, regardless of how many bumps you experience along the way.'

'Will you help me?'

'I already have. I'll call your probation officer if you want, but I already know what he'll say. I've been doing this a long time.'

'But you'll try?'

He went to get my file, then came back into the room, sat down in front of me and dialed. Just as he had predicted, my probation officer asked him to hold me there until somebody could pick me up.

'He says he'd like another chance in the program,' Dr. Neuman said.

I overheard my probation officer say, 'We'll decide whether he can come back after a hearing. He violated the terms of his probation.'

'How long before somebody picks him up?' Dr. Neuman asked.

He held up the phone so I could hear the response. 'I can send somebody over tomorrow afternoon to hold him at the local detention center until we can transfer him back here.'

After he'd hung up, Dr. Neuman looked at me. 'I can't stop you walking out of the front door. I know you're resourceful. I haven't been able to convince you to go to school. You have less than two years until you're eighteen. They can't do anything after that.'

I spent my final night there cleaning up and preparing for my departure. I already knew I didn't want to go back to the self-imprisonment of being stoned all the time. I was free of drugs and would soon be free of Relativity. My entire life lay ahead of me. I'd follow the rules of society. The last place I wanted to end up was jail. Relativity had opened my mind. I would leave a better person, but one who was no more intent on joining society than he had been before he arrived.

BOOK IV

The Pecan Orchard

I still had only a single goal. I wanted to be free of the past – able to wander without affiliation or obligation. I didn't want to be pigeon-holed, praised or frowned upon.

I wanted to be left alone.

I had saved almost five hundred dollars washing dishes and planned to use the money to get a start. I wanted to work with my hands. I wanted to be able to move between jobs when I became bored. I didn't want to be stuck in the same place.

I gave up any notion of returning to Augusta. The only life I knew there was drugs. I was sure my mother didn't want me, and even if she did, I worried I would only remind her of the past I sought to escape. She would hear my deepening voice, observe my unconscious mannerisms and be reminded of my father. I didn't want to remind her of someone I wished to forget.

I sat up in the dining room on my last night at Relativity after everyone had gone to bed and wrote her a letter. I told her I loved her and that I would show my love by not reappearing. I said I had to go find myself. I told her I no longer desired drugs. I no longer lied or stole. I wrote, 'I love you, Mom. Goodbye.'

Then I vanished from her life, just as my father had before me. That was the only part that hurt. I had no choice. As soon as I reminded her of my father and she became irritated, I would seek drugs to dissolve the tension, to dissolve my past. I didn't want my life to become a circular loop. I packed several changes of clothing into plastic bags to keep them dry if it rained and stuffed them into a small backpack.

In the morning I waited on the front steps for Dr. Neuman to arrive. 'I want to thank you. I know things didn't turn out the way they should have, but I learned more than I ever expected to here.'

'Nothing ever turns out the way you expect it to,' he said. 'You'll find your way. I'm convinced of that. I've never turned a blind eye to someone walking away from the program before whom we were supposed to hold. I want you to know that. It's my way of saying I'm certain you'll eventually find the freedom you're after.'

We shook hands and I turned to walk down the street to the Greyhound station. I sat in a plastic chair waiting for my bus.

From the moment I stepped onto it, my life became a blur. I spent the rest of my sixteenth and entire seventeenth year waiting for rides at bus stations and hitchhiking along back roads, highways and interstates, looking for jobs anywhere I could find them. I stayed in shelters, slept in the back of pickup trucks, on the floors of storage sheds, trailers, abandoned homes, cars, in the woods, on riverbanks, in fields, under newspaper at the side of the road and, once in a great while, in the homes of kind old men. I never touched booze or drugs, never drank coffee or tea – it was too hard to find hot water – and only smoked cigarettes occasionally, when I was cold and sleeping outdoors. It made me feel warmer, inhaling the smoke, blowing it out and watching it rise. The only other time I smoked regularly was waiting in Greyhound bus stations and traveling between towns, in the smoking area at the back of the bus, an area marked by a white line painted on the floor, where the rancid bathroom was located and a party was usually taking place among the vagrants passing pints of Old Crow around.

There were always perverts prowling around the bus stations in southern towns, like Macon, Atlanta, Birmingham, Jackson, Tallahassee and the rest, but for all the desperate men who tailed me during that time not a single woman gave me a ride when I was hitchhiking, approached me, followed me through town or even looked at me. Street aggression seemed to belong to men. They buzzed after me like flies on shit wherever I went to shake them off – into restrooms, onto the street, into a greasy spoon to eat. It infuriated me because I didn't

160

want contact with anyone. I didn't want intimacy; I didn't want their money; I didn't want their pathetic love; I didn't want somebody forcing themselves on me; I didn't want to be snatched off the street.

I carried a small knife in a sheath that I tucked into my waist-band while walking and stored in my bedroll tied to the top of my knapsack, leaning between my legs with my fingers resting on it when I accepted a ride. That was the part I liked least of living from place to place. I wandered to be free, to be alone, not to be forced into contact with lonely strangers. Being free and untethered to the past was harder than I imagined. You had to work at it, like a prisoner in a quarry.

I worked a hundred different jobs with people from every walk of life. When I was lucky I made minimum wage and then only if I paid taxes, and less than minimum wage when I was paid under the table – the boss was quick to inform me that 'It came out to the same pay anyway and you ought to be happy to have a job at all.' I worked with Mexicans, who didn't like me because they thought I was taking their jobs; blacks, who didn't like me because I was white; whites, who didn't like me because I worked too hard and didn't eat lunch with them. I walked down fields in freezing rain, picking produce at piece rate with a knife and bare hands, washed stacks of dishes in restaurants too cheap to buy a machine, picked weeds from people's lawns, pruned trees, carried lumber on construction sites, cooked eggs with hash browns as a short-order cook, scrubbed toilets, mopped hallways, laid bricks, mixed concrete, pulled electrical conduit, cleaned grease an inch thick from exhaust fans, changed tires, stocked groceries, shoveled horseshit, carried hay, greeted people, held open doors, chased shoplifters, painted and roofed houses, graded roads, hauled trash, dug holes, built fences, laid pipe for sprinkler systems, plumbed illegal rental units, snaked sewage lines, cleaned septic tanks, buried dead pets, plucked chickens, gutted pigs, loaded water-melons, separated peaches, raked leaves, spread gravel, changed oil, felled trees, cut, split and stacked wood, hung drapes, installed air-conditioners, drove trucks, moved furniture, assembled bicycles, built ponds, set tiles, glued linoleum, stretched carpet, collected cans and bottles, bagged coal, sold Christmas trees and salvaged metal. I worked as a waiter, security guard, parking-lot attendant and baker's assistant. I crewed on a boat, stripped hardwood floors, stocked a lake with fish, cleared rocks from fields, pulled stumps, cleaned windows, sold hardware, helped build a log cabin, hauled water, rerouted a stream, leveled a trailer, delivered flowers, fixed washing- machines and dryers, installed wood stoves, repaired lawnmowers, spackled walls, hung sheetrock, laid railroad ties, set up cubicles in an unemployment office, installed propane heaters and water coolers, disassembled ancient coal furnaces, took tickets at a demolition derby, guided traffic at a bluegrass festival, set up bleachers, scraped barnacles off boats, pitched crabs, worked in a textile mill and on a catfish farm, filled helium balloons, recycled car batteries, rebuilt alternators, sharpened knives and went door-to-door as a newspaper and magazine salesman.

I journeyed between so many towns, cities and states that I'd be hard pressed to say exactly where I had been. I traveled to wherever I heard work was abundant. Sometimes I ventured as far west as Texas or north up into Tennessee or West Virginia, but mostly I explored every nook and cranny in Georgia, Alabama, Mississippi, South Carolina and Florida.

That first year and a half I was free disappeared even faster than the years I had spent on drugs. It was one big blur of finding work to survive, then moving on whenever an employer asked me to stay. I didn't want to get close to anyone. I wanted to be free, but it ended up more a form of self-imposed transient servitude. I was usually the lowest man on the totem pole since I was the newest and often the youngest, which encouraged them to challenge me and see what I was made of. The breaking-in period. They had fun with it. But it pissed them off that even under their onslaught I worked them into the ground. I channeled my anger and frustration into each job. I liked sweating. I liked getting into a rhythm and holding it. I wasn't interested in ten-minute breaks and a half-hour at lunch.

It was only later that I recognized work had become my new drug. I couldn't stop. I wasn't content unless I was going full tilt. The skinny guys rarely kept up and the big guys wore themselves out. When I did meet my match we had the best of times trying to outdo one another, and when one of us broke, the other was gracious in victory. But mostly I was despised for being addicted to work, called arrogant, a showoff, whitetrash, bulldozer, fuckface, shit-for-brains, gabacho, cracker, moron, slave, sell-out. But the names only proved what I had wanted all along, which was not to belong.

I kept this up from town to town and state to state until I found myself on a pecan farm in the southwestern corner of Georgia between Leesburg and Albany surrounded by rivers and swampland. I was exhausted from perpetually looking for sleeping quarters. The farm was only a few hours south of Columbus where my journey to freedom had begun. The owner, Mr. Thompson, had several other businesses in the area. He liked my work ethic and the way I kept to myself. He paid me under the table – a dollar more than minimum wage – and he even offered me a free place to live in an outbuilding that he said I could improve however I liked and he'd pay for materials. He said that when work slowed on the farm, I could go into town to work at his motel.

I spent the last month of my seventeenth year and much of my eighteenth walking between the pecan farm and the motel in downtown Albany. The walk took an hour each way. Mr. Thompson or one of the other workers often offered me a ride when they were going into town but I always declined. Walking was my private time and I didn't want to infuse it with empty conversation. I had stopped moving from place to place and my new daily routine provided a comfort and freedom that moving couldn't. Mr. Thompson rarely checked up on me. He knew I'd finish my duties and then some. He also knew I didn't like to be questioned any more than he did. He lived in a big house near the entrance to the farm, separated from the road by a fence running alongside the street that I had built and painted.

Unlike a fruit tree orchard, pecan trees were huge, often standing more than a hundred feet tall, so though technically an orchard it was more like living in a well-groomed forest. Behind my shack there was an endless tract of undeveloped forest, brambles, bogs and meadows that I hiked through on the rare day that I had time. Even though I didn't own the shed, having my own place to sleep provided an unexpected serenity. An old potbelly stove stood in one corner – I cut wood for it and stacked the logs out front so that I could lean out the door and grab a few to build a fire inside whenever it was cold. For the first time I felt truly free. It didn't matter that I was tied to my new home. I was never in conflict with anybody. Nobody complained that I worked too hard and everyone left me alone.

After Mr. Thompson had asked me to repair a few things around the farm and noticed I had a knack for it, he made me maintenance man at the motel. I learned to fix heaters and replace faulty thermostats on air conditioners. I painted any buildings that needed it, cut and trimmed the lawns, repaired leaky faucets, adjusted antennas and anything else I could find to do. The motel was small, about forty rooms, many of which went unoccupied. Gradually, given the shortage of maintenance tasks, my primary job switched to running the laundry room he asked me to set up. Until then he had contracted a laundry service that had collected big bags of sheets and towels and dropped off freshly washed and folded ones, but when he saw how hard I worked, he took me to a department store to pick up a couple of large washers and dryers. The laundry had to be done seven days a week or they'd run out of linen. Between loads, I'd fix sinks and adjust TVs. Mr. Thompson never checked my hours and rarely came to the laundry room. He trusted me. Whenever I told him how many hours I'd worked that week, he always paid me cash.

Within three weeks of my arrival on the farm I had established my new routine. I woke up in the morning, made a bowl of grits and fried two eggs from the henhouse. I sat on a chair out front staring across the orchard at the perfectly lined trees as I ate breakfast. Then I set out for town, hopping the wooden fence out front and crossing the road to follow a narrow path to the railroad tracks elevated above the forest floor. I climbed up the steep gravel bank and onto the first rail and tried to balance while walking to work.

I played the same game every morning and afternoon. Whenever I started to lose balance I jumped across to the other rail. I aimed to walk the rails all the way into town without ever touching the ground. My ultimate goal was to do it on a single rail.

Most of the maids at the motel were elderly women who worked part-time. Down south you didn't see many young white boys washing, drying and folding bed linen. I was an anomaly and had to prove myself before they trusted my skills.

'I wouldn't use too much bleach if I was you,' the oldest one told me. 'You're going to put holes in the sheets. Nobody likes sleeping under holey sheets.' She burst out laughing. 'We got ourselves a greenhorn here.' She looked me up and down. I started to feel uncomfortable. 'Nareesha's gonna like you.' She started laughing again.

'Who's Nareesha?'

'She's coming in today. She's been on vacation. Let's go find her and introduce you right away.'

It turned out we didn't have to. A few minutes later she walked around the corner to drop off some dirty linen.

'I got somebody I want you to meet, Nareesha. This is our new laundry boy. What'd you say your name was?'

'Sam.'

Nareesha reached out to shake hands in a businesslike manner. 'Pleasure to meet you. I got work to do.' She grabbed an armful of sheets and towels off the shelf and walked back outside.

The maid turned to me and said, 'See? I told you she'd like you.'

I soon learned Nareesha had recently finished high school and was saving up to go to college. Even though Mr. Thompson knew she'd quit before too long he gave her most of the hours. He liked her ambition and drive. I think he had a little crush on her too from the way he flirted with her, but he never seemed to expect anything in return other than friendly banter. Most days it was Nareesha and me, her cleaning rooms, myself washing and drying linen. She soon warmed to me, but I was so shy that I hardly ever said a word to her.

165

I was used to being around drug addicts, loudmouths and laborers, not people working hard to save money for college. I had never met anyone like her. I didn't know how to act and it must have showed, because one afternoon when she came to drop off a load and pick up fresh towels, she remained for a few seconds, and then said, 'Didn't anyone ever teach you manners? You're supposed to greet me.'

I shrugged and looked at the floor.

'I'm not going to bite you,' she said.

I glanced up but I still didn't say anything.

She gazed at me for a while longer, then said, 'Go on your own self,' and walked away.

She wasn't used to being ignored. I could tell that much. Over time, I opened up. It started with short answers to her questions, like 'They'll be done in twenty minutes,' or 'It's on that shelf over there.' In the latter case she responded, 'Well, aren't you going to get it for me? I don't have all day.'

I walked over, picked up a stack of sheets and carried them across the room to her.

She was one of the few women to whom I never said, 'Yes, ma'am' or 'No, ma'am.' The older maids expected it, but I was afraid that if I did the same to Nareesha she might slap me. She slowly pulled me out of my shell.

The first time I said, 'Good morning, Nareesha. How is your day going?' I could see that she felt like a proud schoolteacher

'I'm doing fine, Sam. Thank you for asking.' She smiled.

I smiled back, then focused on folding sheets.

Before she walked away, she said, 'There's a big bag of dirty laundry waiting for you in front of room nine.'

The following week when I went to repair a sink, she stopped me on the walkway in front of the room she was cleaning. 'You should be ashamed of yourself,' she said, 'letting the old ladies working here carry these heavy bags back to you.' Then, to emphasize that she was serious, she kicked the side of the one she had just dropped on the walkway and said, 'I don't want to see your face again today. I thought you had better manners than that.'

166

She went back into the room she had been cleaning and slammed the door. I sheepishly bent down, picked up the bag and carried it around to the back. Soon I was collecting all the maids' dirty laundry, bringing it to the laundry room and carrying armfuls of clean linen to refill their carts so that they no longer had to walk back and forth as they had done for years.

Nareesha began bringing her lunch to the laundry room, where she sat up on the dryer and ate in front of me. Her presence unnerved me. She never asked if I minded her taking her lunch break there. She never asked me to join her. She'd eat slowly watching me go about my work. The only thing I ever said was, 'Excuse me,' for her to move her legs out of the way of the door whenever the dryer she sat on finished its load. She took her time moving her legs.

Eventually, when she'd had lunch there several days in a row, she said, 'You ever plan on speaking to me?'

'About what?'

'Be real.'

I clammed up.

She took another bite, wrapped the remains of her food in foil and slowly slid forward to jump off the dryer. When she saw me watching her, she said, 'Put those damn towels down and help me get off this thing.'

I fetched the footstool and set it in front of her.

She looked at it. 'What do you plan to do with that?'

'For you to step down on.'

'You'd better climb up on that damn thing and get me or I'm going to get angry.'

I stepped up on the stool and held out my hand. She slid up against me, then down to the floor and walked out of the room without thanking me.

After that I wasn't so shy. When I had a chance to talk with her, I took it. Over the following weeks, I stopped by the rooms she was cleaning, and I guess others started to notice.

One day when Mr. Thompson saw me leaving work, he said,

167

'I don't know if it's wise for you to get mixed up with people on the job.'

Of course that wasn't what he meant. If she had been white he wouldn't have said a word. I didn't normally talk back, but by then I enjoyed her company – I didn't want anybody saying I couldn't talk to her. Even when we didn't talk, I still liked being around her. I stood there for a minute, digesting his advice, then said, 'No offense, Mr. Thompson. I appreciate you looking out for me. But I've always made a point of mixing myself up in whatever trouble I could find as long as it didn't hurt anybody.'

'That's just the trouble. People around here talk. You are hurting somebody. You don't know her parents. They don't want you any more than you want to marry me.'

'Who said anything about marrying?'

'All I'm asking is that you respect people's wishes. They've spent a lot of time raising their daughter proper. They have high hopes for that girl. No offense to you, but I can tell by your accent you weren't raised in the South. We've got a long history and tradition here we like to respect.'

A few times a week I worked late so that after everyone left I could draw a tub of water in one of the empty rooms and lie in it, relaxing. The shed on the farm didn't have a bathroom so I was forced to clean up at work. The motel was laid out like a large U with the open side facing the street. The office stood in a small building at the center of the U. The rooms ran around the inside and the doors opened toward the office. There was a concrete walkway in front of the rooms covered with an awning. At the bottom of the U, away from the street, there was a gap between rooms to allow cars to pull into an area out back where another ten rooms ran in a line, parallel to and facing the street but hidden behind the rest of the motel.

These ten rooms were contracted out to Southern Pacific Railroad. Albany had a major switching yard that handled train traffic for the southwest corner of the state, but of the ten rooms, five at most were filled on any given night. Major yard or no, Albany Georgia wasn't Newark, New Jersey. My laundry room was located at the end of the row of the ten rooms in the back, directly beside the five rooms that were typically vacant. Room thirty-eight was closest to the laundry room and that was where I took a bath.

A few weeks after Mr. Thompson's talk, I was relaxing in the warm water when Nareesha slipped through the door unannounced. As soon as I heard somebody come in, I knew it was her. She was the only one who knew my routine, and one of the few people who worked there who had her own master key. We hadn't made any plans but I can't say I was surprised. I lay in the bathtub until she appeared in the doorway. I didn't jump up or try to cover myself with a towel. I just lay there, not moving or making a sound. For a long time she didn't say anything. She looked around the room – at my clean towel hanging on the stand, my clothes bunched up on the floor – and then followed the length of my body in the tub. Finally she said, 'Aren't we comfortable tonight?'

I still didn't speak. She didn't expect me to respond. She stood there a while longer, then stepped back out into the main room, set her purse down, came back in and sat on the closed toilet lid.

'I thought you'd be down here,' she said. 'I had a fight with my parents. They asked about you.'

'What'd you say?'

'That I had no idea what they were talking about. That you worked here and that's all I knew about you.'

'It is.'

'My point exactly.'

'So where do they think you are now?'

'I told them I was going to the library to study.'

'But you're done with school.'

'I'm researching colleges. I already know where I'm going, but I told them I wanted to get some information on a couple other schools.'

'Isn't there one in town?'

'I don't want to be stuck here my whole life.' She looked at the floor. 'Why don't you tell me something about you?'

169

'Like what?'

'Anything would be a good start. Like where you're from.'

'All over.'

'Where'd you learn to talk like that?'

'Like what?'

'You don't talk like people around here.'

'You mean a southern accent? I'm from up north.'

'You fly down here on a spaceship?'

'I moved down with my mother, a long time back.'

'I don't see her around.'

'I left home.'

'You left home?' she asked skeptically.

'Yeah.'

She sighed. 'More like got sent away. What do you take me for?'

I sat up and ran more warm water into the tub.

'I'm waiting,' she said.

I turned off the faucet. 'There's nothing else to tell. Got into drugs. Got sent away. Didn't think it was wise to go home.'

'Where's home?'

'Augusta.'

'Augusta, Georgia?'

'Where else?'

'Capital of Maine – you just said you're from up north.'

'I've never been to Maine. I'm from Ohio. Yeah, Augusta, Georgia.'

'That's where I want to go to school.'

'Why Augusta?'

'Medical College of Georgia. One of the oldest in the country.'

'Don't you have to go to regular college first?'

'There's another school there, Paine College. My parents met there – a black school.'

'You want to go there?'

'Why wouldn't I? It's right across the street from the medical school.'

'You don't mind going to a black school?'

She looked at me to see if I was serious. 'Hello. I'm black.'

170

'That's not what I mean. You're here with me.' I didn't know what to say next.

She saw the frustrated look on my face. 'I can go wherever I want but the other schools never did anything for us. Black schools saved us. Why would I turn my back?'

'Saved you?'

'From ending up like you.' She laughed. 'They gave my grandparents an education when nobody else would. Like I said, my parents went to Paine. It's a tradition for us.'

She fell silent for a minute and looked down as if she was thinking about something. I saw a grin return to her face. I started to say something, but she raised her hand to silence me. 'You'd better get out of the tub before your privates shrivel into a raisin.' She grabbed the towel from the stand and threw it at me.

I reached up and caught it.

She leaned down and grabbed my clothes. 'I'll be waiting for you out here,' she said, leaving the bathroom, my clothes tucked under her arm, as she pulled the door closed behind her.

When I came out she was already in bed. Her clothes were in a pile on the floor beside mine.

'Put the chain on the door,' she said. 'I don't want Mr. Thompson snooping around.'

She turned back the covers and I double-checked the door. Then I came back to the bed and slipped beneath the sheet, but stayed on my side. I didn't know what to do.

'Maybe we should go to sleep,' she said.

She knew how to make me giggle and loosen up. She reached over and pulled me to her. Her eyes were closed. I wasn't sure if I should kiss her right then or wait longer. She finally opened her eyes and said, 'Do I have to do everything?'

I leaned down and kissed her. It was the first time I had ever kissed a girl. I closed my eyes. She was warmer than I'd imagined. My body was still warm from the bath. Sweat rose from the pores on my chest and dripped onto her neck. I leaned down and kissed them off.

'Don't stop now,' she said, when I paused.

171

I ran my tongue gently along her neck and up to her ear, took its lobe into my mouth. She held my head firmly between her hands. She guided me back down to her neck and held me there for a long time, then pushed me down to her breasts and whispered, telling me how to kiss her. I grabbed a nipple gently in my mouth and flicked it with my tongue, then let go and sucked deeper, before sliding my tongue across to her other breast. She told me not to let my mouth leave her body. I went back up to her neck. She let me stay there for a short time, then pushed me down, this time past her breasts to her stomach. I felt her legs part and ran my hand down her inner thigh. She gripped my head harder and pushed me down between her legs. My mouth slid across her belly, over her pubic hair and into her flesh. She pulled me to her and began rubbing her hips against me. Within the small confines, I explored an area of ridges and valleys until I reached a small peak at which point she pulled me tightly against her and started rubbing her hips more forcefully. I heard her moaning, telling me not to stop. I shielded my teeth with my lips and continued licking the tiny peak she had guided me to as her rhythm grew stronger and stronger. She grabbed my head and held me against her so hard that I could hardly breathe. Then all at once she relaxed her grip and I lay there resting my head on her thigh under the covers panting, falling into rhythm with her breathing above.

We revisited that room many times. She'd take me in there at all hours of the day. Soon I was initiating contact. She came into the laundry room and reached up on the shelf and I ran my hand under her shirt and along her spine. She arched her head back and I kissed her neck while I held her waist tightly, pressing our clothed bodies together, until we heard a noise and jumped apart, grabbing handfuls of towels, as if we were busy working, then falling to the floor laughing when we realized it was only a squirrel, and kissing again as I slid my hand up over her breasts.

My experiences with drugs seemed a mild infatuation compared to our obsession. For the first three weeks, we literally made love anytime and anyplace we could. We lost all reason. We took unnecessary risks. We met down by the Flint River, arriving separately and followed a narrow path down into the woods, tearing our clothes off along the way. Another afternoon we made love in broad daylight on the riverbank. A boat of fishermen drifted past on the opposite bank and saw us, intensifying our passion. We explored every part of each other's bodies. She drove out to a dirt road that ran alongside the farm I lived on and parked her car in the bushes. I led her along a short path through the woods to my shed. I held her up on the kitchen counter, kissed her stomach and let her wrap her legs around my head. She lay on the floor, her legs over my shoulders.

Two months later we were still insatiable, but our wits returned. We knew if we were caught that Mr. Thompson would throw me off the farm and her parents would send her to her aunt's house in Atlanta. By then it was only another three or four months before she left for Paine College to find housing and get settled in. She planned to begin in the spring semester instead of waiting through the entire summer and into the next fall, nearly a year away. I learned her parents could easily afford to send her to school, but they had wanted her to work for a year between high school and college so she would understand what it was like to struggle and earn her own spending money.

'Why'd you become a maid?' I asked. 'Why didn't your father get you a job in an office?'

'He said I'd be in offices like him for the rest of my life. If I planned to treat the sick, I needed to see what sort of lives they led so I could better understand the stresses they faced every day while under treatment.'

We tried to stay away from each other more so nobody would become suspicious. I bought a motorcycle from one of the farmhands for fifty dollars. It hadn't run in years. I needed something to displace my intense focus on Nareesha. When I couldn't have her, the motorcycle became my passion. I stripped it down. Working on it was one of the few things that took my full attention: I couldn't let my mind

173

drift if I wanted to remember how it went back together. When I couldn't run my hands across her belly, over her breasts or along her neck, I used a shop hammer to pound the seized pistons out of the cylinders. I cleared the table in the corner of the room and covered its surface with tools, nuts, bolts, solvent and gasket sealer. I studied the shop manual I bought at the motorcycle dealer. For the next three weeks, every moment I had off work that I wasn't with her I tore the bike down to its frame, disassembled the engine, laying each tiny part throughout the shed in the exact order in which I had taken it apart so I wouldn't forget how to put it back together. Each time I came in, I tiptoed between all the parts laid out like a jigsaw puzzle. I slept curled up in a corner.

I didn't have money to buy many new parts, so I learned to hone the cylinder sleeves back to a silky smooth sheen with an electric drill I borrowed. I soaked the frozen main bearings in WD-40 for days and slowly spun the rust out until they eventually rolled freely again. I borrowed Mr. Thompson's compressor and blew the carburetor jets clean. I rebuilt the oil injector, put new springs and bushings in the alternator, sanded the points, found a rectifier at a junkyard, greased the wheel bearings, duct-taped the split seat cover and carefully outlined and cut a custom head gasket from a piece of old gasket paper stored in the barn near the tractor. I brushed and gapped the sparkplugs. Then I slowly put it all back together again.

I stood in front of the shed admiring it before I mounted it, turned the ignition switch and kick-started it. The two-stroke engine fired to life – *rat-a-tat-tat-tat* – blue smoke pouring out. It had the same high-pitched sound as a chainsaw running deep in the forest felling trees. I raced into town, pulled into the motel and told Nareesha to get on the back. The lady who worked the front desk was out front. Nareesha nodded in her direction. I saw her looking at us and waved. She waved back and went inside.

'Get on,' I urged.

'I have to finish this room.'

'We'll come back and finish it together.'

174

She slid over the seat behind me, holding me tightly around my waist. I gunned out of the parking lot and zoomed onto the main road, leaning side to side as we cut up the centerline through traffic. We raced out past the edge of town into the farmland and soon entered the surrounding bogs. About twenty miles on I pulled off the road and around the back of an abandoned mill. I shut the bike off and turned around to her, taking her face in my hands, kissing her, pressing up against her so tightly that I finally slid off the bike and pulled her through an empty doorframe and made love to her on the bare wood floor of the mill, putting my jeans and shirt under her back to protect her.

The next time I saw her she said we had to cool it. People were talking. Her parents had questioned her again, and so had Mr. Thompson.

During working hours she didn't come to the laundry room any more. She told me not to worry. 'It doesn't mean anything. I just don't want to get in trouble. They all know but are acting like they don't, seeing if we get it under control.'

'What's there to control?'

'Everything. I worked my whole life for college.'

'What about me?'

'Don't just think about yourself. You're not even from here.'

I tried to be calm, fearing she wouldn't see me at all if I did something stupid like proclaim my love. I went about my business at the motel, occasionally talking to the other maids or the office lady. I'd pass Nareesha with a handful of tools as if I was too busy to talk. I'd pick up her laundry bag when she was in the room so she'd notice it gone when she came out. I didn't leave rose petals on her cart or love poems folded in her clean towels and she didn't leave any for me. But sometimes she'd look at me from across the parking lot with a melancholic smile.

I arrived home from work one day to find them harvesting pecans. A large piece of farm equipment drove around the orchard from tree to tree with a huge rubber pincher that rose up on a boom, clamped itself around the tree and vibrated, slowly at first, then picking up momentum until it shook so violently that it sent shudders up to the highest branches. Pecans rained down like a storm, piling up on the ground. Mr. Thompson kept the grass throughout the orchard trimmed closely, like a golf course, so that after the vibrating machine was finished, another piece of equipment, similar to those on driving ranges that collected golf balls, could come around and effortlessly scoop the pecans off the grass.

After they were done, I took a grocery bag, walked around the orchard collecting nuts that had fallen into the tall grass near the fence, went back to the shed and sat in a chair out front shelling them. I took them inside, spread a single layer on a baking pan, put it in the oven, then sat out front again while they roasted. I looked out across the orchard and started thinking about my family. I had cut myself off from them, but I still wasn't entirely free. Even though I had destroyed my father's book, his presence still lived silently in the background of my life, in the way I fixated on work to cleanse him from my mind. Maybe I should go home to confront my past more directly than I ever had in therapy. My father was gone but I could still return to my mother to try to understand what had happened and in doing so hopefully open up my future to something brighter than working as a laborer. Part of it, of course, had to do with Nareesha. I daydreamed that if we both left Albany our relationship could return to its earlier intensity. Perhaps in Augusta we could go out in town together, holding hands without worrying about who saw us or what they thought.

The smell of burning pecans interrupted my thoughts. I ran inside, pulled them out of the stove, then came out to shell another batch, promising myself I'd keep a closer eye on them and not let my mind wander.

The next time I saw Nareesha I told her my idea. She didn't reply at first.

'You're the one who said I shouldn't ignore my mother forever,' I finally said. 'You said I should do something more with myself, that I should go back to school, take the high-school equivalency test.'

'You can get your GED anywhere while you think about what you want to do,' she said. 'Maybe it's not the smartest idea to go back to where you got into trouble.'

Her effort to steer me away from Augusta angered me. I became resolute.

'I've already decided,' I said. 'I'm leaving next month. I'm tired of this place.'

She didn't say anything, but after that she must have thought about it because she was nicer. She no longer ignored me at work. She didn't come around and pull me into room thirty-eight any more, but she did acknowledge me when I picked up her laundry bags and she came occasionally to ask how my day was going. I continued bathing in the same room but tried not to think about her so much. I went to the barbershop and had my hair neatly trimmed and bought new jeans and shirts. If I planned on doing something else with my life I had to start by looking more presentable than the farmhand and laborer I was. She seemed to appreciate my effort. Everybody I worked with noticed a change.

I pushed my departure date back a couple of times, hesitating. The idea of seeing my family made me nervous. I had found a level of tranquility without them and feared the reunion might disrupt my fragile balance. Though still far from secure, I was more confident. Nevertheless, I worried Nareesha would lose respect for me if I didn't follow through with my decision, even though I knew she didn't want me to go back to Augusta. Her attitude had subtly changed, though: perhaps she had accepted that Augusta was a big city and it was unlikely we'd ever cross paths unless we meant to. I had no business near the medical college and she wouldn't be around wherever I found work. She became friendlier as my departure neared. I wanted her so much that I had decided it didn't matter if it was the last time we saw each other, as long as I could hold her once more and feel her warm skin against mine.

I tried to act casually. I announced that I would leave in exactly two weeks. She still had another month and a half before she moved so we would be separated once I left. It was more than a month since

177

Nareesha and I had been together so I was surprised when she came to the laundry room one day and asked if I wanted to meet her at the movie theater that evening. 'Don't get any ideas,' she said. 'I just thought it would be fun to go out together before you leave. But we need to arrive separately. I'll meet you in the back row after it starts.'

The movie was *Blade Runner*. I had difficulty focusing on the film, with Nareesha sitting in the dark so close to me. Even though she had told me not to get any ideas she didn't knock my hand away when I slid it onto her thigh or pull back when I leaned over to kiss her neck, but before the final credits rolled she said she had to leave so nobody would see us come out together.

My last week on the job I decided to walk one final time on the railroad tracks into town instead of riding my motorcycle. My concentration had sharpened leading up to my departure and it was the first time I had made it into town balancing on a single rail. I hadn't seen Nareesha since the movie, but she was at work and asked what day I was leaving.

'Why?'

'It'll be strange to know you're gone. I don't want to sit around thinking you might still be here.'

'Let's do something tonight,' I said.

'You know I can't. Besides, my parents are having company. I have to stay home.'

After work I tried to walk home balancing on one rail again but almost immediately jumped across to the other rail to keep from touching the ground. I had given Mr. Thompson notice a week earlier. He let me stay in the shed for my last few days, even though I stopped working. I wanted to spend a day or two relaxing and mentally preparing for my departure. I didn't sleep very well that night and around noon the next day I fell asleep listening to the radio. I dreamed that the program was interrupted to announce the death of Brezhnev, the former leader of the Soviet Union. I awoke a short time later as the announcer and a guest were discussing how his death would change global politics. I turned to another station. Same thing.

Outside my father's disappearance, it was the most stunning news I'd ever heard. I wasn't devastated, as I had been when my father left, but I felt the world shift on its axis, as I had when I'd learned my father was gone. I was too young to remember the assassination of JFK or understand Vietnam. The only wars that had ever personally touched me were the Second World War and the Cold War.

It's over, I thought. In my short lifetime Brezhnev, with his furrowed brow, was more feared than any other world leader – than all the other world leaders combined. I didn't remember Khrushchev and knew nothing of Pol Pot's genocidal campaign until years later. Brezhnev towered above all others in the eyes of the Western world. He had come to power the year I was born and had put fear into me with the 'duck and cover' atomic-bomb drills that had punctuated my early education: a special bell had rung throughout the school as we filed into the hallway to kneel and cover our heads. We waited there for the all-clear bell to ring so we could go back into our classroom. I knew they would never announce it if a real atom bomb was dropped: they'd simply ring the bell and we'd follow the same routine. With every drill there existed the possibility that it might be our last. They told us to keep our eyes shut and not look up because the sight of the blast would blind us.

Each time I heard the bell, I envisioned a building full of blind schoolchildren holding their arms out in front of them as they walked out of the hallway we had crouched in, the only structure to survive the blast, and wandered aimlessly into the surrounding fields where homes had once stood. Now I felt as if I was still in that dream.

I cracked open the shed door, half expecting to see a bright flash illuminate the sky and the perfectly aligned rows of pecan trees disappear. The fierce southern sun shone down between the branches. I stepped carefully out of my dark room and walked through the orchard from tree to tree looking for any sign of life. It was midday and nothing was moving. I walked toward the main house. Partway there I saw Mr. Thompson gazing out into the orchard. We walked slowly toward each other. When he reached me, he asked, 'Did you hear?'

We stood in silence for a moment, a pause of acknowledgment.

'It's true, isn't it?' I asked.

'That's what they're saying on the radio.'

We turned away from each other and stared out across the orchard and up into the sky. It seemed that a great weight had been lifted from our shoulders.

Late that night I heard a peacock screaming relentlessly, perched in a tree somewhere deep in the orchard. The birds rarely shrieked through the entire night, but every once in a while they made so much noise it was impossible to sleep, their screams echoing through the orchard like an alarm.

My final night in Albany I stayed up tidying the shed out of respect for Mr. Thompson and finished packing my few possessions into my knapsack, bagging them in plastic trash bags as I'd always done in case I got caught in a downpour along the way. I had checked the forecast for the state – there wasn't a cloud in the sky but, even so, I didn't want to take a chance. I had learned too many times that things change unexpectedly. In some ways I didn't want to leave Albany – it had given me more than all the other places I had lived, confidence most of all. My time in Columbus had opened doors, but I had left there with no real plan other than a vague hope of finding freedom. I felt as if I was coming to the end of my journey and that I'd soon feel secure enough to settle. I still had no idea what I might do or even where, but for the time being I calmed myself with the thought that Augusta probably wasn't as bad as I remembered it.

After darkness fell, I put on my shoes and went out into the orchard. I wanted to walk between the trees after everyone was sleeping, watch the crescent moon through the branches and smell the night dew rising off the bogs. I stood out in the middle of the trees, then passed the main house on my way back to the shed. Inside I felt more tired than I'd expected. Earlier in the day I'd considered staying up all night, riding my motorcycle through the following day and sleeping in Augusta that first night. I wanted to make sure I got a good night's sleep on my return after years away. I didn't plan to go straight to my mother's. I had decided to go to Broadway, take a room in one of the old hotels for a few days and walk around downtown until I felt comfortable. I was lying on my back trying to remember the name of the street that ran parallel to Broadway when I heard something.

I sat up. The sound fell away. I had started leaning back when I heard it again. I leaped up when I noticed the beam of a flashlight shine beneath the door. I went over and yanked it open. Nareesha was standing less than three feet away. We both jumped. I wasn't expecting to see her and she hadn't expected me to yank open the door so suddenly. My knees went weak. Now I realized why she had wanted to know which was my last night in town. I looked over her shoulder to see if anybody else was around, then pulled her inside.

I started to speak. She raised her hand and slid it over my mouth to quiet me. She kissed my neck, then slid her hands down to my waist and under my shirt and ran her nails up the side of my body until her palms cupped my breast and she pushed me back onto the floor. We pulled our clothes off and began to make love as passionately as we had the first time. I held her shoulders and rolled her onto her back, and we locked into a rhythm that hardly broke over the following hours. There was nothing to talk about. Words lost all meaning. She kissed me the way I had kissed her beneath the blankets on the night she sneaked into the motel, then climbed on top of me. I couldn't imagine anyone as perfect as her. It didn't matter that she was the first woman I had made love to or that she had taught me everything I knew about lovemaking. She was perfectly suited to my body, she knew how to hold me back, when to bite gently on my neck to make my back arch. We rolled around that little room during the short time we had together, the seconds ticking by until we lay facing the ceiling, exhausted.

When she finally said something, it was only to find out the time.

181

As soon as I told her she panicked. 'I have to get home before they wake up.'

'But it's only four.'

'My father rises early. Walk me back to the car.'

I tried to kiss her again, but she was already sitting up, putting on her bra and looking for her shirt. Once we were dressed, I held her hand and led her along the briar path to her car parked behind the mass of bushes where we'd hidden it when I had first brought her here. She was in a hurry now and I sensed her anxiety. I held the car door open and handed the flashlight through the window once she was in the driver's seat. Then I bent to kiss her and whispered, 'I love you.'

She paused for a second, then said, 'I love you, too, baby. We had so much fun.'

I started to say something else, but she stopped me. 'Don't spoil what we had.'

I stepped back from the car, let her turn it around and waved goodbye. She looked back, waved and disappeared.

The night air was crisp now. I came back along the path with a slight chill. I already missed her. I got back to my shed, went over to where we had lain on the floor and pressed my face into the blankets to smell her scent. I ached inside. I knew I wouldn't be able to cry over her again so I didn't hold myself back. By the time my tears dried, the first light of dawn was coming through the window. I got up and put a pot on the stove to warm some water. I didn't have anything to mix it with, so I poured the hot water into a mug, held it in my hand and sipped until I felt warm inside.

I stepped outside for my final morning walk across the orchard to the henhouse to collect two eggs. Back in the shed I made grits while the eggs fried in the pan. During my time on the road I had always loved the feeling of waking up and knowing I was about to embark for someplace new as I packed my bag. I hadn't felt it in ages but now it came rushing back.

* * *

After breakfast I went outside to look over my motorcycle, double-checked the oil level in the crankcase and made sure I had topped off the two-stroke reservoir. I checked the tension of the chain, lubricated it, checked the tire pressure, then pulled the bike up on the center-stand to clean out any slivers of glass or tiny pebbles that had worked their way into the rubber. I noticed a small area on the rear tire beginning to show threads. I spun it looking for other worn spots. The rest looked okay. I checked the front tire. It was fine. I checked the rear tire again. I didn't like the threads showing but figured I could get through one more day of riding before replacing it. It would take several hours to get a tire from the motorcycle shop and mount it, providing they had one in stock, but they didn't open for another two hours. By the time I'd finished, it would be afternoon and my departure would be delayed another day. I wouldn't ever be able to leave town on a higher note than I could right then, with Nareesha showing up unexpectedly last night, so I pushed the bike down off the center-stand and got ready for my journey. I went inside, picked up my knapsack and a handful of bungee cords, carried them outside and strapped the bag tightly to the seat, behind where I'd be sitting.

Mr. Thompson wasn't around when I went out of the front gate. I rode slowly through town before opening up and leaning into a wide, sweeping curve. The two-stroke engine whined as I throttled it into another turn, then rocketed through the blurred green of the south Georgia countryside. Sixty, seventy, eighty, eighty-five miles per hour. I wondered why I had spent so much time hitchhiking and taking slow, smelly buses when I could have been jetting between cities on a motorcycle with fresh air blowing through my hair. I ran the bike harder than normal, excited to be going home. I came up fast on the bridge that crossed Interstate 75 and gunned the bike. Soon I was back in the quiet of the countryside, surrounded by green without another vehicle in sight, racing eastward.

The road had straightened out and I fell into a trance, mesmerized by the coal-colored ribbon of hope stretching in front of me as far as I could see, distorting and bending under the heat rising off

183

its surface. I'm not sure how far up the road I was when I heard a muffled pop and felt the rear wheel give way. I glanced in the rear-view mirror and saw a small puff of white smoke and knew immediately the rear tire had blown. I let my hand off the throttle. I was still racing at eighty miles per hour. I froze my grip on the bars and kept my hand and foot off the brakes – braking at such speeds under those conditions would cause me to lose control and crash. One wrong move and I'd be sliding across the pavement at eighty, using my skin as a brake pad, before slamming into a tree and coming to a full stop. The rear tire slid around as though the road had turned to mud. At least it wasn't the front one. I watched the speedometer slowly dropping – seventy, sixty, fifty. I felt like I was herding sheep. By the time I was at forty I felt confident that I could roll to a stop without flipping over.

Eventually the motorcycle came to a standstill in the middle of the road. I looked in my rear-view mirror to make sure nobody was coming up on my rear – the road was still empty. I glanced ahead: same. I sat there in the middle of the road, straddling the bike. The force of the blowout and the speed I was traveling had shredded the tire.

Once I regained composure, I inched the bike to the shoulder of the road. There wasn't much I could do. I rolled it down the embankment into the dried-out bog below the roadway and jumped off the seat before it hit the bottom. Then I walked down, unstrapped my knapsack from the seat and covered the bike in leaves and branches so nobody would see it from above and when I came to get it with a new tire it would still be there. I walked back up to the road and drove a thick branch into the soft dirt on the shoulder to mark the location, then broke the stick off halfway so it wouldn't bring undue attention. The road was completely still and silent, except for the buzz of insects. The momentum with which I'd started the day dissipated into the muggy air.

I looked up and down the desolate country road several times – still no traffic. I thought about walking back to the interstate. It was at least ten miles away. I knew I wasn't going back to Albany. I could come and get my bike after I'd settled in Augusta. I had lived without it before, I could live without it now. It would be more difficult to get rides on the interstate with cars passing at eighty miles per hour without even glancing at me, and if the police came by, they'd put me back where I'd started. Plus I'd have to go all the way north to Atlanta, then hitch back down Interstate 20 to Augusta, going around my elbow to get to my hand. I didn't feel like touring the entire state. I wanted the straightest route home. I didn't want a million cars rushing past with nobody even seeing me. I decided that, despite the absence of traffic on the back roads, when a car showed its face, the driver would have to stop. Sooner or later someone would be along. I set my pack on the shoulder of the eastbound lane and waited.

I didn't have a watch so I had no way of tracking time beyond the arc of the sun but I sat there for probably close to an hour before I dug through my knapsack for the toilet paper. I had just climbed down into the woods when I heard a car coming up the road. By the time I'd finished and got back to the roadside, I saw its shimmering reflection disappearing in the distance. Another hour passed before a second appeared, heading in the direction of the interstate. It stopped without my signaling and the driver asked if I wanted a ride. I briefly contemplated the other route, then waved him on, deciding to stay with my original plan. At worst, I could sleep near my motorcycle and wait for the early-morning traffic that I was sure used the road. I gave up any hope of reaching Augusta that day.

The exhaustion of missing the previous night's sleep hit me. I stood up from where I had been using my knapsack as a seat, plopped down on the ground and leaned against it, trying to keep my eyes open. Some time later an old van came lumbering up the road. I stood up to make myself presentable and held out my thumb. He slowed before he reached me. A middle-aged man with an unkempt beard and oily blondish hair. He looked like a farm worker. He rolled to a stop. I glanced in the passenger window and looked in the back. It was empty. I leaned in to talk to him. He smelled as if he hadn't showered in a week.

185

'How far you going?' I asked.

'Up the road.'

It wouldn't have been my first choice of a ride on any other day, but at least he'd stopped. I threw my bag behind the seat and climbed in. I started to ask what he did for a living, then decided not to. Those were the rules of the road. You didn't ask anyone where they were from, either.

'I've got work up in Augusta,' I lied.

He didn't respond. I had been in so many cars with so many derelicts through the years that I wrote it off to poor social skills.

'They're hiring,' I said. 'I don't know if you're looking for work, but I might be able to get you on if you're heading that way.'

There was no harm in trying. It had taken long enough to get a ride and I didn't want to wait for another if I could avoid it. Body odor aside, he seemed harmless enough.

'What they doing?' he asked.

'Unloading trucks. Hauling some shit. Not sure exactly what. They need some strong hands.'

'How long it take to get there?'

'If we drive straight through, we can probably be there by midnight. I got gas money.'

'Beer money?'

'I can spare a dime.'

'Maybe it's not a bad idea.'

I had learned not to pressure people like him. He looked as if he had lived his entire life on the road. By comparison I had spent only a short time on it. You make suggestions. You don't say, 'So, you in?' You don't express eagerness. You wait and hope they eventually feel like it was their idea. We drove on for a long time until we came to a crossroads.

'Which way?' he asked.

I pointed left.

He said he wanted some beer and pulled into a gas station.

I got out and used the restroom. I felt good again, even without my motorcycle. I still had the ability to steer a situation in my favor.

186

The day wasn't turning out so bad after all. If I was lucky we'd hit Augusta by midnight and could park down by the labor pool where I'd ditch him, leaving a few bucks on my seat for his efforts. I wasn't a criminal any more but you don't lose your smarts. If he was interested in driving all the way to Augusta, he obviously had no place to go anyway. He came back to the van with a six-pack of Old Milwaukee and cracked one open before starting the engine. He held the six-pack out for me. I passed – I was tired from being up all night. Once I was certain he was heading in the right direction, I leaned my head back and closed my eyes.

I have no clue how long I was asleep.

I was jerked awake.

He had pulled my arms up behind my back.

He was parked off the road.

It was near dusk.

'What the fuck you doing?'

He didn't answer. He didn't need to. He was stronger than me, his arms almost twice the diameter of my own, his thick hands clamped down around my wrists like a vice. He had already opened the passenger door and pulled me out to where he was standing.

'Let's go for a walk,' he said.

I thrashed back and forth, then let my legs fall from beneath me and tried furiously to twist away. He fell hard on top of me, cracking his nose against the back of my skull, but he didn't let go. He had me pinned. He was far heavier than me and remained in the same position for a few minutes to recover his strength and figure out how to get me back on my feet without my escaping. Blood dripped from his nose onto my face, rolled to the edge of my lips and seeped into my mouth. It tasted of rust and salt mixed with sweat. I spat it out. It went into his face, enraging him. He freed one of his hands and punched me directly in the face two or three times. I tasted more blood. I quit struggling.

He pulled me back to my feet and walked me down a slope off the dirt lane he had parked on and into the dried bog below us. We walked far enough into the trees that his van was no longer in sight.

He pushed my arm up behind my back so violently that I feared he would break the bone or pull it out of its socket if he went any further. He reached around and pulled at the button and zipper of my pants until he had them down past my buttocks and then he unexpectedly let go, freeing me momentarily, then elbowed me in the lower back and shoved me down on my stomach into a thick bed of decaying leaves. He sat on my back. I heard him unbuckle his belt.

I squirmed beneath his weight in a final attempt to get away. He slammed his clenched fist into the back of my head so hard that I thought I'd been hit with a concrete block. Everything went black, then bright white. I focused all my effort on staying conscious. I was scared he would kill me if I passed out. My vision came back. He was on top of me. I focused my mind on anything I could other than what was happening. I was completely overpowered. Sometimes to survive you *must* submit. I could no longer ignore the sensation of a searing hot knife in my rectum. He wrapped his hands firmly around my neck – the more intense his rhythm, the more his hands tightened around my windpipe. I was terrified that, at the moment of orgasm, he'd choke me to death. I heard stories about monsters murdering the moment they came. The thought sent shudders through my inner reaches. I was at his will. He held my life in his hands. I felt like I was going to black out again and grasped the only thing I thought might save me.

'Feels good. It feels good, Daddy. Fuck your little boy's ass harder.'

He relaxed his grip slightly and concentrated his effort. I felt like a bag of living flesh being pressed into the forest floor, waiting patiently in the hands of my executioner. I was no longer as tough as I once imagined myself when working as a laborer. The only thing I had was endurance and stamina, but I couldn't outlast him choking me to death.

'You like it?'

'It feels good.'

His rhythm intensified.

'Fuck it harder.'

At the moment he came, his hands briefly relaxed, and a few seconds later he rolled off me. Before another thought entered my mind, I leaped up, holding my pants in my right hand and sprinted, like a deer from a hunter, deep into the woods. I ran until I was sure I was beyond sight and sound, then dropped onto the ground and frantically buried myself in a thick bed of leaves. Dusk was approaching darkness. He came after me like an angry grizzly. I didn't think he'd be able to follow my tracks in the dark or find my burial ground unless he waited until sunrise.

I heard him circling the area in which I had disappeared. I was certain he didn't know whether I had run deeper into the woods or hidden nearby, but he must have sensed I'd stopped since he no longer heard me breaking through the brush. He was a natural hunter. He had already succeeded once in dominating his prey. My heart beat in my ears like a bass drum, so loudly I was sure he could hear it pounding. There was no way to calm it. I held my breath. It beat louder. It beat so loud that it was all I heard. I didn't know if he was still there waiting or whether he had moved on. I didn't flinch. I didn't blink. I held my eyes wide open looking up at the leaves covering my face, quietly inhaling their fragrance, watching the final traces of light disappear.

I waited until the pain of staying rigid became too great. It felt like days had passed. I blew the leaves off my face, holding my body still. I couldn't see anything. I turned my head as quietly as possible to the side and listened. Nothing. I raised my head slightly. Slowly I started seeing outlines. Eventually I made out the twisted shapes of the small trees and bushes surrounding me. I didn't trust my senses. I waited longer, then uncovered my arms and quietly sat up. Dried blood was encrusted on my face. I buttoned my pants. I tried to figure out which way I had come from, and once I felt reasonably certain, I walked in the opposite direction, deeper into the woods, until I reached the water table rising to the surface. I backtracked far enough to circle the edge and finally came to a dirt road running through the dark forest. I stepped cautiously onto its surface.

I walked until sunrise. I came to a field that didn't look as if it had been worked in years. A large house stood on a rise, its silhouette similar to my former boss's house viewed in the morning from my shed at the back of the orchard, except this one was further away. A rooster crowed. Some time later, a screen door slammed and an old woman stepped out with a bucket. I watched her walk to a well and drop it in, allow it time to fill, then slowly hand-crank it back to the surface. I worried she would think I was an intruder but I raised my hand as she started across the field. I didn't have any choice. I was safer there than walking back through the forest to where he had parked the night before.

'Morning,' I shouted. 'Morning.'

I waved my hand in as friendly a gesture as I could. She stopped and peered in my direction. She didn't wave back. After a few seconds she moved up the porch and into the house. The sound of the screen door slamming behind her ricocheted across the field. I walked slowly toward the house. Her husband appeared on the porch. He stood at the top of the steps and waited for me to approach. He didn't walk out to meet me.

'What can we help you with?' he asked.

'I was beat up last night in the woods behind your place.' I pointed across the field. 'I just finished up working on Mr. Thompson's farm down in Albany and was moving on to Augusta. He's in the phone book. You can call him if you want.'

'What's that have to do with us?'

'I need to clean up, sir. That's all. I'll move as soon as I'm done.' I paused, then added, 'I'm scared to go back up the road. I don't want to bump into him again.'

The vulnerability in my voice seemed to set him at ease slightly. But he still hesitated. 'Wait here a minute.'

He went back inside and did something, then came back to the door. 'Go ahead and come inside. My wife's preparing some water. I'm going into town to pick up feed afterward. I'll take you in with me.'

He dropped me off at the Greyhound station. I still had most of the money I had saved – it was hidden inside my boots between the insert and the sole. I learned long ago to keep enough in my front pocket to give anybody who might rob me so they wouldn't become enraged, while hiding the larger portion in my shoes. The little discomfort it caused when I was walking was offset by the knowledge that I still had it. I tried not to think about my other discomforts. I knew then that no matter how much a person might want to confront the past there were certain things you hoped to forget.

BOOK V

Fire Tower Road

When I reached Augusta I walked to Broadway and found a room in a boarding house on a side street. The shared bathroom was in the hallway. The mattress had a depression in the middle where hundreds of people had slept before me, but it was snug. Rent was cheap enough that I didn't have to worry about finding a job right away or think about my mother. I was in no mood for that. I felt dirty inside. I bathed four or five times a day, scrubbing myself until my skin hurt – the woman who oversaw the boarding house told me she'd increase my rent if I didn't stop. I fell into a deep depression. I wondered if my life would ever change. At the time of my attack I had never considered killing him – he would have killed me. But I did watch the streets for his van rolling down Broadway. I bought another knife at a pawnshop on Broadway and practiced pulling it out while I lay in bed. All those years carrying one, and the one time I needed it, my pack was in the back and I was asleep. Thoughts like these spun in my head, driving me mad. When craziness comes you can feel it in your bones – in the roots of your hair most of all. That's the first place you feel it, and scratching your head does no good, but you still scratch insistently as if scabies are burrowing under your skin.

The first time violence rose in me – so fast that I had no control over it – I was eating lunch with a man at a soup kitchen who said, 'You can't blame your emotions on somebody else. You're responsible for the way you feel. You make yourself feel that way, not somebody else.'

I exploded and slammed my tray against the table, shattering the plate on top of it, and slid my hand across the table sending his tray flying. I grabbed him by the collar, stuffed my face inches from his and screamed, 'How does this feel motherfucker? This isn't affecting you a bit, is it?'

Two huge attendants pinned me to the floor until I calmed down, then carried me to the front door and threw me on the sidewalk. 'Your privileges here are suspended permanently,' one shouted.

'You call eating pig slops a privilege?' I yelled, for everyone stepping around me to hear.

I stood up and made it halfway up the block, then started to feel completely disassociated from my body: I was losing my mind. With each passing day it got worse. I felt violent inside. I wanted revenge. I had nightmares about killing people. I walked down Broadway in full daylight fantasizing about pulling out my knife and slitting the throats of people passing me because they looked at me the wrong way. I'd search for his van so I could sneak up behind him in the driver's seat, plunge my knife into his face, gouge out his eyes and leave him there alive. My mind became a cesspool of violence. Finally I woke up early one morning and walked up to the 13th Street Bridge and threw the knife in the Savannah River to stop myself killing someone in a blind act of rage.

For the first time since I was sent away at fifteen, I walked up the street to where the dealers idled and bought a nickel bag of weed. I went to the levee, looked out over the river and smoked my first joint in more than three years. It was the only way I knew to calm myself and I was glad I did it. The tension drained with each puff. I didn't want to talk to a therapist. I didn't want to hear what they thought of my life. I had spent a year in therapy and it had gotten me back here. I didn't want to hear a half-baked counselor repeat that I made myself feel the way I do or have a psychiatrist shackle my mind with pharmaceuticals while he recorded his observations. How could anybody understand my pain without being raped themselves? They couldn't. It would be academic. Empathetic. A case study. I didn't want to be objectified, talked down to or soothed.

I didn't need their drugs. I was able to drug myself on something milder that I could buy when I needed it and stop without their permission. Pot was the easiest way I knew to solve my problems without outside interference. I took another hit as if I was sucking on an oxygen bottle. It would be easier to wean myself off pot than to rot in prison for killing someone. I stretched the nickel bag out for three days, walking to the levee and taking little hits off a joint every few hours before putting it out and saving the rest for later.

When the baggy ran out I walked back up the street and bought a dime bag. Smoking calmed me but it also made me paranoid. I started worrying more about other people harming me than me harming them. If my brain was riddled with violent thoughts, what about all the other homeless people who wandered around downtown? Most were in a worse condition than I was. I hadn't spent my entire life sleeping under bridges. Everything had been going perfectly until that scumbag had taken it from me.

Then I wondered if the confidence I'd experienced in Albany had been false. It couldn't have been. Nareesha would have never been with me, even if all she wanted was sex. She wouldn't have looked at me twice. She was too smart. She'd even said she loved me. I could still hear her as clearly as if she had just spoken. What if she saw me living like this? She'd be disgusted. What if she were raped? Would she end up like this? She was too strong. She wouldn't give whoever harmed her the pleasure of seeing her weak like this. I smoked another joint and ran through the same thoughts for days.

Two weeks later I was sitting in my regular spot up on the levee when a thought hit me with the clarity of the sun's rays illuminating the grass: this is exactly the kind of life that scumbag leads. From city to city and town to town, he lives off the charity of government workers and churchgoers who contribute money to the same soup kitchens I frequented. They kept the crazy fueled. They were feeding leeches, like the scumbag who had attacked me, who drove around between handouts causing mayhem instead of being forced to work like everybody else. He was probably sitting on a levee smoking a joint or drinking beer he'd bought with money he'd picked up from some welfare office, thinking back to his time in the woods with me. I flicked away the joint as if it was infected and walked through downtown that afternoon, repelled by every person I saw working in charity houses and welfare offices. What was so wrong in their lives that they had to help the helpless?

I wanted to scream, 'They're not helpless, you idiots, they're using you. They're more cunning than you – they'll rape your daughter and son, given the chance.' I grew impatient with the sob stories that ever sapsucker I bumped into downtown repeated endlessly. Usually society was screwing them: the rich, big brother, the police. I thought, society is the only thing keeping you alive, you weak piece of shit.

I didn't have any bags to pack. I gathered what little money I had left hidden behind the baseboard of the filthy room I lived in to catch a city bus up to Martinez, on the Columbia County line. On the way to the stop, a guy sitting on the sidewalk with a 'Will Work for Food' sign propped on his legs, said, 'Hey, can you help me out?'

'Yeah, I can, you lazy fuck. Get a job before your ass sticks to the ground.'

I boarded the bus and headed to the county line where I had been told construction sites were hiring anybody willing to work. Riding through town, I thought briefly about my mother. The last thing I wanted was for her to see me in such a mess. It would only reaffirm everything she had ever thought about me.

Hiring anybody willing to work proved an overstatement. I went from construction site to construction site asking to carry boards around or clean up trash for less than minimum wage and was turned away repeatedly. But I needed work so I took rejection in stride. I finally found a job unloading sheetrock at a construction site building a new apartment complex. I bought a bedroll and slept on the second floor in an unfinished apartment – there was no door, no carpet, no drywall, just studs, a plywood floor and a single window that had been recently framed in.

Once the supervisor noticed I worked hard without supervision or complaining about pay he gave me other jobs until I was part of the regular crew. A couple of weeks in, he raised my pay to minimum wage and started withholding taxes. I didn't ask any questions but I took it as a good sign. I worked nonstop to take my mind off life. My demons didn't subside entirely, but by staying busy from sunrise to sunset, I was exhausted enough to fall asleep soon after I hit the floor each night. The only way I knew to keep my life under control was to push it to the max.

The apartment complex was being built in an area of woodlands that had been clear-cut. Deer still wandered through in the early morning. I'd sit up in my room warming water in an aluminum pot on a small backpacking stove to make instant oatmeal and watch them. Horrific thoughts still entered my mind when I was around sharp objects. One morning the supervisor handed me a utility knife to cut the straps off a bundle of lumber. I held it away from me as I did the job and quickly handed it back to him. I had no desire to slice him, but I didn't trust myself.

Part of me had been lost forever on that road between Albany and Augusta, in the same way that another part had disappeared with my father's abandonment. My emotions now seemed a separate entity from my physical self. I doubted I'd ever recover completely, redeem myself or find closure for what had occurred. Like the raised scar on the side of my head from when I had gone through the window years ago, I doubted that the filth I felt inside would ever be entirely cleansed or that I'd recover from the loss I'd experienced. I couldn't correct the past. I couldn't fix it. I couldn't redeem it. I couldn't even seek revenge because I had no idea where my attacker lived. Given the opportunity, I would murder him on the spot or, better, I would torture him slowly, cutting off the fingers that had held my neck, then slicing off his nuts, shoving them down his throat and watching him choke on himself. I would never forgive him. He alone was responsible for my teetering on the edge of insanity. The only thing that saved me was the knowledge that if I fell into the dark recesses of madness he would own me forever. He had ruled my body.

Now he ruled my mind with his constant presence. The only vengeance I could take on him now was to push him from my thoughts and keep him out. I had to guard against freefalling into the chasm of insanity with more vigilance than I would against becoming a drug addict or an alcoholic. Those substances were all that prevented me losing it completely.

I monitored my thoughts, which was so exhausting I couldn't concentrate on intellectually challenging work. Otherwise I might have found a job in a motorcycle shop repairing engines. Laboring gave me the mental space to try to cure myself. Slowly, I learned how to stop replaying things in my mind. To stop thinking about how I could have avoided the attack – by taking the ride back to the interstate I had been offered earlier that day or by going to the shop that morning to buy a new rear tire for my motorcycle. I thought about it rusting beneath the leaves where I had left it. I tried not to punish myself for falling asleep in the van, for believing I had been on the road long enough to judge a person's character. It was a neurosis that consumed me until I'd find myself lying on the ground, holding myself and shaking. I knew if I did not come to terms with it I would not survive.

Thankfully, the apartment complex project continued for six months after I arrived. Living on the site and following the same daily routine provided me with stability. Nobody looked down on me for living on the site. They appreciated my hard work. Sometimes they'd bring me an extra sausage that their wife had cooked for breakfast. The supervisor eventually paid me an extra twenty dollars a night to double as a security guard. He didn't care if I slept: he just wanted me there in case anyone came to vandalize the property or steal lumber. He gave me a small compressed-air horn and told me I didn't have to chase anybody who came onto the site, just lean out of my window, hidden from view, press the button and they'd disappear. I wasn't scared to be alone. I felt more secure: I didn't have to keep my eye on anybody.

The unoccupied apartment complex slowly became my private fortress. As the months passed and the job was almost complete I was saddened. I knew I'd have to move on. As work slowed and I was given time off, I built up the courage to go back into town to find my mother.

One afternoon I took a bus into Augusta and walked up the hill to my mother's place. I was nervous. I didn't expect a celebration. I wasn't coming home in victory, but I was coming home. I tried to hold on to that thought, but as I neared the house, my pace slowed. I decided to walk past once before going up to the door. I went down the block, turned and walked back, this time prepared to go up to the front door and knock.

Going up the front path I didn't see anybody through the kitchen window. There were no lights on in the house, but it was only late afternoon. I picked up the heavy brass knocker and let it drop. I heard the sound echo down the long front hallway with bare wood floors. I let it drop once more and waited. I didn't hear anything inside. I waited long enough so as not to appear impatient, then picked up the knocker and let it drop again, three times in a row. After enough time had passed I decided either no one was home or they had seen me coming and were avoiding answering the door. I stood on the porch for another ten minutes, then stepped down and walked around back. No cars were parked in the driveway. I stepped up on the rear porch to peer into the den. It was empty: no chairs, no couch, no television, no books on the shelves. There wasn't even a lamp in the room. All that remained was the imprints on the carpet where the legs of the couch and chairs had rested. I went from window to window and in each room it was the same. There wasn't a single thing left in the house. Even the curtains in the dining room – my mother had complained about their pattern – were gone.

I looked out over the long backyard. The unkempt lawn ran all the way to the small wooded area near the rear fence where ivy covered the ground. I thought back to the first time I had seen the house and then to my visit when I had come to read the book I had buried. I walked slowly across the dried grass, thinking about the Iron Cross my father had given me. I wondered whether it was still there. I found the place near the tree where I had reburied it. I dropped to my knees and dug in the soft soil with my fingertips. They grazed plastic. I pulled the bag out of the ground, brushed away the dirt and tore at the surface until I held the book in my hand. I opened the cover and saw the medal inside. I pulled it out and held it up to the light – the same as always, tarnished around the edges, '1813' on one side below a leaf and a crown and '1914' on the other beneath a 'W' and a crown. I held it up in the light. It occurred to me at that moment that it had made it through two world wars and all the way around the globe, across the country with my father, then traveled south with me. I was amazed that it was still there. I began to think that maybe it held good luck. I tossed the mildewed book into the woods and slid the medal into my pocket.

As I was walking up the driveway a man came around the corner from the front of the house. 'Can I help you?' he called out.

'I was just looking around. I used to live here.'

He stared at me suspiciously.

'Who are you?' I asked.

'I live across the street. I'm keeping an eye on the house for the owner. I saw you walk around back.'

'My mother owned this house.'

'You must be a Malessa.'

'Sam. Do you know where my mother went?'

'She left almost six months ago. She sold the house to a family transferring here from Texas, but now the father's been held up at his old job.'

'Where did she go?'

'She didn't leave a forwarding address. I think she left the state.'

'Ohio?'

'I don't know. You'll have to ask your brother.'

'What brother?'

'Don't you have a brother named Carl?'

'Carl's been here?'

'After she left he came by a few times with a friend to haul off the coal she had stored in the garage. He said he had a coal stove out where he was living.'

'You have his address?'

'He said he lived out on a small ranch where they board horses near the river. I can't remember the name of the road. It's off Washington, before you come to the big department stores. I was out at the stables with my daughter years ago.'

'Did he say how long he had been there?'

'We didn't talk much. I hadn't seen him around before, but he had the same cheekbones as your mother so I trusted him. Same cheekbones as you.'

I walked away more confused than when I'd arrived. Where had my mother gone? Why had she left? Why was Carl living in town now? Almost four years had passed since I'd been sent away. He had probably finished military duty. But why had he come to Augusta? He had never lived here. I took a bus out to the apartment complex. That night I found a piece of nylon twine and slipped it through the small ring at the top of the medal and tied it securely, then lit a match and held its flame near the knot. The nylon melted slightly and bonded the knot. Once it cooled I lifted it over my head and slid it beneath my shirt. I didn't want to explain why I was wearing an Iron Cross.

The apartment complex had less than a month's work left to complete and even then work was sporadic. Once it was finished I'd have no choice but to move on. I prepared by taking the bus down Washington Road to the Interstate 20 intersection. I figured I'd be able to find work with all the businesses located there. But mostly I wanted to find my brother. Over several days, I followed a half-dozen side streets off Washington into neighborhoods, apartment complexes and storage areas without luck. One afternoon I went further south and saw a small road on the left cutting back into a neighborhood. It wound between houses, then entered the woods, continued down a hill and came to a stop sign at a set of railroad tracks. Just past them a farm road to the left led back toward the interstate. Ahead a dirt road climbed the hill to a small barn and some stables. I saw a man tending horses and decided to climb the hill to ask around. The guy wasn't very friendly or talkative.

'I just come here to take care of my horse,' he said. 'I don't ask names of everyone who comes and goes.'

I walked further up the road to the top of the hill. I heard the faint whoosh of traffic nearby. As I approached the edge of the hill the rush of traffic became louder. At the bottom, some two hundred feet below, the interstate had been cut into the hillside. To the east, less than a mile away, I saw a bridge crossing the Savannah River into South Carolina. When I stepped away, the sound faded, blocked by the earthen wall, and I was back in the countryside. In the direction of the river I saw a small house built beside a stand of white pines and beyond it an open pasture bordered by forest. There were no cars or any other sign of life, but I walked down anyway. Trash was strewn about the yard. I knocked on the door. Nobody answered.

I knocked again, this time harder. When I did so the latch popped and the door swung partially open. I looked in. There was no furniture in the living room, only a couple of pillows and magazines scattered on the floor. Coal was stacked to the left of the fireplace. Another heap stood outside, near the front door.

'Carl!' I shouted. 'Carl, you there?'

I stepped inside. The kitchen was on my left. A wooden table stood at the center with three chairs. The table looked to be about the same age as the house, maybe fifty years old. There was a pot and a frying pan on the stove. I crept across the kitchen. I felt exactly as I had when I used to break into houses. It didn't matter that the door had been unlocked. It still wasn't my house. I didn't have permission to be inside. With it came the familiar rush of adrenaline. I walked to a doorway on the other side of the kitchen and peeked inside – an old worn bed and a bicycle, leaning against the wall nearest me. Clothes were strewn about the floor. A gun rack hung on the wall with a shotgun and rifle. I had never known my brother as an adult. He had been only sixteen the last time I saw him, but it seemed like his room. I walked back across the kitchen and out into the living room to the front door. Before stepping outside I glanced at the periodicals on the floor. Most were about guns, and there was a pile of *Soldier of Fortune*. I had never heard of it before. Men dressed in camouflage clothing were pictured on the cover. Another was titled *Survivalist*. I bent to pick up a copy and flipped through it.

I hadn't been in there five minutes when I sensed something behind me. I glanced around and was startled to find my brother standing silently in the middle of the room with a handgun pointed at my head. His index finger was on the trigger.

I stared at him, without moving, long enough for him to recognize me. A smile spread across his face but he didn't lower the gun. He stood there intimidating me, then said, 'Okay, put the candy down, young man.'

I slowly set *Survivalist* on the floor where I had found it.

'This is going to hurt me more than it is you,' he said, and slowly squeezed the trigger.

I didn't have time to think. I heard the empty clank of metal on metal and the hilarious laugh of a crazy man.

I hadn't taken a breath since I'd first turned around. I felt dizzy. I inhaled, then sighed. 'Still the fucking same,' I said, without any humor in my voice.

'Till the day I die, little bro.'

He took a clip filled with bullets out of his front pocket, slammed it into the handle of the pistol, pulled the slide assembly back, let it slam forward, loading a bullet into the chamber, carefully decocked it and slid the pistol under his belt. 'You that slow?'

'Slow about what?' I asked.

'I saw you coming down to the house. I was in the trees emptying the compost. I watched you go inside and then came in as soon as you started reading. You would have been dead a long time ago if this was real life.'

'This is real life,' I said.

'Nah, this is just a game. I would have blown your brains out without you even knowing if it was real life.'

205

'Then maybe we ought to keep it a game.'

'For your sake, I think we should.' He stood a moment sizing me up. 'What hole are you crawling out of?'

I thought about his question and started to tell him about Albany, but the memory of my journey to Augusta arose. 'Hell,' I said.

He laughed. 'I'm surprised we didn't bump into each other. Looks like we have plenty to catch up on.'

'You seen Mom?'

'She moved to Montana.'

'What's in Montana?'

'Nothing. I think that's the point.'

'Did she say anything? Are you going to see her?'

An expression of impatience crossed his face. 'Nobody ever says anything in this family,' he said, 'and I'm not in the habit of making plans.'

'Did she leave an address?'

'You miss your mommy, huh?'

I looked at the floor.

'She said you disappeared a long time ago. If you missed her so badly maybe you should have stayed in touch. Too good for your family? You're like those little pussies in the army who try to make Special Forces, then get homesick and are shit-canned back into infantry. You probably don't even know how to clean a gun.'

I walked out of the house and started down the road.

'Keep walking, bro, and I'll put a bullet through the back of your head. This time it'll be real life.'

I turned. 'Shoot me, then. See if I care. No more games.'

'I'll shoot your ass.'

'You'll shoot your fucking mouth off is more like it.'

He pulled his gun out and pumped three bullets into the ground in front of me, spraying dirt into my face. A cloud of dust separated us. When it cleared, he said, 'Don't test me, bro. I'm in a good mood today. I'm happy to see you. It's been years. Welcome home.'

Then he turned his back and walked into the house. The guy who wouldn't talk to me earlier was peering around the corner of one of the stables. When he saw me looking at him, he disappeared. I waited a few minutes, not sure what to do, before deciding to follow my brother inside.

He invited me to stay. There was an empty bedroom behind the living room. He said he paid forty dollars a month to the investor who owned the land. 'He likes having me out here to keep an eye on it.' He asked me to pay half if I could afford it. He told me he had saved some money before getting out of the military and wasn't interested in working for a while after what he had been through there. 'I pay my rent. I ain't feeding on Uncle Sam. They don't bother me out here and I don't bother them.'

I asked him why he had come to Augusta.

'Same reason as you.'

'Why didn't you go to Montana?'

'Didn't work out.' That's all he would say about it.

'Why did you stay here?'

'I like Augusta. Reminds me of some of the places I was sent in the army. Plenty of woods around, rivers, swamps. Nobody fucks with you or asks questions. And nobody calls the police when I shoot my guns.'

He got up early seven days a week to go hunting – his full-time job. He didn't shoot game like deer. He hunted rabbit, squirrel, duck, dove, possum, raccoon. When he wasn't hunting, he fished. He didn't get licenses or hunt in season. He didn't believe in government control. The land he lived on was tucked between the interstate, the river bordering South Carolina and thick woods shielding the neighborhoods near Washington Road – no game wardens ever came around. The area was a no man's land on the state border. He was like a modern-day Paul Bunyan. He went to town only to buy tackle, ammunition, shortening to fry with, grits or biscuits for grains, salt for seasoning and, when he felt like splurging, butter. His sole transportation was the bicycle, the yellow Schwinn Paramount I had seen in his bedroom, which he tended like a newborn. He was into fitness.

He took care of his body. He didn't eat processed foods and constantly tried to improve himself.

He seemed like a kook, but he was disciplined. Far more disciplined than I was. And when he worked, he worked even harder than I did. I learned that the first day I was there when he said he wanted to move the coal pile from beside the front door to the side of the house and to clean up the trash. 'Stray dogs always tear shit up out here,' he said. I couldn't keep up with him – he hardly broke a sweat. He was smart too. He could fix almost anything, electronic or mechanical, and he could build traps with his hands to catch animals. He hand-loaded ammunition to save money and tied his own flies to fish with. He knew what plants you could eat when we walked through the woods. He knew how to make a fire without matches. He could build a rainproof shelter from branches he gathered from the forest floor. He could identify any animal in the area by sound. He didn't believe anything the government said and held unconventional views about society and the future of humanity.

'It's nothing but a form of control to keep everybody in order. I know, I used to be one of their executioners. I traveled all over the world. They don't want me talking because I know too much. Think about it. How come all the people they call crazy on the news, the survivalists and anti-government fiends, are former soldiers? Because we know,' he said. 'We know they're full of shit. Notice how they never come after us? They leave us alone. We've done our duty.'

Given that we spent hardly any money, I was able to stretch what I had saved working up in Martinez for a long time. He taught me that it cost almost nothing to survive in the richest country on earth and that you could live better than most, providing you liked nature and didn't mind cleaning your own food. 'It's only when you want somebody else to do the dirty work that life costs money,' he said.

I ended up staying with him far longer than I probably should have. But he was the only family member I had at that point and I still wanted to understand better where I had come from. Besides, I was tired of real life as he called it. I wanted to join his games to get my mind off the reality I was desperate to forget.

He took me down through the woods to the canal every day after he got back from hunting and some days he'd wake me up early to head out with him. He seemed happy to have somebody to share his life with. We crossed the pasture, entered the woods and hiked to the canal. It had been dug some time in the previous century, he told me, to power the textile mills downtown. It ran parallel to the much larger Savannah River, but to get to the river we had to swim across the canal to reach the strip of land that ran between the two bodies of water. The only other way to get there was to drive downtown and take a dirt road that originated near the mills. The road was used mostly by fishermen and the police to keep homeless encampments from sprouting up. Since it was on the Georgia side of the river, it fell under the jurisdiction of the Augusta Police Department. My brother was keen on places where one jurisdiction ended and the next started. He claimed that while the land he hunted on was officially in the city jurisdiction, there was no road into the area and no other way into the woods than on foot. 'You think the doughnut patrol is going to take up hiking into the swamps?' He liked the idea that the cops were too lazy to come into his neck of the woods to check up on him.

Several areas off the canal had flooded long ago, creating swamp-lands where water spilled over its banks into lower-lying areas and filled them in. These were the first places my brother brought me when he started guiding me into the woods. He always wore leather boots and army-issue camouflage clothing. I was surprised the first time he walked fully clothed into the swamp up to his waist.

'Are you crazy?'

He pointed at a rise on the other side of the swamp. 'Can't get there without going through here. That's where the animals hide out because it's not easily accessible to pussies like you. Let's get moving.'

I timidly entered the swamp, water gushing into my boots, my pants immediately soaked. 'What about all this algae?' I shouted.

'It'll come off when we cross the canal.'

'I'm not swimming with all my clothes on.'

'Good luck finding your way home.'

He pushed on through the underbrush until he was almost out of sight. I heard a noise and saw a water moccasin – a poisonous snake – skate across the top of the water past me seeking cover. I sprinted after my brother. I reached him as he was bending over to get through a patch of briars. I followed him through. 'You call this fun?'

He ignored me and continued through the thickets until we finally reached the canal. With its fast-flowing current, it would have been considered a river anywhere else. We silently admired it while recovering from our jaunt through the swamp. Once we caught our breath, Carl said, 'Check this shit.'

He dove off the bank fully clothed, his pistol strapped in its holster, into the rushing current, disappearing below the swirling water. I started counting seconds. When I reached a minute without him resurfacing I began to worry. At that moment, he stuck his arm up through the surface of the water near the opposite bank and fired a round into the air. The unexpected report made me jump. His head appeared. He sucked in air, and yelled, 'Bet you rights to the pistol for the day that you can't clear the canal under water without coming up for air.'

I didn't care about the gun, but the brotherly rivalry that extended back to our childhood fired up inside me. I backed up, took a deep breath and ran forward, diving beneath the surface. Underwater, the pressure of the current was much greater than I had anticipated. I was a strong swimmer but I'd never swum in a fast current. I opened my eyes but I couldn't see anything in the murky water so I closed them to avoid scaring myself. I brushed against some weeds and jerked, then kept kicking. I swam breaststroke underwater as fast as I could. My brother had always been able to outrun me, but I had been the stronger swimmer. I kept kicking and pushing my arms in a wide motion, waiting to hit the other bank with my outstretched hand. My lungs felt like they were going to burst. I used all my energy for one last stroke, then broke through the surface and inhaled as much air as possible. I opened my eyes and looked around. I was in the middle of the canal. My brother sat watching me on the opposite bank.

'Man, I thought you drowned,' he said. 'What were you doing – swimming in circles?'

Later that afternoon when we returned to the house, I asked, 'What are the magazines you're always reading?'

'Work. Stuff to keep up on in case I decide to get back in the trade.'

'Work?'

'The ads in back. Mercenary work.'

'What's a mercenary?'

'Professional soldier. Gun for hire.'

'I thought that was something in the movies.'

'Where do you think the movies get it from? America probably churns out more mercenaries than any country on earth, and when we're not training our own, we train theirs.'

'You can get hired by another country to go to war and still keep your citizenship here?'

'They'll probably congratulate me when I return. Shit's been going on forever.'

'I thought you hated the army.'

'I do. I wouldn't work for them again for anything. I've been corresponding with a guy in the French Foreign Legion. At least they have some class.'

'Don't you have to be French?'

'Why do you think they call it the "Foreign" Legion? It's a special unit so they can sign on foreigners to take care of politically sensitive tasks they don't want their boys involved in.'

'They don't have French troops in their own army?'

'There's French soldiers, but usually the Legion is full of foreigners. Every era's different. Right after the Third Reich was defeated, the majority of the French Foreign Legion were out-of-work German soldiers. A bunch of Krauts still sign on from what I hear.'

'German soldiers with the French? Why would the French hire them?'

211

'To oversee the zones of defeated Germany assigned to the French. You think the French wanted that job?'

'The French hired German soldiers to guard Germany?'

'You sound like every other moron who's never been in the Armed Forces. There are a hundred shades of gray.'

'But why would the Germans do it?'

'They're mercenaries. Everybody knows the Germans don't fight with passion. They do what they're told.' He stood up. 'Full moon tonight. I've got an extra hammock. Let do a mission down at the river.'

'A mission?'

'You really are a pussy, aren't you? I can't believe my own brother came out so soft. Put your boots on and you'll figure it out on the way.' He went into his bedroom and grabbed a small knapsack, took it into the kitchen and loaded it with two small hammocks made from string that were rolled into balls the size of my fist. Several feet of rope were tied to the metal loops to attach them to trees. He pulled a bottle of whiskey out from beneath the kitchen sink. 'Moonshine,' he said, 'distilled by yours truly. Perfect night to drink it.'

With an hour left before sunset we walked across the rolling pasture and entered the trees at the lowest part of the field, less than a quarter-mile from the canal. A soon as we were in the woods, Carl unhooked his belt, slipped off his holster and hid the gun beneath a fallen trunk, a hiding place with which he was clearly familiar. He rolled the dry-rotted log on its side and laid the gun in a slight indent in the soil that appeared to have been dug by hand.

'Why aren't you bringing the gun?'

'Not planning to kill anyone tonight.'

He grabbed a bag of peanuts lying in the hole and slipped them into his knapsack.

'What are those doing there?' I asked.

'A snack in case I get hungry while I'm out. Is it a crime?'

This time, before we swam across the canal, Carl stripped, put his clothes in the knapsack and handed it to me. 'You might like to do the same unless you want to sleep in wet clothes tonight. Don't let that get wet,' he said, pointing to the knapsack. He dove in and swam playfully in the current.

I stripped and packed my clothes into the bag, before venturing out into the current, holding the knapsack in the air and treading water with my legs. It was more difficult than I'd thought. Before I was halfway across, I shouted, 'Get it. Hurry up and grab it. I can't hold it up any more.'

Carl swam to my side and took the bag. I let my arms go limp and drifted underwater, then came back up for air and swam to the opposite bank.

Climbing out, Carl said, 'Where'd you get that?'

I looked down at the Iron Cross hanging from my neck. 'At a pawnshop.'

'You trying to be a Nazi like Dad?'

'I'm not trying to be anything. It's from the First World War. It's the only one I've ever seen.'

'We fought to kill those fuckers,' he said. 'I wouldn't go showing that thing off.'

'I don't. I keep it hidden under my shirt.'

Once we'd climbed up on the opposite bank and crossed the strip of woodland between the canal and the river we put our clothes back on. When we reached the river, we watched the sun setting behind the trees, its orange glow reflecting off the water. A short distance from us the clean massive concrete bridge of the interstate highway spanned the banks – the only civilization anywhere nearby, but with the drivers sealed inside their cars beyond our view, we belonged to two different worlds. There were no other buildings, dams, locks, boats, people or other man-made impediments for miles. Before stripping down again, we stopped to scan the enormous surface of the Savannah River. Nearly a half-mile across, quiet, gentle and flat, it looked like a vast lake being transported slowly to the ocean some hundred miles downstream. Near the center of the river there was a tiny island from which five or six small trees grew. My brother pointed at them. 'That's where we're sleeping tonight.'

Long tree limbs from a grove on the riverbank arched out over

213

the water with Spanish moss dangling like spider webs. We took off our clothes and carefully packed them with the whiskey and hammocks and moved slowly out into the current. The area of the river my brother had picked to cross was shallow and full of large rocks just below the surface, providing secure footing. As we moved further out, the water came up to our waists. There was a submerged rock stratum in that section that allowed us to avoid the deeper pools on either side.

The shoreline receded behind us until we were surrounded by water. Ahead, the small clump of trees waited for our arrival. Carl moved ahead of me, confidently pushing his way through the heavy weight of the current. For me, though, instead of it getting easier with learning where to place my feet, the crossing became more difficult. My legs were sore from holding against the current and my feet kept sliding between the rocks. Watching Carl move effortlessly through the water ahead, I continued, the competition we had always shared driving me on.

When we finally reached the small group of trees, I found the island less remarkable than I had imagined. Instead of being lined with soft soil and grass forming a mat to rest on, it was little more than a half-dozen boulders that a flood had lodged together. The trees, six poplars, with trunks no larger than a foot in diameter, were wedged between the rocks, their roots piercing down into the sandy earth that had collected there. I climbed up on a large boulder and sat beside Carl to catch my breath. It was only a few feet above the surface of the river but it was dry and comfortable, providing a sense of security. We looked back to the Georgia side and then to the Carolina side. Both seemed like distant illusions that might disappear at any time leaving us out there, floating above the world. From the middle of the river everything seemed more distant and doubtful than it had on shore.

Carl opened the knapsack and handed me a hammock. We pulled out our dry clothing and got dressed as the night air cooled. We checked each tree to see which were the right distance apart to string up the small hammocks. He showed me how to unroll them and

214

what kind of knot to make in the rope to keep it from coming undone during the night. Once Carl had strung his hammock up, he spread the tight webbing open and climbed in. A short while later, we lay in our hammocks, talking and watching the moon rise. Carl held the bottle of whiskey against his chest between sips. He had brought a canteen of water to chase it with. We handed the bottle back and forth, until my head felt light. Carl became more talkative.

'What are your plans?' he asked.

'Not sure. Probably wait for my tax return and buy an old motor-cycle to fix up so I can start looking for regular work.'

'Motorcycles are for pussies who aren't strong enough to ride under their own power.'

'I like working on them.'

'Take my Paramount out tomorrow. There's nothing like riding fifty miles under your own power.'

He paused. I was starting to feel drunk but he was hitting the bottle harder than me.

'What about the future?' he asked.

'Find a job like always. Maybe I should get more skills so I can make better money.'

'What about the revolution?'

'What revolution?'

'The rising.'

'Rising?'

'Of everybody we've fucked. Every nonwhite who's been fucked for the last five hundred years joining together, like the Europeans who took over the world and bled countries of their natural resources while murdering anybody in their way.'

'You are a crazy fuck, aren't you?'

He laughed the same way he had when he'd snuck up behind me in his living room and put an empty gun to my head. But lying on our hammocks out on the river, the laughter didn't echo off the walls – it floated out over the water and dissipated.

'We never fucked anybody,' I said.

'Tell that to Africa, Asia, the Middle East. Tell it to Latin America.'

'Is that what they teach you in the Special Forces?'

'They don't teach you shit – except how to kill.'

'I thought Dad was loony. You trying to ace him?'

I was watching the moonlight illuminate the riverbank when his hand clamped down on my neck, clenching my collar and almost pulling me out of the hammock, choking me. 'You ever mention me in the same breath with him again and I'll show you real life.' He released his grip. 'I've been places you don't even know exist. I've seen things. I graduated from the School of Americas at Fort Benning, the most elite school in the western hemisphere for training soldiers in the fine art of fucking over their fellow man. Panama, El Salvador, Honduras, Guatemala . . . Who do you think trains all the dictators and death squads in those shit-hole countries? That's right – we do. Guatemala's D-2 intelligence agency is run by graduates whose soldiers have torched more than five hundred remote Mayan villages in the last decade, murdering villagers just like the conquistadors did centuries earlier. Trained in the good ol' U.S. of A. in the name of kicking Communism's ass. Pulling fingernails, killing women and children – that's just the tip of the iceberg. If they call this peace-time, I'd hate to see war.'

I lay there catching my breath, worried that he was crazier than me, suddenly scared of him. We were hanging above water in the middle of the river. I couldn't run if I wanted to. If I tried to get back to shore, he'd catch me less than halfway there and hold my face underwater. He was stronger, faster. The only way I could escape him was if he let me go. He kept taking shots out of the bottle, staring up at the moon, then started talking again. I sank back in my hammock. He held out the bottle. I reached out to appease him and took a long drink, listening to him talk.

'Maybe it won't happen tomorrow. Maybe it won't happen next year. Maybe not in our lifetime, but it will happen, little bro. Nobody's going to ask questions about who was good and who wasn't. It will be a mission to destroy the people who kept them from getting ahead – and who's to say we haven't? Who doesn't know some stupid white person – I mean literally stupid – who has a hundred times more power and money than they deserve? We'll be the persecuted, just like we persecuted them. Everybody knows this. Nobody talks about it. Do you really think that when the playing field is finally level, when they take power as completely as we have, that they aren't going to repay us? You think they're going to forget five hundred years of conquest? Maybe the rich ones already here and in Europe will, but who do they represent? The rest of the world won't forget.'

A cool breeze blew across the water. I felt as if I was back in the basement again, but everything was inverted. The sky rose infinitely above me and water flowed endlessly beneath me – no matter how hard I tried I couldn't escape the past and now my brother insisted I wouldn't escape the future either. If I submitted to his view I would never be able to prove my innocence, and there would be no reason to confess my ancestors' guilt. I hung there, swinging gently in the breeze. My brother handed me the bottle. I took it and turned it up until I saw the moon reflecting in the bubbles rising through the distilled liquid.

I woke shortly after dawn to the sound of water rushing against the trunks of the trees our hammocks were tied to. The boulders we had sat on the night before had disappeared beneath the surface. Water ran swiftly by less than two feet below us. I rubbed my eyes to make sure I wasn't dreaming. I looked out across the river. Other than the trees suspending us, the river's wide, smooth surface was unbroken. The island was gone.

'Carl, wake up.'

I was dumbfounded. We were both strong swimmers: we could let the current take us downstream as we swam for shore without danger, then walk back up the riverbank, but the enormity of the water was still intimidating.

'Carl, wake the hell up.'

He turned slowly on his side, his movement stretching his hammock, causing it to sag in the middle. His ass touched the water's surface – a fine mist sprayed over his torso. He jerked awake, looked around, then said, 'They opened the locks upriver last night.'

I scanned the water. My eyes moved to the bank.

'Look over there, on the Georgia side,' I said, pointing.

Carl turned and saw a Richmond County Sheriff's car parked on the edge of the road that ran along the levee.

'Do you think he can see us?' I asked.

'Why else would he park there? There's a "No Swimming" sign near where he's parked. Every year someone drowns in the current when they open the locks. But who knows? He might be sleeping his shift off.'

The increased flow hadn't upset the trees. They held firmly against the current, as they had for at least a decade. I looked out across the river again, then back at my brother in his hammock, inches above the water. The knapsack we had set on the rocks was gone.

'We can't swim back right now,' Carl said. 'I don't want to deal with the cops.'

'Why don't we swim to the Carolina side and cross back into Georgia on the bridge?'

Carl scanned the Carolina bank. 'There's nothing on that side except thickets, but I guess we don't have much choice.'

Once we settled on swimming over to South Carolina, there was no hurry to start. The sheriff wasn't going to swim out to us. We lay in the hammocks for another hour, summoning the strength for the crossing. Carl eventually slipped his left leg over the edge of the hammock and lowered himself into the water until he was standing on one of the submerged rocks.

'It's a little colder than it was last night. We should get moving.'

Neither of us was eager to submerge our fully clothed bodies in the cold water. After waiting a few more minutes, Carl finally led by stepping off the boulder into the current. The water rose up to his neck.

'Should we take the hammocks?' I asked.

'I don't want to risk getting tangled in them.'

I slid out of my hammock and into the current. It pulled me slowly out into the wide river toward my brother. We matched one another, swimming side by side, silently monitoring each other in case we floated into a difficult current or undertow. Within a few minutes, the current pulled us into the middle of the wide river and gently carried us downstream. We concentrated on making headway. Partway to shore, we floated across a wide section of gentle rapids. We let our bodies go limp to pass over the rocks below the surface as we were pulled into deeper water, where we concentrated once again on swimming, alternating between breaststroke and freestyle to stay fresh. The warmth of the morning sun caused a veil of mist to rise from the water's surface. As we neared the shore I looked back to where the sheriff's car was parked. Fog shrouded the Georgia side of the river.

The Carolina shore wasn't much of a shore, more a shallow bog covered with algae and brush. The noise of our presence scared a small alligator from its den. It moved with a great splash out into the water, its bulbous eyes protruding above the surface as it let the current drag it downstream.

'Do you think it will come back?' I asked.

'It won't bother us. I just want us to make it through this brush on the bank without shredding our skin in all these thorns.' He looked around. 'Let's walk in the shallows upriver. It'll be easier than fighting those thickets.'

We walked against the current in the shallow water toward the bridge to the north. We pushed through the water for the better part of an hour before we stopped to rest, sitting down in the water. The rising sun had burned off the mist. Looking out at the river, I saw the remnants of the island where we had slept the night before – trees, small puffs of green protruding awkwardly from the river and the barely visible nets strung between them. The sheriff had disappeared.

After another extended effort, we finally reached a place a short distance from the bridge where the steep embankment climbed to the roadway. Within minutes we were deep in thick brush that I was forced to break through to gain ground, scraping my face and arms, thorns sticking into my hands. The firmer ground of the river bottom we had left behind gave way to thick mud and the reeking stench of decaying vegetation. As I slowed, Carl clawed past me and charged through the dense foliage, opening a path. We climbed the nearly vertical hill, using our hands to pull ourselves to the top. Before we stepped out onto the shoulder of the road in clear view of the traffic, we scanned for highway patrol, then hurried out onto the narrow concrete shoulder of the bridge, knowing we were momentarily safe as we crossed the void between Georgia and South Carolina.

'Forget hitchhiking,' Carl said, glancing back. 'We look like a couple of escaped convicts.'

I looked down at eddies swirling in the river far below. I noticed the outline of the small trees in which we had slept. Trucks passed within feet of our bodies pressed against the steel railings. We looked out for police cruisers. As soon as we reached the Georgia side, we climbed over a short wall, dropped into the brush and hiked back into the woodlands near the house, stopping by the fallen tree for Carl to retrieve his gun.

That's how it always was with him. Adventures came one after another with a never-ending stream of apocalyptic conclusions, except he didn't see it as the apocalypse: he saw it as the passing of the torch to the next man even if he were sacrificed along the way. He had no interest in supremacy and viewed neo-Nazis as pathetic clowns, but he nonetheless felt it a moral duty to defend his own. He would no more consider abandoning his home team halfway through the game than he would put a gun into his mouth and pull the trigger. 'You don't switch sides just because you start losing. Our history would be left with no respect at all. Let them talk all the shit they want. There isn't a person with common sense out there who doesn't respect what we've accomplished. Who doesn't want what we have? We ruled this fuckin' earth, bro.' He didn't see himself as an extremist and he had no delusions about saving or perpetuating his race – he saw himself as preparing with dignity for the white man's inevitable decline.

* * *

When my tax return finally arrived, my brother and I had a fight about how to spend it. It was the only time we argued about money. I wanted to use it to buy a motorcycle I could repair so that I wouldn't be stuck out on the farm. I needed to start working. I felt the desire to break free swelling inside me again, and unless I found an outlet beyond hiking and swimming, I knew I'd soon strike out on the road. I didn't want that. I was comfortable at the house – I just didn't want to be pinned down and subjected to his constant views. The fight wasn't about whether or not I'd leave. The fight was about him insisting I didn't waste my money on a motorcycle and bought a bicycle instead.

'I don't give a shit if you're into motorcycles or not,' he said. 'Buy one when you can afford both. But if you can only afford one, get a bike. We can go out riding together. You'll stay in shape. You can get to any job just as easy on a bike as you can a motor and you can use your own power getting there. I don't care how far from the house it is.'

I didn't answer him, but I did take his Paramount out for a ride. He made me carry it all the way down to the paved road at the bottom of the hill near the railroad tracks. He didn't want any dust on it or sand on the chain he wiped clean and oiled lightly after each ride. Neither did he want me to harm the narrow racing tires he had mounted that cost as much as motorcycle tires. My first rides were a peculiar experience. The bike felt flimsy compared with my motorcycle. The tires were so skinny, I worried constantly that they would pop. I was scared to race full speed downhill. Any slight movement of the handlebars caused the bike to jerk to the side and almost crash, but riding did provide solitude and I took it out through the countryside almost every day the following week, then finally rode across town to a bike shop. One of the mechanics showed me several racing bikes like my brother's. There was one in particular I liked called a Motobécane that he said was made in France, but I couldn't get over the price. I could have bought a broken-down motorcycle for the same amount, fixed it and driven across the country. I tucked a small brochure in my pocket and took it home to think about it.

221

I continued riding my brother's bike. Each time I took it out, it grew on me a little more, until I began to understand his point about the feeling of accomplishment gained from riding long distances under your own power. One day I got up early without telling him, walked up to Washington Road, took the bus across town and laid out the money on the counter for the Motobécane. I liked that it had 'Moto' in its name. The storeowner said that the manufacturer had come up with it by combining the French slang for motorcycle – *moto* – and bike – *bécane*.

As I rolled it out of the door, the mechanic who had showed me around the first day yelled over the counter, 'Don't let anybody go messing with your *bécane*.'

Carl wasn't as surprised as I had hoped when I rode up to the house on my new bike. 'I knew you were getting a bike, jackass, especially when I found you gone this morning without mine.'

He took me on a ride along Furys Ferry Road, a secondary road that crossed the river into Carolina about ten miles north of the interstate bridge. He made mincemeat of me going up the hills. By the time I got back to the house twenty minutes after him I wasn't so sure that spending my money on a bike had been the wisest move. A couple of weeks later, he showed me a fifty-mile loop out to the lake and over the dam. The first time we rode it, I stopped at Pollard's Corner halfway and lay on the ground beside the country store, worried I was dying, while my brother went inside and bought a Coke for me and some rolling tobacco to occupy him while he waited for me to recover.

'What are you doing smoking?'

'It's good for you. It opens up your lungs. Gives you energy.'

'Too bad there's not a world championship for kooks. You'd win the gold every time.'

'Yeah, and too bad there's not a world championship for pussies. You'd be undefeated.'

I limped back into Augusta in my brother's draft, begging him to let off the pace so I didn't get left behind. It was one of the few days that he actually let me stay up with him. Each day I got a little stronger. I loved riding so much that even on the days my brother didn't go out I rode with a vengeance, hoping to get an edge on him. Little by little my power increased. Soon I could match his pace on most hills. Then one day it finally happened. I punched it coming over the top of a rise, got a gap on him and nailed it down the other side of the hill. He didn't catch me until I was almost at the top of the next roller. He didn't look amused. He didn't congratulate me. He rode past me, dropped into a bigger gear and started mashing the pedals so hard that I saw bright splotches of light while I tried to hold his pace. I backed off to recover as he stomped up the next hill and left me behind. I decided it was time for me to find a job. I needed money and the space would do us good.

I worked four or five temporary labor jobs, before finding work as a bike messenger. A guy who had recently graduated from college and moved down south from New York had had the brilliant idea that he was going to introduce bike messengers into the South. He didn't take into account that it was often ten miles out to deliver one package, and when you arrived you had to stand around the water cooler for thirty minutes to chat with the good old boy who had hired you so as not to offend him. Then you delivered the next package fifteen miles in the opposite direction, where you were again cornered into a conversation about what a nifty idea bike messengers were before you got on to the next delivery.

I averaged about five packages a day for the month the company lasted, but I got into the most rip-roaring shape imaginable. I raced cars across town, jumped into the draft of trucks and rode inches from their bumpers at forty miles per hour, swerving in and out of traffic, veering across oncoming lanes during rush hour, jumping curbs, dodging pedestrians, sprinting away from vicious dogs. I loved it more than any job I had ever had.

My final day I was speeding up Washington Road toward the interstate to deliver a package to a bank when I heard sirens behind me and noticed the traffic pulling off the road in both directions. Since

I was on a bike I tended to ignore traffic laws and kept churning away until a motorcycle officer came up alongside me and yelled, 'Hey, Pierre, that meant you too.' He pointed sternly at a parking lot for me to pull into and clear the road. I pulled off and glanced back down the road behind me. For a long time it remained empty – an odd sight at midday on the busiest street in Augusta. Five minutes later several other motorcycle cops cruised by, followed by a few more cruisers, and then I saw the motorcade come up over the rise, surrounded by black security cars, another dozen police and sheriff cars and more motorcycles. I realized it was President Reagan – he was in town to vacation for the week at the Augusta National Golf Club. The club was surrounded by tall fences and overgrowth that hid the grounds and buildings within. I wondered why he was leaving so early. He hadn't been due to depart for a couple more days.

The following morning I learned that he had ordered the invasion of Grenada, a small Caribbean nation, while he was at the Augusta National. When my brother heard the news, he told me it was the first major U.S. military operation since the Vietnam War.

'Looks like we're back in business,' he said.

I started looking for a new job. I wasn't eager to go back to work as a day laborer. I wanted something more secure. Augusta had grown on me and I found myself thinking that it would be as good a place as any to settle. The recession had eased slightly since the previous year, but finding work was still difficult. You had to look between cracks to find jobs. I read a newspaper article that said people were going back to college to get government grants as a result of the weak economy. Nareesha entered my mind and I thought about trying to go to college myself. I rode over to Augusta College on Walton Way and talked to Admissions. The woman behind the counter barely hid her contempt behind her smile when I told her that the last school I had attended was Langford Junior High. She told me that only high-school graduates who had taken the SAT were admitted.

'There's no other way?'

'We can't let everybody in,' she said. 'We do have our standards.'

At home that night I reread the same newspaper article about college and saw a sidebar about government jobs being the most secure. I rode back across town to Augusta College in the morning, went to the Physical Plant and asked to speak with the supervisor. His secretary said he wasn't available for another two hours.

'I'll wait.'

While sitting there I completed an application, stressing maintenance work at the motel in Albany and lying about a few other jobs so my life wouldn't appear so transient. After two hours had passed, he put me off for another hour, probably hoping to get rid of me. I didn't have anything else to do so I waited. By the time I sat down in his office, he seemed impressed by my persistence.

'Why didn't you drop off your application like everyone else?'

'I don't want it to get thrown away before you see it.'

'What makes you think I'm going to read it now?'

'Because I'm going to sit here while you do.'

'Why do you want a job like this? You should be in college.'

'I like fixing things,' I said. 'I like cleaning. I never cared much for school.'

He leaned back in his chair, read my application, then looked up at the ceiling as if he was trying to figure out how to say something on his mind. 'Between you, me and that door over there, you'd be one of two white janitors if I hired you. I have forty people working under me. Can you work in those conditions?'

'All I want to do is work. I'm comfortable with anybody.'

'Give me a couple of days to think about it.'

When I returned two days later, his secretary said he was unavailable.

'When is he available?'

'You could try again tomorrow after lunch.'

I came back the next day. I saw him in his office, but the secretary said he wasn't free until later that afternoon. I told her I'd wait. An hour and a half later, she said I could go into his office.

'You don't give up, do you, boy?'

'No, sir.'

'Be back here at eight in the morning. Ready to work.'

'Thank you, sir.'

'Were you in the army, boy?'

'No, sir.'

'The name's Mel Benson. The boys around here call me Mel. I expect you to do the same.'

'Yes, sir, Mel. I'll be back in the morning.'

I left the college so excited that I rode out and did the fifty-mile loop over the dam my brother had shown me, arriving home that night after dark.

I remained at the farm with my brother. He retreated back to his hunting routine and also started working more seriously on a small still he kept hidden in the woods down by the river. He bottled small batches in mason jars and glued hand-written labels on them: 'Savannah River Sour Mash.' He also started venturing into town at night. He only produced a few jars a month but he had no problem finding friends at the local bars interested in buying high-grade homemade whiskey. Stills had fallen out of style fifty years earlier after Prohibition was lifted, but as with many of his unusual ideas, he was certain they would come back into style. He insisted there was a market for homemade whiskey. I think he was motivated by more than market concerns: he liked it because it was illegal, because the government said he couldn't do it.

He often returned from the river around the time I got home from work, and when I was getting ready to go to bed, I'd hear a car pull up out front and people yelling. He'd go out to meet them to head into town for a night of drinking at the Gin Mill on Washington Road or the Whipping Post downtown on Broadway. Most of the guys who started appearing at the house were new recruits from Fort Gordon he had met in the bars. They looked up to him because of his time in the Special Forces and the stories he liked to tell. But some of them were longhairs, as he called them, who wore bushy beards and occasionally arrived on loud motorcycles. Most carried guns. I knew this because of Carl's house rule. If armed company

226

came to the house to drink, they were required to lay their guns on the table. It was the sort of outlaw etiquette that my brother liked to affect and they seemed to appreciate. Sometimes they'd be there when I got home from work if they'd started drinking early.

'Meet my little bro,' Carl would say, even if I'd met them before. He introduced me the same way every time. He never said my name. They were usually polite, sometimes asking me what I did or how my day had gone for the few minutes it took me to get something out of the refrigerator to eat. Then I'd go back into my bedroom, close the door and sit alone cleaning my bike, adjusting the derailleur and the brakes or trying to true the rims. They'd get louder the more they drank until finally they decided to go into town. I started seeing empty Evan Williams bottles around the house. I had never seen my brother drink store-bought whiskey before. In the time we had lived together I sensed a change. After I'd shown up he'd seemed happy for a while. He never smiled much and we rarely laughed, but I could tell he had a good time with me.

I had so many new things I wanted to share with him, but it was difficult to reach him. Even when we were in the house alone and he wasn't drunk, his mind was elsewhere, as though he had deeper things to worry about than the details of my new job that I wanted to share with him. I knew he wouldn't be interested in the fact that I had health insurance as part of my employment. If I ever needed to go to the doctor or hospital, I didn't have to pay. He would have told me they were taking advantage of me by paying minimum wage. After I'd been in the job for a year, they would start giving me vacation pay, one week off for the first five years, increasing incrementally depending on how long I stayed. I would eventually be eligible for sick pay, too.

The benefit that struck me as the oddest but that I liked most was that, as I was a state employee, they put a small percentage of each paycheck into a pension for my retirement. When I first noticed the money being deducted I went to Mel ready to fight to get my money back, until he told me what it was for. He added that if I quit before retiring they'd return any money they'd withheld. I spent the better part of the week mulling over the concept. I had never thought beyond the next couple of days, so considering what I'd do in retirement was like imagining life on a different planet. I doubted I'd live until thirty, much less retire at sixty, but the fact that they were withholding money made me acknowledge that there was more to life than getting through each day.

The only riding I did for the first few months was across town to work and back home, but it was far enough each way that I stayed in shape. Each morning, at a few minutes before eight, we gathered in a room at the Physical Plant to clock in. We weren't allowed to clock in early because the state didn't want to pay overtime, but Mel took note if we clocked in more than a few minutes late, so we'd stand around the room holding our cards and waiting for the clock to strike so we could slide the cards into the machine for it to punch them.

One morning I overslept. I didn't want to disappoint Mel, so I jumped on my bike and raced down the dirt road I normally carried my bike on and sprinted up the hill to Washington Road. From there it was a long way across town, over the crest of another hill, down a long descent and one final long hill that climbed for a couple of miles before I reached the college. At the bottom of the long climb I settled into a rhythm, as my brother had taught me, increasing my pace as I climbed, instead of wearing myself out at the bottom. Halfway up the hill I saw another cyclist ahead, which spurred me to bump up the pace. When I got within twenty feet of him, I rode like my brother did whenever he came up behind me: I stood up, dropped into a harder gear, mashed the pedals past him and continued racing up the hill in hopes of reaching work within a few minutes of eight. At the top of the climb I heard somebody huffing behind me and turned back to see the rider I had passed catching up. He was in strange clothing that clung to his body and wore a small cap with an upturned bill and pointy leather shoes with holes in them.

'Where'd you learn how to ride like that?' he shouted.

He was older than me. I looked at his clothing again and decided he was another pervert, but instead of cruising dark streets in his car, he used his bike to go out on early-morning rides to casually bump into boys riding to school. When the light turned green, I sprinted away, put it in my biggest gear and held it until I was within a couple of blocks of campus. I came to a stop sign and almost crashed when he reappeared on a side street to cut me off.

'You'd be dangerous without work boots and blue jeans slowing you down,' he said.

'Get the fuck away from me,' I shouted.

'Aggressive. Nothing wrong with that.'

When he wouldn't back down, I prepared to pull back and hit him.

'Slow down,' he yelled. 'You're getting the wrong idea. I don't see many people race by me on climbs. You're the first person on that hill who's ever done it.'

I had so much adrenaline coursing through my veins by then that it was impossible for me to calm down. My hands were shaking.

'Go on,' he said. 'Maybe I'll see you on the hill another day.'

He turned and rode away.

A couple of weeks later I was climbing from the bottom of the same long hill on the way to work and heard something behind me. I looked back and saw the same guy following me. I stood up, dropped into a tougher gear and went as hard as I could. Less than halfway up the hill, he pulled up beside me, and said, 'Not today.'

He sprinted off ahead of me. Out of instinct I tried to match his pace but maintained it for only a few minutes before fading. I over-extended myself so much that soon I couldn't even maintain my initial pace and slowed to a crawl by the time I neared the top of the hill. I pulled off to a side street to recover and he wheeled back around the corner.

He held his hand out in front of him like a police officer stopping traffic. 'I'm not here to cause any problems. My name's Wade. Former state road champion. Don't bump into many people who can ride a bike like that around here and when I do I like to meet them. I'm not getting any faster riding by myself.'

He looked to be about forty but it was hard to tell because of his peculiar clothing.

'You'd be a whole lot faster on a better bike with some lighter clothes,' he said. 'Maybe you'd be able to stay with me on that climb.'

'I just bought the bike,' I said.

He looked at it again. 'It's nice. Motobécanes are good. Raleighs are better,' he said, slapping the back of his hand on the top tube of his bike.

Wade was an electrician by trade and, although he was old, he was the fastest bicycle rider in town – or, as he informed me, racer. Whenever he wasn't working construction he wore funny little hats with strange names printed on the upturned bills and the sides, like Molteni, Peugeot, and Renault-Elf-Gitane. The first time I accepted his invitation to come by his garage and see his collection of racing bikes he gave me a Faema-Flandria cap and dug through a pile of old boxes until he found a pair of leather cycling shoes with wooden cleats on the bottom that fitted my feet.

'My gift to you,' he said. 'Athlete's foot.'

He had a corny sense of humor, but he was good-natured and seemed interested in nothing more than finding somebody younger than himself to fill his old cycling shoes. He was married and had a daughter, but didn't seem interested in having her out on the street training. It didn't take him long to win my trust. Even though he worked full time and had a family, he went out of his way to take me on training rides.

He gave me hand-me-down wool jerseys and a couple of pairs of old wool cycling shorts that clung to my legs like the ones I'd seen him in. The shorts had a chamois sewn into the middle, a thin piece of leather to prevent saddle sores, tiny boils that developed on your crotch making it impossible to sit down. Before we headed out on rides, he'd dip his fingers into a jar of Vaseline and lubricate the chamois to reduce the friction even more. It took a lot of getting used to. I felt like a cross-dresser, but I enjoyed the camaraderie.

It was like joining a secret society. I liked the idea of wearing the strange clothing and the cycling cap, but I was too embarrassed to bring them back to the house, so for the first months I stored them in his garage. I'd drop by after work and we'd suit up like a couple of European pros, then head out for a hard ride. He was heavier than me and I soon learned that I could push it on the climbs and sometimes drop him, but on the flats he cranked along like a motorcycle. He taught me how to draft, staying within a foot of his rear tire and letting him block the wind so I could conserve my energy and hold his pace. He knew every strip of pavement surrounding Augusta.

Since he preferred riding on flat roads to push the pace he often took me on the Bomb Plant Ride – every ride had a name. We'd head out on Sand Bar Ferry Road and cross the bridge into Beech Island, South Carolina, where he had a ten-mile time-trial course set up on Atomic Road, a narrow stretch that led to a government gate that entered the Bomb Plant – officially known as the Savannah River Site. He took me out there and timed me on a course he had set up to check my progress. On the first ten-miler he clocked me at just over twenty-four minutes. He wasn't overly impressed, but he wasn't disappointed, either.

That ride intrigued me because of its name. Wade didn't seem to know much about what went on behind the gates. He just liked the remote road without much traffic. When I asked my brother about it that night he said that in the early fifties the federal government had cleared more than three hundred square miles of low-lying land on the Carolina side of the river to built five nuclear reactors in a remote location away from the population centers of the northeast that could be easily secured to process war-grade plutonium for the arms race. He said they still churned out the poison. Once I learned this I avoided the ride, encouraging Wade to show me others.

Every once in a while I convinced Carl to go on a ride with me. By then I knew more places to ride than he did. He was lighthearted when he rode. We'd race through the countryside, sprinting for city-limit signs and trying to drop each other over climbs. I never felt freer than when I was out riding and I loved riding with Carl: Wade had introduced me to the technical aspects of riding, but without Carl I wouldn't have had a bike. I would have been riding through the countryside on a motorcycle without ever experiencing the exhilaration of powering myself from one place to the next.

Riding was more meditation than grueling exercise. More about freeing your mind than grunting up the next climb. You had to work to experience freedom, but the effort of pushing over the next hill was rewarded by the views you saw and the places you passed through. Whenever I rode everything else melted away. It was an addiction, but so much better than any drug.

I couldn't understand why Carl didn't embrace cycling more. It was exactly what I had been looking for my entire life to escape the past. It helped me live in the present by concentrating on each revolution of the crank-arms. I wanted him to experience the same freedom I felt. He clearly understood it or he wouldn't have made me buy a bike, but when I tried to interest him in it, he'd pull away.

Wade tried to talk me into entering a race, but I was hesitant. I treasured the freedom of riding. I didn't want the expectation of results to destroy the pleasure of riding – and, more importantly, I didn't want to disappoint him. I hadn't shaved my legs, but I was no longer embarrassed to be seen around town in cycling clothes, wearing pointy shoes and my Faema-Flandria cap. I didn't care what other people thought. They would never know that my cap was from the same team the greatest cyclist of all time had raced with. Eddy Merckx, The Cannibal, had won every major road race and the Grand Tours in France, Spain and Italy multiple times, securing 525 career victories – Wade had stacks of old cycling publications piled up in his garage: I'd roll up a couple in my back pocket before heading home each night and read them until I fell asleep.

He finally convinced me to ride the Statesboro Century with him. A 'century' was a hundred-mile ride through the countryside, cycling's equivalent of a marathon. Months before the event the organizers sent out flyers to bike shops throughout the state and people like Wade would show up from all over to spend the day together, sharing their passion. It wasn't officially a race, but it was inevitable that the cyclists became competitive, especially in a place like Georgia. In a way cyclists were the misfits of sporting enthusiasts. With baseball, basketball, football or golf, you could always find a pickup game, but cyclists in Georgia rarely saw other riders. Race results were never posted in the newspaper. Other than an obscure monthly periodical printed on recycled paper that Wade subscribed to, the cycling world didn't exist – except a few times a year when we drove for hours and gathered in a place like Statesboro.

After waking at five, riding across town to Wade's house, dis-assembling our bikes, stuffing them into the back of his Datsun B-210 and driving across the state, as the sun rose over the forests and swamps, the century proved an epiphany. Several hundred riders of all shapes and sizes huddled beside their cars pumping up bike tires, pulling on jerseys, filling water bottles and collecting bananas or fig bars to carry with them. Some were drinking coffee. I saw one smoking a cigarette, like my brother, another doing push-ups, some-body else oiling his chain, a few sleeping on the hoods of their cars and a woman attaching a trailer to her bike so she could bring her daughter along. I felt completely at home.

By the time Wade had found a place to park and we had assem-bled our bikes, changed our clothes and filled our jersey pockets with food, they were already gathering on the starting line. A man with a bullhorn was shouting orders, 'Don't go too fast through stop signs and don't fall asleep in the middle of the road if you get tired. We'll be here all day waiting for you and we'll keep the chickens from roosting on your car if you don't get back until nightfall.'

He pointed a starting gun in the air and fired three shots. 'The other two are for good luck,' he shouted, as we passed.

Soon I was in the middle of a sea of cyclists, a swelling body that flowed this way and that, people shouting at the front to warn everyone that a turn was coming up. We were so far out in the countryside that there wasn't a single car. I heard people who hadn't met since the last century, the year before in Dalton, telling each other about their kids in school, a car they had bought, the repairs they had had to do to their bike to come out on the ride that day.

As time wore on people formed different groups, depending on their abilities. I followed Wade through the pack as he went from one person to the next asking how their business was doing, did their son graduate from school, if they knew of any other centuries or races being organized that year, and introducing me along the way.

Around the twenty-five-mile mark, Wade went to the front and increased the pace. The crowd began breaking apart until there were only ten riders left at the front. I rode along at the rear of that group, not wanting to get in the way or cause trouble by swerving in front of somebody or braking too quickly. Occasionally I glanced back over my shoulder, and once saw a guy race across the gap to join our group. The mass of cyclists eventually disappeared from sight and for a long time there was a smaller group behind us, but five or ten miles later they had disappeared as well. I was too shy to talk to anyone, so I stayed at the back and looked at the countryside and the farms we passed, spinning along. The only other people I had ridden with were my brother and Wade, but never both at the same time, so the experience was new. When we passed a hand-painted sign on the side of the road indicating the fifty-mile mark I rode past the others to Wade at the front and said, 'I'm going to drop off to pee.'

'You did great,' he said, reaching out and patting me on the back. The other riders chirped in, congratulating me for staying with them so long. One guy said he looked forward to riding with me again on the next century.

Once they'd finished I drifted off the back, pulled over to the side of the road and ran into the woods to relieve myself. Then I got back on my bike. The group that had been behind us earlier hadn't come back into view during my stop. I could still see my group in the distance, on the flat, straight road. I stood on the pedals and found a comfortable rhythm, then sat down and pushed it harder, riding bigger gears until I was flying along, gaining ground on them. I was most comfortable riding by myself, without worrying whether I was going too fast or too slow. Nonetheless, I felt obligated to ride in Wade's group since he had driven me down and paid for the gas.

When I caught up with them, I rode up to the front to let Wade know I was back. They had been riding with their heads down, concentrating on their cadence, and looked up now, as if I had said something wrong.

'I thought you were stopping,' Wade said.

'I did. I stopped back there.'

Wade turned to the riders behind and shouted, 'Did Sam drop off the back?'

'He wasn't with us,' one said.

Two riders were ahead, a few hundred yards up the road.

'See if you can catch them,' he said.

'You don't want me in this group?'

'We'd love to have you here. I just want to see if you can catch those guys.'

'And then come back here?'

'No, ride with them the rest of the day, if you want. Let's see what you've got.'

I glanced back. The rest of the guys in the group were staring at me. I shifted gears, stood up and got back into the rhythm I had been riding to catch up with them. I quickly caught the two guys ahead. They appeared startled when I asked from behind whether it was okay to ride with them.

'Sure, sure,' one said. 'Better yet, why don't you ride in front a while?'

'Come on, give the boy a rest,' the other said.

I rode behind them for a while and then we started trading off, each person going to the front and blocking the wind while the others followed behind. We continued rotating, concentrating on going faster and faster, until we settled into the highest pace we could maintain as a group. When I finally looked back to see where Wade was, he had disappeared.

'Should we wait for Wade?' I asked. Wade was well known in the group and they all seemed to look up to him.

'Hell, no, I've been trying to drop that bastard for years,' the one up front shouted.

'Thank God he brought you along today,' the other one chimed in.

From then on we raced along, without speaking, all the way back to Statesboro. When we neared the finish, one asked, 'Should we sprint?'

The other said, 'No, let's just roll in together. We've had enough fun for the day.'

On the way home Wade announced that he was entering me in something he called a citizens' race the following month. 'It won't cost you a dime, I'll pay for everything. And if you don't like it, you never have to race again.'

For the next four weeks I trained with him every day after work. Some days were recovery rides, Tuesdays were dedicated to sprints, Wednesdays we went on long endurance rides, Thursdays hill climbs and on weekends we headed out to do a little of each, simulating racing conditions. I also still rode to and from work each day. As the race approached, I asked Carl if he would come and watch.

'I gotta meet somebody that day,' he said. 'Plus if you're not going to be around, I don't want to leave the house alone.'

Whatever his reasons, I knew he wouldn't change his mind. He could be stubborn. There was no use in trying to convince him; I'd only irritate him.

On the morning of the race, Wade drove out to the house and picked me up before dawn so I wouldn't have to waste energy riding to his place. 'You live way out,' he said, when he arrived that morning. 'I didn't know there were any houses up here.'

'This is it,' I said. 'Just us and the horses.'

'Well, it looks peaceful enough.'

We headed out and got on the interstate. This time Wade hadn't brought his own bike. His focus was on making sure mine was ready and helping me prepare. We arrived almost two hours before the race.

'Just relax in the car,' he said. 'I'll get the bike set up.'

There was a different energy than there had been at the century we had ridden. People were preparing for the race, rather than asking about each other's families. Once Wade had put my bike together and I'd changed into my cycling clothes, he told me to go out and ride for a half-hour to warm up and familiarize myself with the finish area, paying particular attention to the 200-meters-to-go mark. 'At full effort, that's the furthest a person can sprint. Don't jump before two hundred meters from the line.'

I went out and previewed the course. I kept replaying everything Wade had told me to do over the previous weeks.

'Stay with the leaders if you can and ride behind them to conserve energy,' he had repeated, every time we had gone on a ride. 'The only time I want to see you come out front is with two hundred meters to go when you sprint for the finish line.'

When I returned to the car, he seemed more nervous than I was. 'You sure you know what to do?' he asked, three or four times.

'Yeah, just ride, right? You're starting to make me nervous. I thought we were coming up here to have fun.'

He topped up my water bottle and had me sit in the driver's seat of the car and hang my legs out while he rubbed them down, massaging my calves and slapping them back and forth. 'Gets the blood flowing.'

It felt strange having a man massaging my legs in a parking lot, but I tried to ignore it, knowing I'd soon be riding and out on my own. The referee called the competitors to the line. He began shouting a list of rules. None of the racers paid much attention. When he was finished, he set his clipboard on the ground and asked if we had any questions. Nobody responded. As he reached in his pocket for his starting pistol, everybody stiffened. I looked around, unsure whether I should as well. Maybe I wasn't as nervous as I should be.

The gun sounded, creating a confused rush as everyone rolled forward, slipping their feet into their toe-clips and cinching the straps, securing their feet to the pedals.

I rode as hard as I could until I reached the first ten riders strung out single file. I slowly moved up until I reached fifth position, exactly where Wade had told me to ride. From there I followed his instructions exactly. Never go to the front and never let more than five riders ahead of me. If a rider tried to get away by himself, I was supposed to sprint after him if nobody else did so. If they did, I was to follow their wheel. They attacked one after the other. I wasn't sure who to follow, but I stayed as close to the front as possible. At first the other racers screamed at me to pull through and take a turn up front, but each time somebody yelled at me, another sprinted away, causing the group to splinter, as we all tried to catch up with the first rider. Each time we lost a couple more riders off the back, until halfway through the race there were only four of us left in the first group. I followed the last rider as Wade had instructed, but it wasn't a popular tactic. The others kept yelling at me to go to the front. Eventually the pressure became too great and I took a turn at the front, pulling into the wind while they lined up behind me. When I let the next rider take his turn, they attacked and sprinted up the road together. I put my head down and went as hard as I could – so hard that my abdomen started cramping, but I didn't stop. I slowly clawed my way back. I was huffing like a vacuum cleaner. They were startled that I had caught them, then irritated again by my presence.

'Get back on the front. Take a turn, you leech.'

It took me a long time to recover. I stayed at the back and ignored their insults. They yelled whatever cruel things came to mind, until they could see it had no effect. After that they ignored me. They seemed to know one another and appeared to be carefully trying to guess each other's moves in advance. Whenever one attacked, the other two were immediately on his wheel, with me following in fourth place. At the five-mile-to-go mark they began launching a series of sharp attacks against each other. The guy ahead screamed for me to go to the front and chase down the rider who had just attacked. Having been tricked the last time, I refused, but whenever the gap opened too wide I jumped across to the first rider as fast as possible, attached myself to his rear wheel and recovered. After five or six attacks in succession, the only thing I was able to focus on was waiting for the next, which would inevitably come. At the exclusion of all else, I focused on staying behind the first

238

rider – especially after another guy in our group dropped off the back, reducing us to three.

The guy in first position hammered like Wade had on the Bomb Plant ride. He went full speed like a motorcycle, making sure that the guy who had been dropped wouldn't make it back. I started cramping again. Another rider fell off the intense pace. When we passed a large placard with '1 Mile' scrawled across it, I realized the only racers left were myself and the rider whose tire I was drafting. He began yelling at me to take a turn at the front. Wade had explicitly stated I should not go to the front until I could see the finish line. Each time he pulled to the side, I pulled to the side behind him.

We looked back. The other two other riders were together now, but they looked too far behind to catch us with less than a mile to the finish. The leader snaked back and forth, trying to move me out of his draft, until he finally got so mad that he put on his brakes. I followed his example and nearly came to a stop behind him. We glanced back again. The other two riders were gaining on us. The leader suddenly sprinted as hard as he could and got a slight gap on me. I sprinted up to top speed behind him and eventually caught back up and glued myself to his rear tire. He kept the pace high to make sure the two guys behind us wouldn't reconnect. From there on, he seemed unconcerned about my presence.

At the '500 Meters' sign, he glanced back to see if I was still there. I reached down to tighten my toe-straps and tossed my water bottle into the grass, as Wade had instructed, to reduce my weight. I still couldn't see the finish line. It was hidden around a sharp bend on a slight upgrade. I waited for the other rider to sprint, knowing that the race would soon be over. Right before we reached the corner he swung wide to throw me off his wheel and into the open wind while he entered the turn at full speed.

Instead of trying to follow his wheel, I took the inside curb nearest me, leaning my bike over the way I used to do on my motorcycle, then straightened it up and started sprinting. By taking the inside line I immediately came back even with him without expending the energy he had used to go wide. I violently swung my bike from side to side. I felt like I was going to lose control, my lungs ready to burst, my legs searing with pain. As I crossed the finish line, I swerved to avoid a spectator who had jumped out into the street to watch the sprint. I came to a stop. Somebody grabbed my arm and slapped me on my back. Then I heard Wade's voice: 'You won! You won the goddamned race! I can't believe it! Your first goddamned race, boy!'

Driving back to Augusta I was flying higher than a kite. A big trophy sat on the floor, with a marble base and a bicycle racer on top, leaning against my legs. Wade kept telling me to pick it up so he could glance at it. He was as happy as if he had just won the race himself. He kept saying, 'I can't believe it.'

When we passed a car with two women up front and another in the back, he beeped the horn and yelled at me to hold up the trophy. We laughed like schoolchildren, overwhelmed by the feeling of victory. We were a team.

'You're getting licensed,' he said. 'No more centuries or citizens' races. We're going to see how you do against the big boys.'

He explained that there was a governing body at the Olympic Training Center in Colorado called the United States Cycling Federation. Since cycling hadn't developed along the lines of the other pro sports in the country all elite riders were affiliated with it. The organization sanctioned races around the country, creating a feeder program to the training center for the national team, which was decided by results throughout the season. USCF races also formed the backbone for what was essentially the professional racing circuit in the country, with competitions taking place from city to city, state to state and region to region throughout the year. Wade had spent the better part of his twenties racing the USCF circuit before he got married and became an electrician.

I couldn't imagine uprooting again and traveling from one place to the next now that I had found a job that was paying into a retirement pension, but I liked the idea of racing, especially after winning.

And I liked Augusta more each day and didn't want to go back on the lonely road. I would have never met Wade if I had continued that lifestyle and I would have never been hired at the college.

Carl was more excited by my victory than I'd expected. He was sitting on the front steps smoking when we pulled up to the house. He was as surprised as Wade that I had won the race. He went inside, dug through his room and came back with a sealed mason jar of whiskey to give Wade for helping me. 'A friend of mine distills it,' he said. 'Don't go shouting it from the rooftop, but feel free to share it. Special blend to drink among friends.'

It might not have been the most appropriate gift, but Wade had grown up in Georgia and I doubted it was the first bottle of moonshine he'd seen. He didn't lead a hard life like my brother, but he occasionally drank beer after rides so I didn't think it would go to waste. I could tell that he was touched.

My brother set the trophy on the kitchen counter so that whenever company came over he could show it off. It motivated him to dust off his bike and start coming out on rides with me again on Saturday mornings. He'd wake up with a hangover and insist that he was well enough to ride when I tried to let him off the hook. By Sunday morning he'd be too hammered after drinking heavily on both Friday and Saturday nights. Wade spent Saturday with his family. Carl and I usually rode the Graniteville Loop. We'd take back roads into downtown then roll across the 13th Street Bridge into South Carolina and climb the long hill up Georgia Avenue into North Augusta and continue out of town, past Belvedere. Every time we did the ride, pushing the pace up the first long climb and picking up speed through Belvedere, he'd pull over on a side street and puke up last night's drinking session. I always said the same thing, 'Want to call it off? We can roll back into town easy. There's no reason to push it today. I'm going on another training ride tomorrow.'

'Give me another minute here, okay? We got to keep your miles up, bro. I don't want anyone pounding my little brother into the ground.'

When he had finished puking he climbed back on his bike, and

241

ten minutes later he was at the front insisting on pulling me into the wind, while I rested in his draft. If he had put his mind to it, stopped drinking and smoking, slept at night and eased off his other training, he would have ridden me into the ground every time. We turned right and raced along a desolate road until we came to the top of a long hill that looked over the valley in which Graniteville was nestled. On the right, a narrow dirt road ran into the forest to a series of old rock quarries that Wade had shown me.

We rode our bikes carefully into the woods, hid them in the bushes, stripped to our shorts and walked out into the massive pools of bright turquoise water. Wade had explained that a mineral in the earth turned the water that color – it was crystal clear beyond the blue sheen.

We swam out into the blue hole and floated in the water. Those were my best memories with Carl, away from the house, the guns, his ideas of coming wars – just he and I lying on our backs in the middle of the forest on radiant blue water, flipping over and diving to the bottom with our eyes wide open, seeing who could go deepest, then letting our bodies drift back to the surface, flipping onto our backs and floating with our eyes closed as the sun warmed our skin.

The first sanctioned race I attended was in Charlotte, North Carolina. Wade drove me there, registered me and took care of me. The race was a criterium – a one-mile circuit around several blocks at the center of the city to be covered thirty times. When the referee fired the gun the field of a hundred riders sprinted off the line and never let up. I kept waiting for the pace to slacken before the attacks, but it never did. They attacked straight off the starting line, attacked out of every corner and attacked all the way to the finish line.

I was dropped, unable to match the group's pace, ten laps into the race and pulled out by the referee as the leaders were about to lap me. I could hardly face Wade. He kept assuring me it was okay, that I simply had to adjust to the speed and warm up more next time. I had been unprepared for the relentless attacks from the start.

There was no civility, no talking to fellow riders in the first few laps. Nobody even yelled at anyone to pull through to help block the wind up front. They simply attacked and dropped you if you didn't. I realized then that centuries and citizens' races were a thing of the past if I hoped to compete at this level.

It was a two-day race weekend, common on the circuit, Saturday and Sunday, so we left Charlotte early and drove up to Blowing Rock, North Carolina, for the race the following day.

'Don't worry about it,' Wade said. 'They'll be fried from holding that pace through the entire race today. You'll be fresh tomorrow. It'll be your chance now that you know what to expect.'

The Blowing Rock race was smaller. The field was about half the size and the course held on a tighter circuit, but it was the same kind of race, a thirty-lap criterium. Blowing Rock was near a small college town, the racecourse lined with students. This time I warmed up for a full hour before the race and reached the starting line drenched in sweat. When the referee fired the starting pistol I was first off the line and sprinted as hard as I could on the first lap so avoided being swallowed by the field and spat out the back, like I had been in Charlotte. Less than halfway through the second lap the entire field swarmed around me, fighting for position each time we entered a corner, sprinting wildly out of every turn and onto the straightaways, but this time I raced as aggressively as they did, bumping shoulders and not backing down when somebody tried to nudge me out of a turn.

When I'd drifted to about twentieth position I knew I was too far back, especially when I glanced over my shoulder and noticed part of the field was already gone. We weren't even ten laps into the race and attrition was taking its toll. I saw Wade on turn four screaming for me to move up. I fought my way back up through the field until I was around fifth position. I never let myself drift back more than a place or two and never went to the front. The pace didn't let up. Every few laps they'd ring a prime bell, indicating a cash prize on the next lap to the first rider over the line, a tactic organizers used to keep the race animated and the pace high.

I ignored the primes, letting the other riders sprint for them, and concentrated on not getting dropped. By the time the referee announced over the PA system that we had twelve laps to go, I was sure I could finish the race.

My confidence waned when I drifted off the wheel of the rider ahead of me as the pace intensified. I waited for the guy behind me to come around and fill the gap so I could keep a steady pace without sprinting back up. After a couple of seconds nobody came around and I glanced back.

There was nobody behind me. We were a half-lap ahead of the rest of the pack. By clinging to the wheels of the four riders ahead and ignoring the rest of the field, I had made the winning move of the day – a five-man break. I had been concentrating so hard on holding my position and the pace had been so fast that we had drifted off the front without ever really attacking when the guys behind us had let gaps open. At that point I focused on nothing but staying with the riders ahead, ignoring their individual attacks, their jostling for position, their setting up for the final sprint, their attempts to read each other's tactics. I hung on for dear life. With each successive lap they were going faster and faster, like a runaway train with myself as the brakeless caboose. Their speed rose again as we entered the final turn. I came across the line a few seconds behind them in fifth place.

When I found Wade, he was as happy as if I had won. Even though I didn't make any money or bring home a trophy, he still took me out afterward. We ate like kings, ordering the biggest steaks Sizzler sold.

On Monday morning I woke up at seven and rode across town to work. I was still grateful to Mel for giving me the job so I tried to keep my building cleaner than the others to show my appreciation, but some of the janitors had been assigned to their buildings so long that it was impossible to find a stain on the floor or dust on the blinds. I had been hired to replace a man who was fired for sleeping on the job. I cleaned from the time I clocked in until the end of the day, but there was always something I missed.

The college was built on the site of the Augusta Arsenal, whose buildings dated back to 1828. It was proud of its history, and brochures lay around the administrative offices that I was assigned to clean. I picked up a stack and took them home to show Carl since he kept up with military history. The administrative buildings had gone up as a fort and were still surrounded by loop-holed brick walls five feet thick and twenty feet high, with tiny slots cut into them every fifteen feet to stick muskets through and fire at invaders.

When I showed Carl the brochures he read them and dropped them in the trash. 'Never the whole story,' he said. 'Typical government bullshit.' He told me that General Sherman had been stationed at the Augusta Arsenal for six months, in the buildings I cleaned, shortly after graduating from West Point and twenty years before the Civil War. After Georgia had seceded from the Union, the Arsenal became the secondary manufacturer of war materials to the new Confederate Powder Works built downtown alongside the canal – the only buildings constructed by the Confederate States of America. It had produced 30,000 pounds of powder a day and supplied the entire Confederate ground forces throughout the war. 'Back then it was the world's second largest gunpowder manufacturer,' he said. 'Without it the Civil War could have never been fought. The Arsenal and Powder Works made Augusta the ammunition and war materials center of the Confederacy, churning out goods around the clock to maim and murder the North.'

After that, whenever I mopped the floors at the college I thought about what my brother had told me and about the people, from generals to slaves, who had walked down the same hallways I kept polished. I found it odd that a place whose original purpose had been to store and produce materials to kill had been transformed into an institution to educate. I wondered how many of the present students went on to become engineers at the Bomb Plant, the modern equivalent of the old Arsenal. It bothered me that, more than a century after the Civil War had ended, there weren't more black students walking down the halls that their enslaved ancestors had once maintained. I wondered whether anything had changed in Augusta since the Civil Rights movement of the 1960s, less than twenty years earlier. I hadn't grown up there, but the lines were clearly drawn from one neighborhood to the next. No matter how close to the white neighborhoods the blacks lived, their own houses were tiny by comparison.

Around that time I became interested in educating myself, especially since, as an employee there, Augusta College provided the perfect opportunity for me to learn. Each day when I cleaned classrooms, I studied the diagrams and outlines the professors had written on the chalkboards before I took my bucket of water and wiped them clean. Beneath the desks I collected books that students had accidentally left behind and started taking them home to read at night. I sometimes stood silently in the hallway outside a classroom, listening to a professor lecture. I didn't care that they hadn't formally admitted me: I was there, standing among them, listening to their lectures, studying their notes on the chalkboard, trying to make sense of their textbooks late at night. I found a dictionary with a broken binding that I covered with duct tape to hold it together and carried it in my backpack so that whenever I came across a word I didn't know I could look it up.

As the months passed I liked my job even more. I'd wake up early, eager to ride across town and join the students walking through campus. I saw myself as a professional student who had been hired to keep the building clean and paid an hourly wage to absorb the same information that the students paid thousands of dollars to learn. The math classes were beyond my comprehension, with their abstract symbols and enigmatic formulas. The history classes were the most interesting, but more for the lessons they left out than the ones I found outlined on the board and printed on class syllabuses students threw away. When studying the Civil War there was no mention that Augusta was the war-manufacturing center of the South, or when studying the Cold War they never examined Augusta's proximity to one of the largest plutonium production sites in the country. They rarely touched on the genocide of the Indians, who had once lived along the Savannah River. In criminology they studied the disproportionate crime attributed to blacks, but I found no mention of the limited economic opportunities that forced them to seek other ways to find equality with whites.

To my uneducated mind it appeared that for everything they taught there was another block of knowledge that was ignored – rather than systematically suppressed. It was a bit like an old woman with a wart on her nose. She had worked hard her entire life but still couldn't afford to have it removed, so nobody mentioned it.

Wade had taken me to another half-dozen races and though I had yet to claim victory, I had finished among the top ten in all but two. Slowly my presence became known, but less for my consistent results than my odd appearance: I was the only member of the pack whose legs were covered with hair, I wore outdated wool shorts and jerseys and raced a bike whose quality was more appropriate for weekend pleasure rides than elite competition. I was tired of staring at their perfectly shaved legs at each race, the smooth skin revealing every ripple in their calves and quadriceps as they laughed at my over-growth, pointed at my inferior factory-built Motobécane and ridiculed my worn wool clothing in contrast to their shiny Lycra.

My only revenge was making the breakaway in almost every race as ninety percent of the field, on custom bikes, faded off the back. The greatest feeling was in criteriums when our breakaway, a group of four riders, lapped the field and we raced up to the front through the pack of riders on whom we were now one lap up, making it virtually impossible for any of them to place higher than us. When that happened, they never laughed at my clothing or hairy legs.

Once Wade was convinced I was committed to the sport, he took me out and bought me a set of Lycra clothing, thin synthetic shorts that clung to my legs like a second skin, and jerseys made of similar material that absorbed sweat and whisked it away from my chest.

247

We retired my Motobécane and he set me up on one of his old Raleigh racing bikes that hung from the ceiling of his garage.

The first time I shaved my legs they bled like a chicken being plucked alive. I didn't want my brother to see me doing it, so I asked Wade if I could use his bathroom the night before a big race. He gave me a pair of scissors to trim the hair, an electric razor to buzz it closer to the skin and a handful of disposable razors with a can of shaving cream to finish it off. Then he went downstairs to have a sip of my brother's whiskey while he waited. He never told me I had to shave, but he suggested it would reduce wind resistance and make leg massages more practical. He also said that if I crashed and got road rash from sliding across the pavement, hairless legs healed faster and were less prone to infection. What he didn't say – and the main reason I knew I had to do it – was that my peers would never truly consider me a racer until I shaved them clean.

It was far more difficult than I'd imagined. The dip on the back of my leg, behind the knee, was hard to get at while the kneecap, the surrounding bumps and indentations were a constant source of nicks. The skin near my ankle was more delicate than that near the center of the calf and more likely to peel if I pressed the razor too hard. There was also the question of how far up the leg to shave. Cycling shorts came to just above the knee, longer than short pants. Unless you wore only long pants when you weren't cycling it seemed essential to shave higher than the length of tennis shorts, and if you were going to shave that high, why not just finish the thigh where it connected to the torso? Once you reached the torso, new considerations arose. Shaving was an art form and it was difficult not to admire – with furtive glances – anyone with a skilled hand.

When I came downstairs and showed Wade, he raised his glass in a silent toast. His wife, Janet, came in to see how I had done, used to her husband's long-standing habits. She wasn't terribly impressed with the nicks that covered my legs but she seemed to admire my courage.

I knew that Wade was trying to relive his past through me, introducing me to every aspect of racing, and grooming me for victory, but I didn't mind because his past was a future I had not yet experienced – I had never won a major race. Our relationship formed a happy collision of lives moving in two different directions. I usually traveled forward into the unknown to see if I could achieve the elusive victory we chased. He often traveled in reverse, digging through old boxes of bike parts, resurrecting a retired frame that carried memories in its metal tubing that seemed to reappear in his mind when he lifted it down from its hook on the garage ceiling. Our collision seemed to make us both more complete. It made me think back to my father's desire to teach me history that I felt had little to do with me: Wade wanted to teach me a physical action that had everything to do with me. I wanted to win a sanctioned race more than I had wanted anything in the past.

The Graniteville Loop emerged as my primary training ride. I started putting in more miles than Wade could keep up with. I still rode to work and back home, but I also cycled an additional thirty miles, clocking fifty a day on average, often arriving at the house after dark. At first my job inhibited my training, but I soon corrected that by taking my cycling clothes to work, changing before lunch and slipping off campus. Lunch hour was automatically docked from our timecard, so we weren't required to clock out and in at noon and one. I took advantage of this by rolling away through the back parking lot at a quarter till noon to hammer out the Graniteville Loop, which provided the perfect mix of flat terrain, a long climb and a series of rollers on the way back into town. It was the first time I ever consciously took advantage of an employer, working fewer hours than I was paid for. My fitness rose in increments – I could see small but steady improvements in the time-splits I kept for every hill and the gears I pushed over the climbs.

It was around then that I started thinking about Nareesha again. To reach the 13th Street Bridge from Augusta College, I descended Central Avenue to 15th Street and worked my way across town to the bridge to cross into South Carolina and complete my loop. Paine

College stood on 15th Street across from the Medical College of Georgia. I rode past it almost every day, keeping my head down, concentrating on my form, knowing I had to get my miles in and back to campus before my supervisor noticed I was missing.

After a few weeks of passing Paine daily, it became harder to ignore. My life was better than it had been in Albany. I had a good job with benefits, I was competing regularly, rode an expensive racing bike, even if it wasn't mine, dressed in Lycra clothing worth many times the amount I'd ever paid for work clothes, and I was learning even though I wasn't enrolled at the college. I wasn't discouraged that most of what I read was beyond me without the guidance of a teacher, because I was increasing the scope of my knowledge. The physiology classes in particular interested me – I'd pore over the teacher's handouts about glycogen, lactic acid, oxygen uptake, fast- and slow-twitch muscle fibers.

Yet no matter how I tried to occupy my mind, each time I passed Nareesha's school I thought about her, until soon I was thinking about her almost as much as bike racing. I started rolling through campus each time I went out on a lunch-time ride. At first I convinced myself I just wanted to see where she went to school and compare it to Augusta College. But then I was wondering about ridiculous things – like trying to get a job there as a janitor. As she had told me, it was a black college and I stood out whenever I rolled through, but with the Medical College across the street and other businesses nearby it was plausible that I was taking a shortcut. Each time I came through I rode slower, checking out students, hoping to bump into Nareesha. After a couple of weeks' seeing the same people, I started getting strange looks.

One afternoon a security guard who had seen me creeping through dozens of times walked out and asked if he could help me – I had stopped to examine my bike. He caught me at the wrong moment. My mind was fixated on the rim I had just bent jumping over the curb from the street onto the sidewalk. It was one of Wade's most expensive racing wheels and I had damaged it beyond repair. I was trying to figure out how to explain it to Wade when I realized what the man had said, and retorted, 'If I was black you wouldn't be asking that, would you?'

The second the words came out of my mouth, I regretted them. I felt like a racist, spitting in his face, mocking him.

Before he could say anything, I added, 'I didn't mean it like that.'

He turned around and walked away.

I lifted up the front wheel and rolled the bike across campus and out through the parking lot. As I was crossing it, I heard a group of girls returning from lunch, climbing out of a car, laughing. I recognized the laugh. One of the girls looked up and we locked eyes. Nareesha. When she saw me, she fell silent. I didn't know what to say, whether I should just walk by quietly, acting like I didn't know her, or whether I should say hi, acting like our meeting was a random encounter. In the space of a second, I knew I should walk away. I knew I shouldn't say anything. But I didn't want to wonder for the rest of my life if she had been waiting for me to speak and would be hurt if I walked off like she wasn't there. I tried to tear myself away, to have enough willpower to let her go and just be happy I'd seen her again. She had already turned away to get her books out of the car, when I said it.

'Nareesha.'

Another girl looked at me, then turned back to Nareesha. 'You know that guy?'

Nareesha didn't acknowledge her question. 'I'll catch up,' she said. She straightened up, the books in her arms, and marched over to me. She didn't look pleased.

I tried to fill the moment of awkward silence. 'I know I look strange,' I said, touching my cycling clothes. 'I'm on a racing team. I work up at Augusta College.'

She didn't look at my bike, my clothing, or comment on my job. She looked straight into my eyes. 'I told you not to spoil what we had. We had something good. That was a different place, a different time. Appreciate it for what it was, not what it is.'

I didn't have a chance to respond.

She turned around and walked away. She didn't say goodbye.

251

Like a moron, I watched her go, half expecting her to glance back and smile before disappearing around the corner of a building. She never did. I was forced into making comparisons. I was a janitor; I rode a bike to work; I lived in the boonies; I paid half of forty dollars a month for rent; my brother hunted squirrels and made whiskey in the woods. She was in college; she had parents who loved her; she was going to be a doctor. Everything I had accomplished in the last year seemed meaningless, and a hole opened up inside me. I walked up the hill, numb.

Back on campus, I changed into my street clothes, walked over to the Physical Plant, told Mel's secretary I had eaten something at lunch that made me ill and asked if I could go home. I pushed my bike over to Wade's house, sneaked into his garage and hid the damaged wheel behind a bike carton. I grabbed another off a hook and rode across town.

I didn't bother dismounting at the bottom of the hill near the stop sign to keep my bike clean. I rode up the dirt lane, not caring whether or not grit got on the chain. My brother was out when I got to the house, but he appeared less than an hour later. I was lying on my back in the front yard, staring up at the sky.

'What are you doing home?'

'You got any more of that whiskey?'

'What happened?'

'Bent a rim.'

'Looks like somebody wrapped one around your forehead.'

I got up and followed him inside. He dug a half-filled jar out of the cabinet. I asked him to get shot glasses.

'That bad?' he asked.

I took the jar and filled the glass, picked it up, shot it and refilled it.

When he realized I genuinely wanted to drink, he sat down and started pouring shots. We went through the remains of the bottle in less than an hour.

'You got more?'

'Let's take it down to the canal,' he said. He brought another jar

252

out of the bedroom. 'We won't get interrupted by one of my friends coming up here to go out tonight.'

If Carl had a favorite pastime it was drinking, but we never really sat around and shared his love the way we had bonded over cycling. He had never pushed it on me, but I could hear in his voice that he wanted to get drunk with me if I was willing. He knew something had happened, though he didn't try to pull it out of me.

I was already feeling tipsy when we climbed the fence and started across the pasture. I stuck my foot in a gopher hole and smacked my head on the ground.

'Man, you must have really bent the shit out of that rim, bro.' He laughed his stupid laugh.

I staggered behind him across the field and into the woods. We went to a part of the canal he hadn't taken me before. It was further upstream. His private fishing spot. A folding aluminum lawn chair was stashed in the bushes that he pulled out and let me sit in. A fishing pole he had made out of a long branch leaned against a tree and he had hidden a small cache of fishing line, hooks, lead weights and a shovel to dig up earthworms.

'Where's that knife with the compass on top?' I asked.

'What are you talking about?'

'Remember up in Indiana? Our canoe trips?'

'I don't live in the past,' he said. 'Not worth it.'

'What do you think about?'

'The future.'

'I mean besides wars. What other future?'

'All the places I'll go when I leave here.'

He opened the whiskey jar and handed it to me.

'How are you going to get there?'

'The FFL.'

'The FF what?'

'I told you before, the French Foreign Legion.'

I didn't want him to start talking about Armageddon, so I fell silent and stared across the canal into the woods on the other side. I was only talking to get my mind off Nareesha. I didn't care about his knife or whether he wanted to join the FFL or live like Daniel Boone for the rest of his life. We drank in silence, lost in our separate worlds. The alcohol took control of me. I closed my eyes and let my head hang back, then climbed out of the chair and onto the ground where my brother was sitting. He held out the bottle. I took another drink.

The ground was spinning. I closed one eye to see Carl clearly. My hearing was playing tricks on me. His voice came and went. I couldn't hear him properly but I could see him laughing at me. He pointed and held out the bottle for me to take another round. I reached for it. My body went limp and then I felt tears running down my face and onto my shirt, but I didn't feel bad. I didn't feel anything except the alcohol coursing through me. I tried to sit up. I reached for the bottle again, but my hand kept grabbing air and falling to the ground. My brother clasped my hand and pulled me over to him. I lay down at his side. He slipped his arm around me and held me close to him. I wiped my face. There was grit in my mouth and dirt stuck to the tears on my face. My brother rubbed my chest and whispered into my ear, 'We were born to hurt. It makes us stronger. It separates and bonds us. We were born to hurt and born to die. There's no use holding it back. Embrace it, little bro. It'll make you whole. It'll make you stronger.'

The next morning I awoke under the bright sun to the sound of insects humming in the bushes and the sight of my brother sitting a few feet away fishing in the canal, glancing back to see if I was okay. When he saw me open my eyes, he pulled up a stringer of fish and held them in the air. 'Breakfast.'

Then he held up the last sip of whiskey, swishing it around the bottom of the jar. 'Coffee.'

He finished it off, then turned back to the canal to check his bobber and slung the empty jar out into middle of the canal. It floated for a time, swirling in an eddy, then took on water, bubbled and disappeared below the surface.

I rolled onto my back, closed my eyes and let the sun warm my face. I could still taste dirt in my mouth but I didn't try to spit it out. *We were born to hurt*, I heard him whisper in my ear. *We were born to hurt. Embrace it and it'll make you stronger.*

Macon, Charleston, Savannah, Atlanta, Chattanooga, Birmingham, Memphis, Winston-Salem, Greensboro, Durham, Tallahassee. On weekends Wade drove me all over the southeast to races in which he had once competed. We'd finish up our workday on Friday afternoon, meet at his house that evening and pack the car. Then he'd drive out and pick me up around five in the morning on Saturday to drive four or five hours to the races. Sometimes we slept at camp grounds on Saturday night, occasionally he rented a hotel room, but most of the time hosts let us stay in their homes, aging racers like Wade. He briefed me on the particulars of each racecourse on the drive: 'Slight rise on the back, fast off-camber descent out of the fourth corner, loose gravel if the course isn't swept, straight flat finish.' He talked about where the attacks would likely be launched, who to watch out for, my strengths and weaknesses in relation to the course. I continued to break the top ten at every race if I didn't crash or flat. My highest placing was third in a three-man break and sixth in a field sprint.

While I was considered a motor, a person who could stay on top of a big gear and wear out the competition, sprinting was not my forte. I had raw power and acceleration, I could attack and bridge a gap, but when it came down to the final two hundred meters the pure sprinters with their explosive burst over ten seconds defeated me every time. I began to race more aggressively, going to the front and pulling, launching attacks and living by every athlete's motto: 'No pain, no gain.'

The more I hurt, the more I knew everyone else hurt – and the harder I pushed it once I started hurting, the sooner I knew my competitors would snap. It was a psychological game. They had no way of knowing if I hurt as bad as they did and was simply bluffing, but when I increased the pace at such moments it made them think I still had more in me, even though I was on the verge of cracking.

When successful, I'd immediately establish a gap with a few other riders who were able to withstand the pain. By then I had learned how to blow apart the field and narrow the competition down to a select group of riders – usually the same ones. But approaching the line with three or four other guys, I usually came in last. Nonetheless, my results in the breakaways were still among the highest places in the race and I was known to work hard to establish those breaks. Racers, coaches and sponsors became aware of my presence.

At the Palmetto State Games, the criterium championships for South Carolina, I made the lead break of six riders early in the race. We were evenly matched and rotated through the paceline, taking our turns pulling into the wind. Our momentum was so fast that we came up on the back of the field at the halfway mark and looked at each other, communicating silently, and jetted into the field, attacking again to take another lap out of them for the hell of it. Lapping the field was the ultimate form of domination. By the time we were a lap and a half up on them, the referee held up the five-to-go card and we started watching each other closely. Winning solo was considered the most prestigious but most difficult victory and to do so you had to launch your attack close enough to the end that you could hold the gap while avoiding being swallowed when the riders behind you started to sprint.

I marked the riders I felt were dangerous – the riders who might attack and try to win solo with one or two laps to go. These attacks were known as flyers – where you attacked the other riders and flew solo off the front and hoped to God you didn't crash or blow up before you reached the finish line. Most flyers were suicide missions, but you never knew for sure without trying, and in bicycle racing it was better to die trying to win than accepting your fate and being defeated.

With three laps to go the strongest rider in the group took a flyer and we all chased him down, quickly reeling him in. As we caught him, with two laps to go, another rider unexpectedly counter-attacked and took another flyer, forcing us to chase furiously to pull him back before the bell lap – the final lap.

256

Right as we came up on him, he looked round, knowing he was doomed, and backed off so he'd still have something left for the sprint. As he slowed there was a momentary pause as we caught our breath and tried to force somebody to the front and pull – to their disadvantage – into the final section of the race. Acting purely on instinct, I attacked at the exact moment the other riders paused. I flew past the guy still dangling off the front and got a gap on my competitors. From there it was a grind to the line. I put my head down, dropped into the biggest gear and wound it up so fast that it was hard to hold my line going into the final turn. Quickly recovering, I looked under my arms to make sure I still had a gap – it had increased – and cranked out the last section of the course, rolling across the line solo, punching the air with my right fist in victory.

If riding bikes was addictive and racing was like a drug, winning made cocaine seem like watery coffee, angel dust a sugar rush. I was on fire as I crossed the line in first place. It was like flipping a switch. Second place might as well be last. The difference between winning and losing. All of my past third, fourth, fifth and sixth placings were meaningless now that I'd won. That day I learned that there was a chasm between making the breakaway and coming to the line within feet of the winner, and that it was impossible to know this until you had won. And once you'd tasted victory – unless it was a fluke and you had won due to another rider's error – it suddenly became hard not to win every time.

I soloed to victory in the next two races. My trademark move was turning on the turbo-jets with one lap to go and making toast of the sprinters as they tried bridging back up to me before the finish, leaving them vying for second place. Once they wised up to that move, I had to attack earlier and try to solo in from two or three laps out. After a while it got harder to win, because everybody in the race tracked my every move and raced against me, instead of me racing against the rest of the field. But by then I had enough victories under my belt for a sponsor to approach me – a distributor of Italian racing bikes owned by a man named Craig based in

Columbia, South Carolina. He wanted me to move to Columbia and race with a team he was building.

'You'll have some of the fastest riders in the field working for you,' he said.

The only team I had ever ridden for was Wade's and mine, which wasn't really a team. It was a devoted mentor and his protégé. We both knew that for me to reach the next level and win bigger races, I needed to join a real team. Wade and I had never thought beyond winning a few races. Whether it was because neither of us truly believed I would reach this point or we were just too caught up in the moment, I can't say. He took me racing because he loved and missed it. I had gone along with him because it was fun, it gave me someone to hang out with, it took my mind off things I didn't want to think about, and it made me feel good about myself. Along the way I discovered I had a natural athletic ability. But that was as far as it went.

When the opportunity presented itself that required me to move away, I hesitated. I had laid roots in Augusta. I had a good job, Mel was like the grandfather I'd never had, looking out for my life far into the future, and Wade provided the stable home in which I felt welcomed. I wasn't sure I wanted to give that up to go out on the road, sleeping in vans and on strangers' beds, searching for elusive victories to satisfy my cravings.

Craig said he'd keep a slot open for me and asked me to make my decision within two weeks. When he invited me to join the team we were headed into the heat of the summer and a lull in the racing season in the southeast. We never discussed benefits or pay or housing. There wasn't any money in cycling: it was an underground or minor sport with little coverage. The people who raced did so because they loved it. The people who sponsored teams did so because they had made enough money to give some to the sport they loved. It was a losing proposition from a sponsor's point of view, but that didn't stop people like Craig founding teams. A few riders got stipends from the national team to hold them over between Olympic years, but the amount was negligible. I could tell from the car Craig drove and the bikes he distributed, which were popular on the racing circuit, that he had made a lot of money.

I didn't get back to him within the two weeks he had given me, and since there weren't any races coming up for the remainder of the month, I never saw him out on the circuit again that summer. Instead of deciding right away, I went out on long rides by myself, meditating on different outcomes and trying to work out what I ultimately wanted from life. It was the first time I had consciously set out to consider long-term goals and to come up with a plan for my life other than freedom. I explored new roads I had never been on and found new training rides. I wasn't concerned that I hadn't responded to Craig: I felt confident that if I decided to join his team, he'd take me. There weren't many other riders in the southeast who were capable of winning and the ones who could were already affiliated with other teams. Above all, I wanted to be sure I was making the right decision. And I wasn't sure I could win consistently with a sponsor breathing down my neck. I needed to go out and hammer some hills alone, see if I could notch it up to the next level before I committed to having people sacrifice their own chances at victory to race for me. As the competition became more elite, riders would work for me early in the race and I would no longer race on my own in an attempt to win.

I spent a few weeks timing myself on various hills, but still hadn't found a training ride that I felt truly tested my abilities. There weren't any mountains around Augusta so I had to be content with launching myself up the steepest hills. Wade took me back to the Bomb Plant Ride, near the Savannah River Site nuclear facility that we hadn't been to since we'd first met and timed me over the ten-mile time-trial course. The last time we had been there I had come in at just over twenty-four minutes. This time he stopped the clock at twenty-one minutes and eight seconds on a regular training bike.

'I'll mortgage my house myself and sponsor you, if you can maintain that,' he said. 'You're flying.'

259

He was excited. I was nervous. Maybe it had been a fluke. Maybe the wind had been behind me on the way out, then turned somehow and pushed me back. I didn't want to be pressured, so Wade left me alone while I went out into the hills each day, searching for the answer.

In the process I discovered a ride that neither my brother nor Wade knew about, even though it was only a few miles into South Carolina over the Furys Ferry Road Bridge. Whenever we went out that way we were always racing for the lake to cross the dam and snake through the country roads along its shores. At the top of the climb beyond the river, the road swerved to the left and followed a high plateau through the forest until it reached the road to the dam. As it veered to the left, I saw a narrow makeshift road off to my right, cutting at an angle back into the forest. It was surfaced with gravel and sealed with a coat of tar. My arms rattled so much as I turned onto it and entered the forest that it was difficult holding onto the bars, but I continued, curious as to where it might lead and more interested in an adventure than putting in miles that day.

Less than two miles on, I came to an abandoned fire tower in the middle of the forest. A tall chain-link fence encircled its base with an old rusted sign that said 'No Trespassing.' The top of the fencing was bent down in places where people had climbed over the top. It looked like a giant metallic redwood tree towering over the surrounding forest. At the top there was a small room that the lookout had occupied. I still wanted to see where the road led or if it simply disappeared as it joined logging roads within the vast forest, but I decided to climb the tower on the way back.

Further down the road I came to a vista and the forest opened up. I saw the narrow road descending through the trees below and took off down the hill, cranking my biggest gear, pretending I was at the front of a race, flying through the woods with a pack of a hundred riders chasing me. The road swooped and swerved deeper into the forest, no houses or other buildings along the way. Eventually it flattened out and passed through a swampy area, then over a small bridge.

I turned and rolled back across the bridge toward the climbs I had just descended. I picked up momentum and switched to the big chain ring, even though a series of stair-step climbs loomed ahead that would normally have required small gears to scale. The resistance of the rough road made it harder to ride fast, but I wanted to find out how strong I was. I got on top of the gear and started picking up speed. When I came to the first stair-step, I stood up and hammered over the rise without shifting down, regained my momentum at the crest and stomped over the next climb, one right after the next, until I came to the final short steep wall where I had stopped and looked down into the forest after passing the fire tower. I dug deep, raced to the bottom, stood up and threw my bike back and forth as I pushed an enormous gear over its crest. When I reached the top there was no doubt in my mind: I knew I could go to Columbia with confidence and lead the team without worrying whether or not I was strong enough.

But by the time I got back to the fire tower, I was thinking about all the rides around Augusta and my positive memories from the previous year. I leaned my bike up against the fence and slipped my fingers through the chain link, climbed to the top and dropped down on the inside. A narrow flight of stairs within the exposed frame zigzagged to the top. I was less than a quarter of the way up when I became frightened – the rails holding the stairs in place were thin and narrow. I convinced myself that numerous people had climbed them before and continued up, at first surrounded by trees and then rising above the forest, clearing the treetops, holding tightly to the handrails in case my feet slipped.

The trapdoor entering the small room at the top was padlocked. I sat down on the narrow steps beneath it to rest. On the Carolina side there was an endless panorama of pine trees. Looking toward Georgia, the Savannah River snaked through the forest heading into downtown. I had never been so high in the air or seen such a wide-open view of wilderness. I thought again about Columbia, living in the middle of a busy city and traveling wearily from town to town to race.

A breeze passed over the top of the forest below me and the tips of the pines shimmered. I noticed the red clay banks cut into the hillside and vast blankets of kudzu growing out over the canopy. A hawk swooped by at eye-level, gliding out toward the river.

Up there, I decided I didn't want to leave Augusta. It didn't matter how strong I was or how well I rode, I wanted to make Augusta my home. I didn't want to return to a transient life or give up a secure job. It didn't matter if I passed Nareesha in the mall one day with a new boyfriend or if I went to the hospital and she turned out to be the doctor who examined me. I had been through more in life than losing a girlfriend. I had already learned more in Augusta than anyplace before and I didn't want to risk leaving it behind.

It was late Friday afternoon when I returned from my ride. I decided to wait until Sunday morning before I told Wade of my decision. My brother was out, as he always was on Friday and Saturday nights now. At least he and his friends hadn't gathered around the kitchen table to get drunk. I flipped through the collection of textbooks I had carried home from the college. Most were still beyond my comprehension, written in a cryptic language or the Latin terms in which biology was described, but that didn't stop me studying them. I figured that if I spent long enough I'd slowly unlock their secrets.

I liked the idea of educating myself: I was able to direct my course of study without adhering to the narrow requirements of college. I had even learned a new term that described the process by which I learned: autodidacticism. Self-education. I'd read about it in the college library and learned that most teachers looked down on it because they felt self-educated people learned in a scattershot fashion, absorbing anything they could get their hands on, rather than systematically. I wondered if it was really so bad to learn on your own, especially if you couldn't get admitted into the learning factories. I found it ironic that many of the people they studied and much of the knowledge they focused on was developed by autodidacts like Thomas Edison, Benjamin Franklin, Abraham Lincoln and Socrates. But, even so, I still fantasized about being formally enrolled in college and learning alongside other students. I envied them.

I fell into a deep sleep. I was dreaming that I had been admitted into Augusta College after building up a library of lost textbooks when I was awakened by a loud crash.

I sat up in bed.

A wave of fear passed through me. Was someone breaking in? Then I heard my bike hit the floor and my brother moaning. I heard him stand and pick up the bike, then another crash. I flung off my blankets and went to rescue the bike. When I walked into the living room, Carl was lying on the floor, clutching his shoulder. I saw blood on his hand, then a large splotch at the center of his shirt and droplets on his forearms. I panicked and dragged him into the middle of the room. He kept trying to get up, but I held him down, telling him to take it easy. I tried to pull his shirt over his head, but I couldn't get it off. There was blood everywhere.

My mind raced. How could I get him to the hospital? Where was the nearest phone? We didn't even have a street address – how would the ambulance find us? I wanted to see how badly injured he was. He struggled with me, but I finally I got his shirt off and ran my hand across his chest and down his stomach looking for an incision or bullet hole.

There was nothing. His face wasn't beaten either. I rolled him over, but I couldn't find any injury on his back. I searched carefully around his chest and under his arms, to make sure I hadn't missed anything. He was exhausted and lay staring at the ceiling, waiting for me to finish. I couldn't find anything. There was hardly any blood on his pants, other than what had dripped down from his shirt, so I didn't take them off. I lay on the floor beside him.

'What happened?' I asked.

He didn't look at me or answer. I asked him again, but he still didn't say anything. He leaned up, got his balance and started to stand. I tried to help him, but he shouted, 'Get away from me.'

I backed off. He stumbled out of the living room, through the kitchen and into his bedroom, slamming the door behind him. His torn, bloody shirt lay in the middle of the room. I stared at it, then went into the kitchen to wash the blood off my hands and arms.

I walked back through the living room, went into my bedroom and lay on the bed. I was wide awake. My mind was still racing, the alarm clock ticking loudly in the background. I lay awake all night, watching the sky through the window turn slowly from black to faint blue as dawn bled into day. I lay there without moving until the sun shone and I had to change position to keep it from shining in my eyes. But I still didn't get up. I waited until I heard my brother stir. I heard him walk into the living room, then back into the kitchen. I waited a while longer, then cracked open my door and walked quietly out into the living room. His shirt was gone, but there was still blood on the floor, more brown or black than red now. I went into the kitchen. Carl was sitting at the table, his head in his hands. The shirt lay on the floor beside him. His handgun was in the middle of the table. He looked up at me standing in the doorway. We both remained silent a long time.

When I turned to leave him, he said, 'You gotta help me take care of this. We gotta get this place cleaned up.'

I went outside and sat on the front steps. I heard him in the kitchen filling a bucket with water. He carried it into the living room and set it on the floor, then came to the front door, and said, 'Come on, bro. This can't wait. I'll go get everything ready while you clean the living room.' There was still blood on his forearms. He disappeared into his bedroom.

I looked at the bucket with a rag hanging out of it and my bike leaning up against the wall. I noticed a spot of blood on the seat tube where he had tried to pick it up last night. I stood up, grabbed the rag and scrubbed the bike down. At first I was angry, then resigned. I couldn't think straight. I cleaned the living-room floor in circular patterns, like I did at work, from baseboard to baseboard, then took the bucket out into the yard and dumped it in the bushes.

When I started back up the front steps, Carl appeared in the doorway with a sheet slung over his shoulder, stuffed with all the clothes he'd been wearing the night before. He saw the rag in the bucket. 'Give me that,' he said.

I handed it to him.

He tucked it into an opening in the sheet. 'Get your sheets,' he said.

'For what?'

'Get them. I don't have time for this.'

I went into my room and pulled them off the bed.

'Run out to the gate and see if there's anybody around the stables.'

I did as I'd been told. I didn't see anyone. I motioned to him. He came across the yard and we climbed the fence into the pasture. He adjusted the sheets hanging over his shoulder by grabbing all four corners to make a bag and we set off across the field. We hiked to the same place alongside the canal he had brought me the night we got drunk. He set the bundle of clothes down, pulled out his handgun and laid it on the ground, kneeling beside it, disassembling it piece by piece. As he took it apart I caught a faint whiff of burned gunpowder combined with the smell of the gun oil he used to wipe it down. He put each part on the ground, until the only thing left in his hand was the handgrip and receiver – the shell of the gun without its barrel, hammer, slider or any other component attached to it. I noticed the words Sig Sauer P226 on the black slide assembly he had tossed to the ground near my knee. I didn't touch it. He looked out at the water, back at the receiver, then slung it into the center of the canal as hard as he could. It made a small plop and disappeared.

He picked up each piece one at a time, turned them over in his hand and threw them into the water, until all that remained was the barrel and the magazine of bullets. He picked up the barrel first, peered through it at the canal, then tossed it in. He ejected the bullets from the magazine with his thumb and threw them into the canal one at a time. Finally he picked up the magazine and flung it after them.

Then he walked to the edge of the clearing, collected a stack of sticks and built a small fire. We sat there until a bed of embers glowed at its base. He added more wood, then dropped his clothing into the flames, making sure not to smother the blaze.

'I'm going into town tomorrow to make some phone calls,' he said. 'One of my buddies from the army lives out in Waynesboro. He can set me up until I leave for the FFL. You need to think about moving out of the house.' He said something about shipping out to Angola or some other place I had never heard of.

I was torn. This was the person who had introduced me to cycling. The person who had essentially given me freedom – the same freedom I had traveled for years to find. Now he had shackled me with the unstated knowledge that he had possibly killed somebody. I had seen him come home drunk in the middle of the night with blood splattered on him. I had walked beside him to the canal and watched him disassemble his favorite gun and toss it into the water. I had watched him burn his bloodstained clothes. Whatever had happened, I alone could solve the crime for the police.

But in doing so I would lock up the person who had freed me. I didn't agree with his worldviews – I had listened to them endlessly, as I had to my father when he'd rambled on about German-Americans. On my long rides through the countryside I had often thought about the things my brother told me. His beliefs had slowly made me despise whites and everything we stood for. I wasn't convinced that nonwhites would one day persecute us the way the Germans had persecuted the Jews, but I had decided that if his paranoid fantasies ever proved true I would never defend myself. How could I defend the behavior of my ancestors? At the same time I couldn't prosecute whites, no matter how much I rejected them. I certainly couldn't bring myself to turn in my own brother. He had helped me find myself. There would be no heroic outcome for me. Heroic deeds belonged to my ancestors, when they had conquered and settled new lands, and – if my brother's prophesies proved true – to the future people who redeemed their ancestors' defeats. At that moment in history we were lost. It didn't matter whether Carl went off to another country to fight with a foreign army or not. Our dreams lay not in the future but buried deep in the past.

* * *

266

The following morning I rode out to Fire Tower Road again. I rolled past the tower and descended the rough road into the forest. The sun was high overhead but the forest seemed darker than yesterday as I raced down through the trees. I turned on the bridge without stopping and started back up the road at full speed, racing for the climbs to burn the fear and frustration out of my body. My mind was someplace else. I didn't feel the hills. I hit them harder and faster than I had before, thrashing my bike up the climbs. I let out a scream as I came over the top of a sharp rise and a flock of birds rose out of a tree beside the road and disappeared into the forest.

When I reached the fire tower again, I flung my bike against the fence and yelled. I climbed over and scaled the narrow metal stairs with less caution than the day before. When I reached the top, I leaned my chest against the railing and beat my fist against the trapdoor above me. My foot slipped. I clung to the railing and looked down at the long drop below me. The trapdoor was too heavy to break through. I looked down again and my head spun – but I didn't have enough balls to try to kill myself, too frightened I might land on the ground alive, paralyzed and unable to move. I noticed a section of clear-cut trees I hadn't spotted the day before and another small clearing near the bridge where people had dumped trash for years.

I gazed out at the river snaking through the forest, flowing through Augusta and past the Savannah River Site that was churning out war-grade plutonium, past the remains of the Confederate Powder Works alongside the canal. How could General Sherman have marched all the way from Atlanta to the sea, I wondered, without passing through Augusta and burning it to the ground like he did every other place? It had been practically on his way and it had provided the Confederate Army with the explosives that had killed countless Union troops. If there had been anyplace that had deserved to be destroyed it would have been the factories in Augusta. Perhaps Carl had been right when he'd told me – on the day I had given him the brochure – that Sherman had probably avoided Augusta because he had good memories of staying there in his youth: he knew several members of its upper class through his parents' political connections. He had known he could defeat the South without decimating Augusta so instead he had followed a path through the center of the state, wrecking inconsequential towns along the way. I wondered how many events throughout history had been shaped by one individual's memories of a single place, either good or bad, that had compelled them to spare or destroy it. How else could Augusta have emerged from the Civil War more prosperous than it had been at the start?

Augusta, with its Master's golf tournament, was the quintessential peaceful southern town, its blooming azaleas beaming out across the globe each spring during the televised tournament. As peaceful and quaint a place as it projected itself to be, much of its economic foundation was rooted in developing weapons of mass destruction and enslaving people to work plantations. I decided then that I would go to Columbia to join the team as soon as I could find a ride out of town. I looked back at the river. I saw a tiny island near the center that reminded me of the night Carl and I had slept suspended above the current. I wondered if the hammocks were still hanging in the trees.

I climbed down, picked up my bike and spun the wheels to see if I had damaged them, then headed back into town. I couldn't ride fast enough to burn all the pent-up energy inside me. I wondered if there would ever come a day when my future wouldn't turn on a dime and slam me into the ground. I could stand up. I could be life's punching bag if that was my fate, but if there were a God out there, I prayed he would show me a different route eventually. He had to. I no longer had anybody else to turn to.

When I got back to the house an El Camino was parked out front and a man over six feet tall stood on the front steps watching me approach. I could tell by the way he stood – his posture casual and erect at the same time – that he had been in the Special Forces and had come to pick up my brother. He let out some sort of call with his tongue and lips that I'd never heard before to alert my brother to my arrival. Carl appeared at his side. 'My little bro,' he said. 'We'll be back in a minute.'

He came over to me, took the bike and leaned it up against the bushes. 'Let's take a walk,' he said.

I pointed down at my cycling shoes.

'We're not going far.'

We walked to the fence, climbed over and stood on the other side in the pasture. For a while he didn't say anything, looking out at the rolling hills that fell away and entered the forest.

'I want you to move on. I don't want you out here alone. I'm leaving in less than an hour. I'm not coming back. I'm sure your buddy Wade will put you up while you figure it out.'

'I already got it figured. I'm going to Columbia.'

We fell silent.

'This isn't the way I planned to end my stay in Augusta,' he finally said. 'I don't want to go into details, but sometimes people push you. I thought we'd get our moment in the sun here, but some shit had to come my way like usual.'

Out of the corner of my eye I saw him look out across the pasture to the edge of the woods, beyond which flowed the canal and the river. 'We tore this motherfucker up. The army and the Arabs together would have had trouble penetrating our training ground. Take *that* on the road. If somebody is hurting in a race, grind them into the ground.'

I glanced at him. 'They're already dead.'

He wrapped his arms around me and hugged me. His muscular chest pressed against my thinner body. He held me for a while longer. 'I'm sorry for bringing you into my world. You were the last person I ever expected to walk out of the dead and back into my life.'

We went to the house and I sat in my room with the door closed, staring at the small library of books I had brought home from the college and arranged alphabetically on my shelf. I listened to my brother's friend helping him carry some stuff out to the car and load it into the back. I put the little bit of clothing I owned and my work boots into a backpack and set it near the bedroom door. Once they were finished, my brother knocked on the door, opened it and peered in.

'We gotta clear out. I don't want you here alone.' He looked across the room at the neatly organized bookshelf. 'You want those? We can load them up and drive them to Wade's.'

'No, I'll leave them here. Too heavy to haul from place to place.'

'You sure?'

'Yeah, I'm sure.'

'Then grab your bag and clear out. Head down the road. We're going to hang out here a minute. I'll catch up with you near Washington Road to say bye again.'

I slipped the pack onto my back, walked out of the front door and down the steps to my bike, still leaning against the bushes. I mounted it to start rolling down the hill. They came outside to get something from the car. When I reached the railroad tracks, I dismounted and pushed my bike across to avoid getting a flat or one of the skinny tires slipping between the rails to send me crashing to the ground with the extra weight on my back. Once I'd cleared them, I stopped and looked up the hill one last time. Nobody was around the stables, and the horses were all out in the pasture together, running in a herd down in one of the lower meadows. From where I stood, the farm seemed abandoned. Beyond the stables, obscured by the hilltop, I saw a small plume of smoke rise near where our farmhouse was hidden. I climbed back on my bike and rode as hard as I could up the hill. I wanted out of there.

When I was near Washington Road, the El Camino pulled up beside me. My brother grabbed my hand as I rolled beside the car toward a stop sign. 'I love you, man.'

I nodded, awkward in front of his friend.

They pulled out into the flow of traffic and disappeared. I waited for a clearing and sprinted across to another side street and worked my way through town. When I reached Wade's house, he was in the driveway washing his car. We made small talk for a while and I helped him dry off his car, then asked him to drive me to Columbia.

'It'll only take you a little over an hour to get there,' I said. 'You'll be back home in time for dinner.'

'What are you talking about?'

'I made my decision.'

He looked at my backpack. 'Come on, spend the night. Let's talk about it. You can't just up and go like that. You need to give it some serious thought.'

'I have. I can go down to the bus station if you're busy.'

'Of course I can take you. You're catching me off guard here.'

We had been friends long enough that he knew once I'd got something in my mind there was no changing it. He started to say something, then stopped himself.

'I'll tell you what,' he said. 'I'll take you on one condition. If you join Craig's team, you don't stop there. You owe him nothing.'

'I'm not stopping there.'

He went in to talk to his wife. I walked into his garage and changed out of my cycling gear into street clothes. I hung his Raleigh on a bike hook, returning it to him. I saw my Motobécane resting at the back of his garage, too worn to race at the elite level. I didn't even go to take a closer look. We drove out on Walton Way, up Wheeler Road and merged onto Interstate 20. I leaned back in my seat as he picked up speed. I hadn't called Craig to tell him I was on my way to accept his offer. Nobody at Augusta College had any idea I wouldn't be back. I wasn't going back to collect my final paycheck or the money they had withheld for retirement. I was on my way, as I had always been.

There were things I loved about Augusta and things I hated, I thought, as we crossed the river and entered South Carolina on the same bridge my brother and I had once struggled to reach from the river below. As we started up a small hill on the Carolina side of the river, I knew from previous trips that, once we descended the other side, the bridge and Georgia would disappear behind us. The state had created the person I was, nearly destroyed me, then challenged me to rise again. I refused to bow to it or even look back when we crested the rise and started down the other side to continue east, but I would always respect the place I had come to see as home, even as I left it behind with no plans to return.

271

BOOK VI

Five Points

We drove into Columbia early on Sunday evening. I knew from the racers I'd met on the circuit that Craig would probably be around his shop. Even if he wasn't there, I could hang around until he showed up on Monday morning. I had been on the street for longer than a night before. Craig was more successful than Wade, but Wade disliked everything about him. On the drive he told me that when they were both in their late twenties they had escaped the field in a two-man break at the Carolina Cup – a prestigious race – with five laps to go. They were equally matched sprinters so they had settled on it being a toss-up – until the last corner when Craig had glanced down at Wade's rear tire and shouted, 'Looks like it's going flat.' Wade looked down at the moment Craig attacked and opened a gap that he couldn't close before they reached the finish line. Craig glanced back with a sly smile and threw both hands in the air to claim the coveted silver cup.

'I was so disgusted, I didn't bother stepping up on the podium to accept my second-place medal.'

They had seen each other at races dozens of times since, and Craig had seen me with Wade, but they had never spoken again. Wade told me it was part of sports, part of life.

'You don't have to like your competitors and they don't have to play fair.'

He knew Craig had more money than any other sponsor in Georgia or South Carolina so he didn't try to persuade me against him, but I realized as we drove into town and he became silent that he expected me to keep my promise not to stop here.

We drove slowly past Craig's shop and, sure enough, there he was near the back sitting at a truing stand, spinning a wheel and twisting its spokes with one hand while lifting a beer with the other. Another man sat on a stool nearby, laughing at something he said, and a woman held a hand over her mouth. Wade drove around the block. I asked him if he thought Craig would set me up on a new bike. I had known as I hung up the Raleigh he had lent me that he'd never let me take it to Columbia for Craig's benefit.

'He'll give you a bike,' he said. 'You'll be outfitted by tomorrow night if he wants to keep you in shape. That's what sponsorship's about.' He dropped me off curbside with my backpack.

I stood on the sidewalk, watching him drive away, thinking of how much effort he had selflessly devoted to helping me succeed, before picking up my backpack and walking to the shop. I took a deep breath and turned the door handle. It was locked. A bell on the other side of the door rattled when I shook it and they looked up. Craig set his beer down and came to open it. At first he didn't recognize me – he had never seen me without cycling clothes on.

'I came over to accept your offer.'

He glanced over my shoulder, seeing if there was anybody with me, or if I had a car parked out front, then looked at the bag slung over my shoulder. A mild expression of shock crossed his face when he grasped that I hadn't come over to talk to him, that I had arrived unannounced on his doorstep to live. He looked out into the street again. 'Did you bring a bike or anything? Sleeping bag?'

I shrugged my shoulders.

For all Craig's cutthroat tactics, which Wade had warned me about, I saw another side of him: he knew how to roll with whatever he was dealt. He hardly missed a beat once he understood that he'd be putting a roof over my head and feeding me from the word go, and this had all occurred to him before he had walked across the room to introduce me to his company. Bike racers had always been gypsies: it was part of the sport – he knew it as well as anyone.

'I hope you don't mind sleeping on the floor in the back between bike boxes.'

'Anywhere's fine.'

He introduced me to Sally, an athlete and apparently his girlfriend, before turning to the other man and introducing me more formally by my full name. Then he turned to me and said, 'Treat Janek right. He's the one who keeps the bikes up and running.'

As soon as Craig finished speaking, Janek took my hand, shook it and repeated my last name. 'Malessa?'

'I prefer Sam.'

'Polish?'

'Not exactly. My father's from there. It was split between Russia and Poland – East Prussia.'

'*Prusy Wschodnie*? It's exact place I'm from. My mother lives there.' Then he returned to my name. 'You know Emilia?'

'No, I don't think so.'

'Emilia Malessa – member of *Armia Krajowa*. How you say it in English?' He paused to translate it in his head. 'Polish Home Army. She fought in Warsaw uprising like my father. Order Virtuti Militari.' He reached into his shirt and pulled out a medal affixed to a leather cord. 'Virtuti Militari. My father's,' he said.

I didn't dare touch the similarly shaped Iron Cross hidden beneath my shirt. My head felt light, then heavy with the information that flooded my mind from the research Dr. Neuman had helped me with when he was trying to convince me to come to terms with my past. There were maybe eight hundred Malessas in the world, but I was never sure if any or all of them were related and had decided before leaving Relativity that I didn't want to know any more about the few who lived scattered around the world – a Lithuanian family of Balt Prussians, a clan of Ethiopian Jews, several ministers in Germany, a group of snowmobile mechanics in Wisconsin, members of a secretive Bavarian village thought to hide Nazis in the Andean foothills of Chile, a community of farmers in Manitoba, a South African precious stones dealer and now a member of the Nazi resistance movement in Poland.

I was confused. I had a hard time finding something to say. He was waiting. I became frightened that he might be angry if he knew my origin. I complimented his medal, turning it back and forth in my hand at his insistence. He was full of energy now, more so than when he'd first heard my name. He slapped me on the back.

'I'm American,' I said. 'I don't really—'

He cut me off. 'American, too. Soon. We celebrate tonight. I buy.'

'Looks like you found a new friend,' Craig said. 'Sally and I are heading out. We'll leave you two alone. Get Sam some bedding, Janek, and lock up before you leave.'

'He stay with me tonight. My guest.'

Craig picked up his keys and wallet from the truing stand and put them into his pocket. 'You two have a good time,' he said. 'I'm glad you decided to come, Sam. You won't regret it.'

Before Craig left, he pulled out a large roll of cash, peeled off several bills and handed them to Janek. When he saw me staring at the money, he said, 'What are you looking at? He earned it. I'll start paying you when you earn it.'

Janek and I stepped out onto the dark sidewalk in front of the shop. He locked the deadbolt. Within a couple of blocks the sidewalks were filled with people. A discernable energy was in the air that I later came to see as associated with every city that was home to a major university – where races were often staged. The University of South Carolina was a few blocks up the hill and its students flooded out into the section of town where Janek took me to meet a group of his friends.

When we reached the bar it was so packed that we had to push our way inside. He told me to wait while he merged into the massing bodies to see if they had arrived. A few minutes later he was back at my side, 'Come, come.' I followed him through the crowd. They were pressed close together near the rear corner of the bar, close enough to be able to shout orders to the bartender, whom they knew. Janek introduced me as 'Mr. Malessa.' Most of them had a beer in hand, but with my arrival Janek insisted on a round of vodka, his treat. Once it had been poured and we were all holding our glasses, Janek raised his and shouted above the noise of the room, '*Na zdrowie.*'

278

Between their thick accents and the noise in the room, it was hard to hold a conversation, but I felt comfortable surrounded by them joking to one another, mostly in Polish and occasionally including me with a gentle insult in English. Their mannerisms were familiar – they reminded me of my father, but I was well aware that if they knew his background they'd be offended at the suggestion. The mild residual guilt that clung to my insides hiding my identity slowly washed away with repeated rounds of vodka. Soon they had me toasting '*Na zdrowie*' and '*Stolat*' alongside them. I felt completely at home with them. The only other people I had felt equally familiar with since leaving Chagrin had been Dr. Neuman and the handful of Eastern European men who had put me up while I was working as a transient laborer. My father had talked about Poles when I was young, saying that his cousins had been left in East Prussia and were raised to speak Polish. To my knowledge they still lived there, my second cousins. My father spoke rudimentary Polish, which he had used to communicate with a few bakers he had once hired in Cleveland. For all his ranting about German-America, we seemed anything but pure.

My mind drifted back to the room when I heard Janek telling his friends in Polish about Emilia Malessa, flashing his Virtuti Militari medal, which they had all clearly seen before. I tried to distract them from whatever Janek was saying by holding a drink up in the air behind him and making funny faces until they broke out laughing.

Janek turned. 'Hey, you poke fun at me?'

'Not at all.'

He snatched my drink out of my hand, set it carefully on the bar and grabbed me playfully but firmly in a headlock. 'You want to play? We have fun.'

His friends laughed louder.

'My new bike racer,' he told them. 'It will make him tougher.'

They laughed more, ordered another round and toasted my future victories. We partied late into the night. After everything that had happened, my only desire was to get so drunk that I wouldn't remember anything about my decision to come to Columbia. I wanted to wake up the following morning and fall into my new life the way I had so many times before, without thinking about where I had come from or why. Whatever happened to my brother, I didn't want to know about it. We had come back together, gotten to know one another and were now torn apart once more, moving toward our separate destinies. I wondered if we'd ever cross paths again. He didn't know how to contact me and I didn't know how to contact him. We were both free from the family and pain that had created us, free to fly or fall where we might, to wander out into the world as we had been born to.

My head was swimming in alcohol. I prayed Columbia would turn out better than Albany, better than Augusta, better than Chagrin, better than all the other places I had lived, however briefly. I had never been welcomed so quickly or with so much festivity into any place I had arrived and treated as kindly. Nor had I ever experienced the optimistic energy I felt in the bar and out on the sidewalk of that thriving section of the city.

As the night wore on I learned that Mr. Grezlik, the eldest and most popular man of the group – who had also bought the majority of rounds – owned a construction company and had created a small empire, building houses throughout South Carolina, hiring recently arrived Polish immigrants. Mr. Grezlik was formal but not stuffy or pretentious, as I might have expected someone in his position to be. By the end of the night he made his way over to me and asked if I wanted a job. I was struck by his unexpected offer and felt bad telling him I had to concentrate on bike racing first in hopes of satisfying my obligation to my new sponsor.

'You have a place if things don't work out with the bicycle,' he said.

As we departed, we shook hands with each other firmly, one at a time.

Walking back to Janek's apartment, I asked him why he didn't work in construction with his friends. 'The pay must be better. Plus you'd be around friends.'

'I'm a bike racer,' he said. 'Fourth at World's in 1975 on the track.' He wasn't a bike racer any more, but it was the culture he had grown up in, the sport he loved. He slapped his plump stomach and said, 'Make no mistake, I'm still fast.' In a way he reminded me of Wade. He was past his prime but still as enthusiastic about bikes as he had always been. By working as a mechanic, he remained connected to racing, part of the clan, and contributed an essential element to victory, as important as a coach and teammates. Without his expertise in repairing bikes or changing flat tires quickly during races, we'd have no chance of winning. He had moved to Columbia and stayed because his wife's relatives had settled there after arriving in America long before he had. He was divorced but said he wanted to stay near his children.

In a moment of silliness to change the subject, he declared himself 'Janek the Mechanic.' Other than the rhyme, I didn't understand the joke at first, but he was so affectionate that I couldn't help laughing with him and placing my arm around his shoulders as we staggered down the sidewalk to his apartment. Over the following weeks I learned that he was known as Janek the Mechanic in the shop among customers and young racers; he had a good sense of humor and even tolerated the Polish jokes to which he was subjected every few days, even though I could tell he didn't like them.

When we got back to his apartment he poured a couple more rounds for nightcaps. I looked at him: I would have to work with him every day. He was responsible for keeping my machine running flawlessly. I didn't want to deceive him. After I set down my glass, I said, 'Janek, I have a confession to make. My father isn't Polish. He's German – East Prussian.'

'Your father's German?'

'Yes, German. My grandfather, all of them. Maybe some Polish in there somewhere along the way, but German as far as I know.'

He considered this for a moment. 'Don't worry, my friend. We're in America now. We're Americans.' He poured another shot, then added, 'Just don't tell my friends, okay?'

'No problem,' I said. 'I just want things clear between us.'

Before we went to bed he taught me the Polish word for 'good-night' and made me say it before we turned it.

'*Dobranoc.*'

'See?' he said, delighted. 'You're Polish now. *Dobranoc*, my friend.'

The following morning I awoke to rain pattering against the window. Janek made a pot of tea and we sat at the table drinking it, too groggy from the night before to talk much. Afterward we went down to the street, then sprinted up the block, racing each other, dodging people clutching umbrellas and jumping over rain-filled gutters, until we reached the store and ducked inside. Craig was already there. The light in his office was on and he had pulled several bike boxes out from the storeroom. Because of the rain there weren't many customers, so Craig and Janek devoted most of the day to building a new bike for me. The frame was bright yellow. Craig clamped it into the bike stand to attach components to it. The word 'Italia' was stamped beneath the bottom bracket. I sat watching them insert the spindle into the bottom bracket and carefully adjust the bearings, snug the crank-arms to the spindle, attach the shifters to the down-tube, string wire from the shifters to the derailleurs, press the headset in place.

Craig carefully measured my inseam, the length of my torso and arms, made several calculations, then selected the proper size stem to hold the handlebars in place and measured the precise height of the seat from the pedal in a downward position. Watching them work like scientists opened up a new realm of racing. I had never paid attention to the length or height of anything, other than when my legs ached once and Wade told me my seat was too high. All I had ever done was get on a bike and ride. I had no idea that it could be custom built from the ground up to fit my body. The day before, when Wade had mentioned a new bike, I had assumed Craig would simply pull one down off the rack for me. It was almost dark by the time they finished.

'Take it upstairs,' Craig said, pointing to a door at the back.

The shop was located in a brick building a hundred or so years old. The worn wood floors, creaking hinges and swollen door frames hadn't been maintained through the years, but for all its decay it had a warmer feel than a newer building. I carried the bike to the door, climbed the narrow staircase to the second floor and went into a room with rollers and windtrainers set up beside each other. A stereo rack with a big amplifier stood at the edge of the room and there were two huge speakers in the corners. A single bulb hung from a wire affixed to the ceiling. I pulled the cord and illuminated a dozen large posters on the walls of cycling champions climbing the Alps, descending the Pyrenees, sprinting up the Champs-Élysées and battling over the Dolomites.

Craig bounded up the stairs, Janek following close behind.

'Let's crank it up and see what you're made of.' Craig tossed me a new pair of cycling shorts and a jersey with the team name – Venezia Cyclery Columbia U.S.A. – embossed on them. 'Over there,' he said, pointing to the restroom. 'I don't want to see your pencil dick.'

I went to change while Craig got into a skinsuit in the corner of the room near a clothes rack on which hung a half-dozen jerseys and shorts turned inside out for the chamois to dry. The room had the musky smell of a gym, combined with the scent of bicycle grease and chain oil. The combination of scents produced a gravity that I had not experienced in relation to cycling before, hinting at the seriousness of the task at hand. Windtrainers held the bike in a stationary position, the forks and bottom bracket clamped in place, while the rear wheel spun on a small metal cylinder attached to a fan whose resistance increased the faster you pedaled. Craig, however, favored rollers: unlike the windtrainer, they required the rider to maintain perfect form to keep his balance. Once you reached a high enough speed the momentum of the wheels allowed you to maintain a fragile balance on top of the spinning rollers, as if riding on the open road, but if you touched your brakes, decreased your speed too sharply or made any abrupt movement, you crashed to the floor. Craig didn't race any more but, like Wade, he stayed in shape. Janek picked a clipboard up off the floor and entered some data on it, then fiddled with a stopwatch. 'You ready to do some intervals?' he asked.

I nodded.

Craig told Janek to put some music on the stereo. My rollers were positioned near it. Janek winked as he approached me, then flipped through a stack of Craig's workout records. Most of them were by a band named Kraftwerk, a German word I recognized that translated to 'power plant.' I glanced at the album titles: *Autobahn*, *Trans-Europe Express*, *The Man-Machine*. 'What kind of music is it?' I asked Janek.

He shrugged.

I called over to Craig above the whir of the rollers. 'Who's the band?'

'Euro Jet Trash,' he shouted. Then he yelled to Janek, 'Let's break him in.'

Trying to balance for the first time on a set of rollers spinning at twenty-five miles per hour with my new coach at my side was disorienting, but when he put the music on and cranked it so loud that the window nearest me rattled, I felt as if I had entered another realm. The music was strange and disconcerting: there wasn't a single acoustic instrument. Right down to the drums everything was electronic – staccato, machine-like beats. The music was mostly instrumental, but as soon as I started getting comfortable with the strange new sounds, a garbled synthesized voice, moving between German, French and English, entered the mix.

Janek raised his arm, then dropped it, signaling the start of an interval.

I pedaled as hard as I could. Between my hangover from the night before, the intense effort and the music pounding in the background, I thought I was going to pass out. Between each interval, Janek placed his fingers on my jugular vein to take my pulse. We did interval after interval until the room was spinning around me. I started feeling sick – maybe I'd made the wrong choice in coming here. Maybe I should have spent the night at Wade's house, as he had asked, and thought more about it.

The electronic beat pounded through me. Janek's hand kept reaching out to my pulse while Craig stared at me with a menacing smile, pushing the pace faster and faster, until I couldn't keep up with him any more and lost my balance, slipping and crashing to the floor. The needle bounced off the record and the room fell silent, except for the whir of Craig's rollers and him laughing in the background as Janek sprinted for the trash can while I clutched my stomach to stop myself throwing up on the floor.

Within a few days my new surroundings no longer felt so alien. The weather warmed up and the rain stopped. I spun around town on my new bike to learn the street patterns and different neighborhoods, riding up through campus and around the state capitol building. Craig kept telling me he was going to introduce me to the team masseur, a guy named Nick, but he was always too busy doing other things to follow through. We didn't have any races coming up anyway, so it wasn't essential I meet him right then, but I liked the idea of having a team masseur. I quickly learned that with Craig you had to wait until he was ready to do whatever he had promised instead of reminding him repeatedly.

At least he took the time to introduce me to another rider, Devin. He was a political-science student at the university and had won a big race the previous year. He was known as the strongest sprinter in the city, but Craig hadn't been able to convince him to join the team. He said he didn't want to interrupt his studies by training too much or traveling to races, so instead Craig gave him occasional freebies – tires, jerseys – so that he'd come out and whip us in sprints to keep us fast.

Devin showed me different training loops outside the city limits. On the way out of town, I got a flat. We stopped and repaired it. On the narrow roads deep in the swamps, my tire flatted again. 'How many tubes you got?' he asked.

'That's it.'

I knew exactly what he was getting at and we laughed. Flats tended to come in threes. If you got one, you were safe. But if you got two, it was almost a given that you'd have a third before you got back to town. It was a superstition that proved true often enough for every racer to be aware of it. Even so we usually carried only two tubes, fearing that if you carried three you were asking for it. More importantly, we didn't like weighing ourselves down with extra equipment stuffed in our jersey pockets.

'You going to pay me now or later?' Devin asked, producing a small patch kit from his jersey pocket.

'I'll give you the honor of fixing the next one.'

'Yeah, right, and I'll give you the honor of wiping my ass when I stop to shit.' He tossed me the patch kit. 'I don't want to dig for it when I hear the next tire pop.'

I caught it and stuffed it in my jersey pocket as we pushed off. Ten miles down the road, I flatted again, racing down a descent. Devin hadn't flatted all day.

'Well, at least that's out of the way,' he said.

Devin was a genuinely nice guy and provided a perfect tonic to Craig's more abrasive style. Whatever reservations I felt toward Craig, he had introduced me to good people – so far, between Janek and Devin, I couldn't have asked for better.

After I had been in town about a week, Craig called a formal team meeting to introduce me and take us out on a group-training ride. Before the meeting started, he pulled me aside and told me he couldn't say I'd been brought in as the new team leader. 'You'll have to win the respect of your teammates to earn that position.'

We went into the shop. The riders were gathered in the mechanics' area, sitting on the floor and on work stools. He clapped his hands to get everyone's attention, while I sat on the floor to listen.

'We have a new rider. You should all know him from the circuit. I didn't invite him here to take over the team, but the same rules apply as always. If he proves himself a better rider, you work for him, just like he'll work for you in races where you're better. I don't want any inner-team rivalry. We're here to get the best rider that day across the finish line first.'

My new teammates looked at one another, bored, having apparently heard his lecture many times.

Craig changed the subject. 'Who thinks racing's fun?' he asked.

'About as fun as frying in hell,' a rider at the back of the room shouted.

'That answers my next question. Racing isn't a game. The way you raced in Wilmington when Sam won without any team support, while you guys had each other to fall back on, was pretty sad. Sam's here because he kicked your ass. While you guys were out there playing, he was busy racing.'

'We had three mechanicals that day,' a rider interrupted, 'not to mention Jerry's crash. It's an unfair comparison.'

'I guess you were too busy to notice Sam flatted that day, too. He took his free lap and went on to win. Racing is war. In a one-day race, the strongest rider doesn't always win. The smartest one does. That day Sam was the strongest and the smartest.'

'Rizzo doesn't seem too bright to me,' a rider joked.

Everybody laughed. The rider sitting beside me explained that Rizzo was the leader of a rival team in Florida.

'Okay, Rizzo aside,' Craig conceded, 'the strongest rider doesn't always win. Nobody wins a battle by doing stupid things. You save your strength – you don't show your hand early. Patience is synonymous with winning.'

'What does synonymous mean?' a rider asked.

'It means your dumb ass won't be riding today,' Craig said. 'You just selected yourself driver of the day.'

I soon learned that nobody wanted this job – it meant he had to drive the motor scooter behind which the team followed single file as he led us out of town to the narrow roads Devin had taken me on, which wove through the swamps near Hopkins and Gadsden. This method of training was called motor-pacing. It was faster and harder than regular training – in fact, it was the most difficult, intense training I had ever done. Much of riding was still new to me – each aspect of training took on fresh and unexpected angles I hadn't anticipated. The motor scooter forced us to maintain a higher pace: the leader had to stay within inches of its rear tire, as the rest of the team strung out single file behind, each rider nearly touching the wheel of the guy ahead of him. Drafting required great trust between teammates – if somebody hit their brakes unexpectedly, the entire team risked crashing like dominos at high speed. Abrupt and unexpected movements were prohibited – you had to ride conscious of those around you. At high speeds if you accidentally let a tiny gap open between riders, you fell quickly out of the slipstream, forcing the riders behind to use precious energy sprinting around you. Naturally you did everything within your power to remain in the slipstream so that those behind you wouldn't be cut from the group because of your weakness.

On the most intense days any rider who fell off pace was left out in the swamps to ride home alone. We rarely waited for teammates unable to keep up. This was one of Craig's cardinal rules: if you weren't strong enough to stay with the group on fast days, you had no business being on the team.

He justified this by saying, 'Racing is harder than training. If you can't keep up training, you're not likely to be of any use in a race.'

Like most of Craig's coaching methods, it was a tough-love tactic – we all had off days, but nobody wanted to ride twenty miles back into town alone – and motivated you to keep up. On the days that we motor-paced, we circled a ten-mile loop out in the swamps because it was inevitable that, no matter how strong we were, we'd drop off the pace eventually when the motor scooter hit top speed.

We started out motor-pacing at about twenty-five miles per hour. The driver increased the pace by two-mile-per-hour increments. A few laps into the training session, with the various grades climbed at top speed, we were flying, and it became too much for even strong riders to hold on. One at a time, riders lost contact, until there were only three of us left. Climbing one of the short hills, another rider snapped, leaving only myself and one other holding onto the machine's searing pace. The final rider able to stay in the slipstream of the motor scooter at the end of session won that day's honors. This was also how Craig established the team's hierarchy and appointed a leader going into that weekend's race without bickering among the members.

Going into the last lap that day, my legs burned worse than during any race I had competed in. I was in so much pain that all I wanted to do was drop off the back to release myself from the self-inflicted torture. I hung on until I was sure my lungs were going to explode and then, just as I decided to let go, I saw the other rider struggle momentarily, losing his form, snapping like a rubber band and flying past me in reverse. I buried myself, holding the motor scooter's pace, and rolled out the final lap, just myself and the motor scooter.

On the way back into town, cooling down, spinning our legs out, Craig dropped back and said, 'Good ride, but I'm not impressed. If you're going to lead the team, that's what's expected of you.'

That's the way it went for the next month as we geared up for the fall races that marked the end of the season.

When I wasn't training, I met more people around town. Craig introduced me to a local sportswriter, who wrote a short profile of me as his new team captain; the article was dominated by a large picture of me standing beside my bike wearing the team jersey. The article ran before the fall races and helped drum up a little business for the shop. He also introduced me to the owners of other businesses near his store and numerous customers who held positions up at the capitol and the university. It felt peculiar being introduced so formally. I was used to anonymity, but now part of my job was to represent Craig and his business so I had to dress sharper, in clothes Craig purchased for me, and carry myself in a professional manner. Until now I had done little socializing but talking to people was surprisingly easy. I relished the attention. I had never been respected before.

I finally met our masseur, Nick, by chance one afternoon while out picking up lunch for Craig. As I was walking back to the shop with my arms full, a tall lanky man with dyed purple hair wheeled past me on roller skates, stopped in front of a store and took out of his backpack several brushes and small jars of paint to finish the sign he had stenciled on the window. As I neared him I noticed he

289

had glued a line of glitter around the soles of his gold skates. It looked bizarre – but there were all kinds of odd people in the neighborhood near the university.

'Nice skates,' I commented, as I passed.

He looked down to admire them. 'You're the first to say that. You skate?'

'Can't say I do.'

He looked at the bags in my hands. 'For Craig?'

'Yeah – how did you know?'

'Who else around here eats a garbanzo-bean wrap for lunch every day?' He rolled his eyes. 'You must be the new guy. I guess I'll have to introduce myself since Craig doesn't seem to have the time. Nick,' he said. 'Nick Baly. I designed your team clothing.'

'You're the masseur?'

'When Craig pays me. With the races coming up, I guess I'll be back on call.'

'What are you doing painting?'

'I do a lot of things around this part of town. Jack of all trades, master of none – don't tell anyone my secret.'

He was gregarious and never at a loss for words. I liked him immediately.

'You must eat lots of pasta,' he said.

'All the carbos I can get.'

'Stop by my house tomorrow night. I'm having my annual Pesto Party. Tell Craig he's invited.'

I had no idea what pesto was, but didn't want to embarrass myself by telling him so. He wrote down his address and told me to be there by seven.

The following afternoon, when I reminded Craig near the end of the workday, he said that a woman he had dated years earlier was going to be in town that night and they had already planned dinner. 'Tell him we have races coming up and I'm going to need his lazy ass to come by and start doing some rub-downs.'

I felt awkward going by myself, but I didn't have anything else to do and looked forward to a big meal. Craig fed me enough to keep

290

my calories and energy up, but I was always hungry. When I got there, Nick was squatting in his garden just off the front porch yanking up basil stalks. He saw me and glanced at his watch. 'What time did I tell you yesterday?'

'Seven.'

'Sorry about that. I meant eight. Hope you're not too hungry. You can help out. Go on in and have a look around. Put some music on. There's a stack of records inside the front door.'

I stepped inside and quickly realized that it wasn't your average house. After my tour through it, with someone who lived there, the dinner party and the music, played live and on the stereo, I left around midnight, as disoriented as I had been on my second night in town when Craig had taken me to the indoor training room and worked me over. Except this was the total opposite.

Instead of ending the night throwing up in a trash can, I floated out across town to my little nook between bike boxes in the store-room to sleep, trying to make sense of the world Nick inhabited. He lived in a large house, high on a hill, that I learned was known around town as the Commune. It was divided into separate apartments with a large communal kitchen on the first floor. Each member was expected to share duties, preparing meals for the others and cleaning dishes, so that they had more time to spend with their families. Nick lived with his daughter, Natasha, in the once formal dining room on the first floor that he had converted into an apartment. Another family occupied the living room, which had been sealed off from the rest of the house with a neatly built wall painted with mountains, forests and tiny flowers. The children entertained themselves that night by sitting on the floor and adding grass, rabbits and squirrels to the scene.

Upstairs Sondra – the mother of Nick's daughter – lived with her husband Ignacio and their two younger children, who had been delivered at home with Nick acting as midwife. Sondra and Nick had never married. Sondra's husband was a musician from Argentina. They performed an original repertoire of folk songs at festivals around the southeast. Ignacio seemed to enjoy Nick's presence. They were warm with one another and he told me that Nick often looked after their children when they had to play a gig out of town. Their relationship was unlike any other I had known in the past – it didn't resemble the hippie façade of happiness and unity I'd seen during my time on the road but was based on genuine mutual respect.

An old turntable sat in the front hallway on top of a milk crate filled with records that the children and adults took turns playing so that music drifted constantly through the house. Most of the night they switched between five or six records by a musician I had never heard of named Joni Mitchell. At first her high, lilting voice irritated me, but Nick sang along to the lyrics of almost every song with such optimism that it grew on me. When the adults went out back to smoke pot, I sat down in the hallway to look through the records. I learned that Joni wasn't simply a folk musician – she played complex compositions as well, backed by legendary jazz musicians, such as Miles Davis's former saxophone player Wayne Shorter and an inventive fretless electric bass player who made his instrument sing like a horn section in several songs on *Don Juan's Reckless Daughter*. She sang about love, peace, war and greed – typical hippie themes – but in a poetic way unlike the rock music I used to listen to. There was rarely a trace of sappiness or romanticism in the songs I heard that night – most were infused with stark images that made me think differently about many things, such as Nick living with his child's mother, who was wed to another man, yet there was no tension in the house. It was a different galaxy than the one I'd grown up in.

In South Carolina my life expanded. I had already traveled and been through so much that I wasn't sure there was much else to learn. My arrival there was probably no different than it had been for many generations of students joining their freshman year from farms and small towns. Everything seemed possible. The ominous cloud of doom that seemed to have hung over my head since birth had been replaced by the radiant optimism that pervaded the city. I lived in a section of town called Five Points – a natural depression in the earth that held the heat of hot summer nights like an oven – where five roads converged. It was composed of a half-dozen city blocks or so, and artists, athletes, chefs, students, businessmen, congressmen and others gathered there each night. From student bars, like Group Therapy, to high-class lounges, like Goat Feathers, there was a place for everyone to meet, toss back drinks and plot their dreams.

A small theater called the Bijou played independent films, where I saw dozens of almost incomprehensible movies shot in forms I had no idea existed. A used-record store, Papa Jazz, was located in the basement of a building where its frizzy-headed owner played chaotic free jazz as background music. There were numerous coffee shops and the bike shop that I lived in, along with Nick's dance studio where he taught yoga in the morning, worked as a graphic artist in the afternoon, gave a few massages before dinner and taught modern dance at night.

Nick was a guru of sorts. People from all walks of life sought his counsel – always free of charge – on whatever spiritual problems ailed them. He never advertised his services or sought a following. People found him. Many were lost, wayward souls like myself, but he never refused anybody and had accepted that part of his purpose on earth was to help the suffering.

In the evenings – after putting in a few hours at the shop and focusing on the training regimen Craig created for me – I was free to wander the city. Of all the places I had lived, I'd never been in a community like Five Points. Everybody seemed to be making their life up as they went along, intent on learning something new every day and sharing what they had learned with others, including strangers like me. Through Craig I met people I'd never imagined I could get to know. When they learned I was the new team captain with several victories under my belt, they often tagged along at the beginning of training rides to chat before the pace got too fast for them. I had never received so much attention from strangers. At first I thought it was just part of living in a big city. One of my team-mates was a student in the medical program at the university and invited me to his apartment after training rides. Large books with the skeletal and muscular structures of humans lay spread across his table and scattered on the floor. He raced to take a break from his intensive studies. A lawyer often went on easy training rides with me and engaged me in conversation as if I were his peer, asking for advice on riding faster. Several riders on the team were students. After a few months in Columbia, the Greyhound buses, the jobs in concrete block rooms behind motels, the janitorial, the dishwashing, the day-labor jobs, the nights of sleeping on the side of the road, in shacks, shelters and halfway houses, seemed to belong to another lifetime entirely.

I had been saved – by a bicycle my brother had insisted I buy. I had been saved by the fact that I had been late for work one day and had met Wade. For all the things I disliked about Augusta, I doubted that such an absurd turn of events would have happened anyplace else.

The following month I went to Washington DC with Janek and won a silver medal at the East Coast Criterium Championships, held on the circular drive in front of the White House, missing victory by the width of a racing tire. On my return I announced the news as soon as I entered the shop to my teammates who hadn't made the trip. Craig congratulated me, then waited until I'd finished telling the others the details of the race before he asked me to come to the storeroom.

'Listen,' he said, 'you did a good job and I won't take that from you. But don't go bragging about second place – I brought you on to captain the team. Those guys aren't going to sacrifice themselves for you if the best you can do is second.'

'Give me some credit,' I said, crestfallen.

'I did – I said good job. Forget all that little-league, parental-encouragement bullshit you hear me telling kids whose parents buy bikes from me. You're in the big league now. No matter how close the top two finish, nobody remembers second and they sure as hell don't take pictures of the runner-up for the newspaper. If you're going to race for second you might as well hang up your cleats now.'

'But—'

'You keep riding like that, you might as well start turning wrenches for a living.'

Without giving me a chance to say anything else, he slapped the ten-millimeter open-end wrench he had been holding into my hand, reached up, slid a bike box off the rack, and said, 'Go assemble this. The lady who bought it will be by before closing time to pick it up.'

He walked away without even tossing me a sarcastic smile.

I beat the entire eastern seaboard, save one guy who nipped me at the line, and he's going to call me a loser? I turned to the bike box he had slid in front of me and kicked it so hard that my foot punctured the cardboard and got caught in the spokes of the front wheel. When I twisted free, I heard a *ping* and saw a broken spoke poking through the hole in the box.

'Fuck!' Not only did I have to assemble the bike, now I had to repair it, too. 'I'll show you,' I muttered, as I dragged the box up to the mechanics' room. When I went in everybody stopped talking and turned to assembling the bikes hanging on their stands without looking at me. They had heard the commotion.

I tried pulling the bike out of the box, but the loose spoke got stuck in the cardboard, wedging the bike in place. After pulling at it for a few seconds longer, I became frustrated. 'Screw this stupid, cheap-ass piece of shit.' I dropped the box and kicked it again. Now everybody was staring at me. 'What are you guys looking at? Let's suit up and go training.'

'I don't know if Craig'll be happy about us cutting out before closing time.'

'Fuck him. I'll take the blame. Let's go.'

As we were wheeling our bikes to the front door, he came out of his office and asked what was going on.

'That bike you wanted me to put together needs a new wheel. Tell the lady it'll be ready tomorrow.'

'You can't leave like that.'

'Fire me if you want. I just spent ten hours in a car driving back from DC and haven't trained in two days. If we're going to win any races we need to train, not assemble bikes.'

As we prepared to roll out, I glanced back at the front door to see if Craig was still standing there. He had a big smile on his face.

'You piece of shit! You did this on purpose!' I yelled.

I threw the chain on the big ring and stomped on the pedals – there was no warm-up that day, just straight-up balls-to-the-wall hammering out of town. When we reached the outskirts, somebody shouted that only three of the five riders were still in the paceline. 'Should we wait?' he asked.

I didn't respond. I attacked the guys on my wheel. The race for the Mount Zion church was on. They all knew the route. Come as a group or straggle in one at a time, I didn't care right then. I was still undefeated up that local climb and I was going to make damn sure nobody beat me that day.

In some ways it felt as if the idealism of the early seventies had arrived a decade late in the South Carolina capital. Even with limited education and few skills I was repeatedly approached and asked if I was interested in helping different social and political organizations to collect signatures or distribute pamphlets. I was weary of pamphlets and overenthusiastic young people, especially after reading my father's account of growing up in Nazi Germany, but I sometimes wished I felt less inhibited so that I could join in.

Nick took me to a small counterculture print shop in the warehouse district. He hired them to print advertising materials he designed for businesses around town – his way of supporting them. The shop mainly printed pamphlets that seemed to protest almost everything the government did. I had no idea such places existed and found it odd that the workers dressed in ragged clothing, even though they were clearly wealthy enough to afford better, wore their uncombed hair long and grew shaggy beards like the hobos I had met working transient jobs. It was almost as if they were disguising their backgrounds to appear poor. When

I asked Nick if the print shop was illegal in some way, he assured me it wasn't.

'We have to exercise free speech,' one of the men showing me around said. 'What good is our constitution if we don't?'

I had been taught never to express myself in public. I was scared I might get into trouble for protesting. I'd spent a year of my life in an institution, but nobody working there looked like they'd ever been sent away. Regardless of Nick's assurances, I was sure there was something illegal about printing so many pamphlets at a shop hidden in an industrial section of town, just as I was sure my father had broken some sort of law by writing a story he was scared to share with anyone but me. The only thing I wanted to do in life was win races and I knew I couldn't win them by protesting the rules. The last thing I was interested in was getting involved in politics.

Devin called me a few days later to congratulate me on taking second in the DC race and to make plans to go on the sprint-training loop he and I often trained on. 'Time to bring you down to earth,' he said.

'Craig already took care of that.'

He laughed. I suspected that was one of the reasons he hadn't joined the team.

That afternoon we rode out of town and circled a five-mile loop, rolling through the hardest sprint on the first lap to warm up, a slightly descending section of road. It was our favorite because of the high speeds we hit approaching the landmark that was our imaginary finish line – a large broken limb sticking off a dead tree. Like everything else in cycling, each sprint had its own name, in this case Broken Limb Sprint. We rode another lap to get ourselves psyched up for the effort and came back around to the straightaway where we could see the broken limb, about a quarter-mile away, and started picking up speed, taking turns at front on the slightly downhill section. Pretty soon we topped out at around thirty-five miles per hour and broke into the final furious effort, going neck-to-neck at some forty miles per hour in an all-out sprint when a car approached from the opposite direction traveling at twice our speed. We were too deep in the heat of competition to let up, so we held our line in our lane to make sure the car had plenty of room to pass and concentrated on completing the effort.

In the space of a couple of seconds and, without at first realizing what was happening, I saw the driver's dark hand throw a brick out the window. It sailed toward our heads like a projectile. I screamed as it flew in front of my face and Devin ducked. The brick clipped his earlobe as it sailed past. We pulled over to the edge of the road in disbelief, hyperventilating from the sprint, adrenaline tearing through our veins as the car disappeared up the road.

We climbed off our bikes, our legs swollen from the intense sprint, causing slight cramps – we hadn't cooled down by spinning our legs out. We dropped the bikes and sat beside each other. I reached over and wiped a drop of blood from Devin's ear. Ten minutes passed in silence – our breathing and heart rates slowly returning to normal as we contemplated the close call.

'There was only one reason for that,' Devin said. 'He doesn't even know us but he tried to kill us.'

I didn't say anything. Unfortunately, such events were part of the job description. Cars hated us interrupting the flow of the traffic. Rednecks threw Coke bottles and beer cans out of their car windows at me regularly, and once an irritated woman had flung a Styrofoam cup of lukewarm coffee that had splattered across my jersey. Businessmen tossed periodicals, as if they were trying to swat a fly. Nobody liked cyclists slowing them down and they made sure we were aware of it by screaming that they paid taxes to drive on those roads. We knew the risks of training on public roads and usually brushed off the daily dangers without a second thought.

But I had never before had a brick slung at me and wondered why he had had such easy access to it. I figured he was coming home from a construction site at which some jackass white boss had screamed at him all day and, in a momentary fit of rage, had snapped and thrown the brick out the window. Enough bosses who relished their power had tried to break me down in the past – I could think of no other reason why he had targeted us. But maybe my distorted guilt

298

at being white was making me try to justify his behavior. I doubted the same thing would happen if he passed us again. I was willing to write off our brush with death as a freak, random occurrence. I had to think that way – otherwise I'd have been too scared to go out on the road and pursue the thing I loved most.

Neither of us blurted the N-word right after it happened. What good would it have done? He was a straight-up psycho and his race had nothing to do with it. That day, pedaling home was more difficult than we usually found it, glancing over our shoulders as we rolled along, both knowing we couldn't dwell on the incident.

Three days later, I called Devin. 'Ready for the next round, Senator?' I had started calling him by that name partly as a joke and partly to encourage him in his dream. He was still the best sprinter in the city, and if I planned to leave the South as a result of my skills on the bike, I could only afford to train with those capable of beating me. 'Where we plan on training?' Devin asked.

'Where else? Brick Sling Sprint. This is the day I'm going to destroy you, Senator.'

A long pause ensued at the other end of the line, followed by a sigh. I worried I had pushed it a little too far. Then I heard his voice: 'Dream on, Georgia boy. Give me an hour to finish studying.'

I didn't beat Devin that day, but I was beating him at Brick Sling before I took off near the end of the season to drive to Miami in the rusty VW team van. Craig sent four teammates along for support. I won my first race there in a mass sprint against a field of 125 riders. It proved my only victory that autumn.

I settled in for the winter, moving out of the bike shop to a small room in the back of Nick's dance studio. Although we hadn't spent much time together we felt kinship and comfortable in each other's company. I started working out at the gym up at the university to build my core muscles, following the regime Craig drew up for me, and used the dance studio when nobody was there to stretch and do calisthenics in front of the mirrors. Then I'd sit up late at night in the middle of the floor, cross-legged, with my eyes closed, visualizing winning races.

Cycling had altered every part of me – the structure of my muscles, the shape of my body, the way I walked, where I lived, how I thought, what I ate, who I interacted with. I built up a small library of cycling books that I had borrowed from Craig and sat through the long winter nights reading up on the sport that had transformed my life.

The bicycle was unlike any invention that had come before. It was the first complete synthesis of man and machine and remained the world's most efficient use of human power. It consumed virtually no oil. It improved health. Before the car, it had been a principal mode of transportation and had remained so throughout the Eastern world for most of the twentieth century. Millions had once ridden through city streets simultaneously without traffic jams, noise or pollution.

It had also altered the structure of society. In the nineteenth century, feminists had called it the 'freedom machine.' Susan B. Anthony declared that it had 'done more to emancipate women than anything else in the world.' Bicycle infantry was used in both world wars. The British Army Cyclist Corps in the First World War had formed ten battalions. Japan had used fifty thousand bicycle troops to invade China in 1937. The Viet Cong had ferried supplies on bicycles along the Ho Chi Minh Trail to avoid detection by U.S. forces and had driven the French out of their country by attacking them at Dien Bien Phu with stockpiles of ammunition they had carried into the jungle on bicycles. Cycling was also one of the world's most popular forms of recreation.

Each morning when I entered the bike shop, Janek looked up from the stand were he was working and said, 'Dzień dobry.'

'Morning, Janek.'

'No, say it right.'

'Dzień dobry.'

Unlike my father, Janek relished speaking his own language and sharing it with others. Nobody else who came around the shop had much interest in speaking Polish – students at the university preferred to learn Italian or French, the languages of two great cycling nations, and occasionally used them when talking about races – so I became Janek's pet project. I often returned from a training ride around the time he was locking up the store and would ask how his day had gone. His response rarely varied.

'*Tak sobie.*' So-so.

At lunchtime, I often cleared off the workbench to make room to eat while he went to the refrigerator to get kielbasa and onions. We'd sliced up the cold sausage and lay it on a plate and he'd hand me a whole onion, which I bit into as if it were a raw apple between pieces of sausage. I liked it because it cleared my system. Chewing raw onion was like breathing fire. While we ate, he told me racing stories from his time in Poland. He considered one of the races he had competed in there to be the greatest in the world – the Peace Race, a multi-day event, known to Eastern Europeans as the Tour de France of the East. It traveled from Warsaw to East Berlin to Prague. Janek had won a stage ending in Krakow. His hero was a competitor named Ryszard Szurkowski, a world champion, who had won the Peace Race four times.

'Ryszard would have won the Tour de France easy.'

Janek explained that despite having many of the greatest cyclists, Eastern Bloc countries weren't permitted to compete in the Tour because of its professional status. Theoretically, all full-time athletes in Soviet countries were amateurs, which allowed them to compete in the Olympics – no professional athletes were then permitted to take part in the Games.

'You must compete in the Peace Race,' he said. 'Stay with my relatives.'

He then started talking about the Olympic Training Center in Colorado. 'All Polish coaches,' he said. 'My friends. Defected from Poland.'

'Why aren't you there, coaching or working as a mechanic?'

'My children. I had my day. Now I concentrate on making sure they have theirs. Their mother likes it here so I stay.'

He told me about the training camps they held each year and

301

urged me to apply next winter once I'd had another year of racing experience. 'I help you,' he promised.

I had never thought about the Olympics or living at the Olympic Training Center. It seemed a remote fantasy. Only a short time ago I'd been riding to work in Augusta on my bike. I was never much of a dreamer. I knew my place in the world. But hearing him talk about it in such concrete terms, the fact that he had ridden for his own national team and personally knew the national coaches here, made it seem more realistic. 'How do I apply?'

'Race, get results, then write a letter at the end of next season.'

From that moment forward, I couldn't get it out of my mind. I envisioned the Olympic Training Center as a castle located deep in the Rocky Mountains. I wondered how many people lived there and if the athletes from different sports interacted together or were kept sequestered in their separate chambers awaiting their chance of glory. I couldn't shake the idea from my mind, and from then on I trained with the sole goal of gaining entry to the training center the following winter. It would be my ticket out of the South and my badge of self-respect. It no longer mattered if I was unable to get into college: I had a more important goal.

With the first early-season races approaching in two months, Craig briefed me on a new criterium that would circle the state capitol. It was the only big race during the coming season to take place in Columbia. He wanted to make a strong showing there – he wanted me to win. To facilitate the process he took it upon himself to start personally motor-pacing me four days a week. We went out by ourselves, him driving and me tucked in behind the motorbike, racing at many times the speeds I was capable of maintaining while training by myself. He wanted me to get used to race pace before the season started and to be sure that my fitness was better than the other competitors'.

Between motor-pacing sessions, he sent me out with Devin for sprint training or with the other guys to do intervals up Mount Zion.

Craig said that in order for the human organism to grow it had to be stressed. You only reached the next level by pushing yourself beyond your ability, breaking down, then recovering and thereby reaching a higher level than before. To increase muscle mass you had to stress your muscles, microscopically tearing fibers, damaging them so that they healed with more muscle fibers than before. He claimed the mind was similar.

'You put it through intense pain until it reaches its snapping point, then back off, recover and go again, allowing yourself to become conditioned to higher and higher levels of pain each time you train. If anyone ever tells you there's no truth in the saying that the farther you fall the taller you'll stand back up, don't trust them,' he said. 'They've never had their ass kicked enough to know.'

Craig was the most self-centered, egocentric person I'd ever met. He formed not only the center of the world but was the world. He rarely called or approached another person. You were expected to come to him. His telephone was for receiving calls, not making them. If he invited you into the kitchen to grab something to eat with him, you were expected to prepare it. To know how to prepare it. You served it to him first, then quickly served yourself. I would have preferred a more independent life, but as long as I raced bikes full-time under his sponsorship, I was expected to be at his service – in the way that many immigrants become indentured to their sponsors after being admitted to America. I tried to ignore this because my life was good.

Besides, in another way, he was incredibly generous. He often invited me to expensive restaurants. On other occasions, he might pull a twenty-dollar bill out of his pocket and hand it to me without comment. I never thanked him on such occasions, just as he never thanked me for preparing meals or picking them up in town. In fact, I never thanked him for anything, since I would have been thanking him every time I turned around, which would have made us both uncomfortable. He also provided travel costs to races, gave me bikes and repaired equipment, sometimes at great cost, especially since my less-than-finessed riding style tended to destroy expensive wheel-sets within months. He let me keep my meager race earnings. There was little money in cycling, but I often won several hundred dollars at each race that I split with teammates.

But for all the things I liked about Craig, I found his subtle attitude toward blacks unforgivable. About once every other month, the store was broken into and bikes were stolen. He instinctively blamed them. On several occasions he took me out with him to find the stolen bikes. The thieves usually smashed the plate-glass window with a rock or piece of concrete, jumped inside, grabbed a couple of bikes and disappeared – Columbia wasn't known for sophisticated robberies. Craig viewed the police as incompetent. He knew where to look for the bikes and over a week, driving back and forth, they often reappeared, ridden down the street by a kid, a teenager or an old man. They were easily identifiable – they were an obscure Italian brand that no other shop in the state sold and came in only one color: bright yellow. When spray-painted a different shade, as they frequently were, it was obvious even from a distance. We made our living with those machines and knew them as well as a horologist knows watches. He kept a slip of paper in the ashtray of the car in which he had written down the serial numbers of each stolen bike.

Whenever we came upon one of his bikes being ridden, he was confrontational and expected me to be the same. If I failed to express my loyalty to him in this way, I risked being thrown off the team and losing my livelihood. His confrontations consisted of casually pulling over ahead of the cyclist, stepping out into the road and forcing the rider to skid to a stop. At this point he grabbed the bike and yanked it out from under the rider, who often flipped onto his side in the middle of the street. I was expected to stand close behind Craig and watch his back, prepared to fight if needed. If the rider protested, or a group of people swelled around us – and this happened on more than one occasion – Craig produced his evidence from the ashtray of the car, made his case, then quickly laid the bike in the trunk of his car and drove away. If somebody tried to block his departure, he'd say the same thing each time, 'It would please me greatly if you got out of the way. Otherwise I'll assume you don't mind being run over.' Invariably they moved.

Craig had a way of persuading people to see things his way, even when they didn't. He never called the police and I suppose, as a result, he won some respect. If a rare racing bike was stolen that he had no luck in locating, we drove to a place where you could buy drugs while you sat in your car and waited for somebody to approach. If you got out, they wouldn't come near you.

'What can I get for you folks tonight?' a dealer asked.

Craig would peel a hundred-dollar bill off his roll, making a show of doing so, and say, 'I'll be back tomorrow to pick up a piece of anonymous information that I thought you might be able to help me out with.' He would explain exactly what the bike looked like, when it had been stolen and ask the man to find out whether or not anyone had seen it around the city. He was well connected at the state capitol, he would add, and would see that business on the corner was shut down if the dealer refused to participate. The following night when we rolled back around, more often than not the bike would be leaning up against a lamppost. As we approached, the dealer would nod to a kid standing nearby who would push it to the car and apologize while the dealer looked on. Craig would pop open the trunk with a button inside the glove box and the kid would lay it carefully inside.

Other than that, Craig had no contact with the black community. Not only did he have no contact, he passed back and forth daily through their neighborhoods, as if they didn't exist. He made it crystal clear that there were two communities in the city who rarely interacted with each other. To Craig I realized, community was not about bringing people together: it was about keeping them apart. I wondered whether this was true elsewhere.

'The first rule of crushing your opposition is to attack when they're weak. You never attack when they're strong,' Craig said, as we were rolling out to the swamps together for a day of spinning – recovery

305

training. 'You find the nicks in their armor and you exploit them. You crush them so they don't consider clawing their way back into contention.'

He told me that bike racing was unlike running or triathlons where you went out hard and held the pace through the entire race. Cycling was more complex – one of the most complex sports of all, in fact. He called it 'chess on wheels.' Only the smartest and strongest were capable of winning races, but never the strongest alone. It was not a sport of brawn and bravado. It was a sport of patience. Letting dangerous attacks go up the road. Having teammates cover them. Reeling them in during the last third of the race. Setting up the team leader to attack or counterattack. He explained pacelines, double pacelines, echelons, double echelons, and how they could be used to push the pack into the gutter in a strong crosswind and split the field apart. You could attack from the front and go on a suicide mission early in the race, in hopes of getting enough distance on the field before the final to stay away, no matter how hard they chased, no matter how efficient the trains rolling behind you were.

'Out of sight, out of mind,' he said, like a mantra. 'Out of sight, out of mind.'

He said that if you attacked and got far enough up the road that the other riders couldn't see you, sooner or later they'd forget about you, even though they knew you were still out there, and would focus on the riders surrounding them. 'It's human nature. If you're dangling off the front where they can see you, you're like a carrot on a stick. They'll chase you down every time, no matter how fast you ride.'

There were only three elements keeping you from going a hundred miles per hour on a bike, he said. Air resistance, road resistance and gravity. Those were cycling's laws of physics – the only things holding you back, aside from fitness and intimidation by other riders. I asked him what I should do if I were climbing a long mountain pass in a race and flatted as a huge gust blasted down the mountain and had no team support to get a new tire or block the wind or help pace me up the climb.

'In that case, you're fucked.' He looked at me to see if I was serious.

I cracked a smile.

He said the pack moved in a counterintuitive symbiotic relationship, sharing duties pulling into the wind, setting pace, slowing for crashes and nature breaks even as they raced against each other. There were mercenaries who hired themselves out to other teams, while riding under their own colors in covert operations to split prize money, or who had been paid in advance at small races to help give a hometown rider victory. There were specialists in different forms of battle – mountain goats, time-trialers, sprinters, rouleurs, domestiques, captains, lieutenants and, the rarest, the all-rounder. There were races of attrition in which the sun, rain, snow or terrain ate away at the riders more than their tactics and strategies.

As time passed, the line of demarcation between Craig's encyclopedic knowledge and mine faded. His knowledge became mine. Neither of us had been born into a cycling culture. Our ancestors had never raced. We weren't Italian or French. We had never seen races on television or listened to them broadcast over the radio – but we were cyclists. Cycling had given us a sense of purpose that all the other areas of our life had failed to provide. It had brought discipline, honor, self-respect, commitment, competition, duty, health, solace and peace. Each time we faced adversity we looked out for each other. Each time we won we celebrated together. When we lost we mourned as one.

As the race neared, Craig put Nick back on the payroll as team masseur. Even though I saw him each morning when I was leaving the studio to start my day, he brought his massage table to the bike shop and set it up in the indoor training room on the second floor. A full massage typically lasted an hour. At first I felt uncomfortable having somebody focus so much on me. I had always been the worker, the one doing things for other people, but when I was lying on the table the situation was inverted. I couldn't deny how relaxing it felt, my legs going from tense to jelly over the course of the hour. He'd start on my quads and calves, then turn me over and work out my gluteus maximus with his elbow, then move up my back with the base of his palms, pressing in deep, alternating strokes along each side of the spine, stopping when he felt a knot to locate the pressure point into which he dug his thumbs.

I asked him to look at my knee, where I'd felt a small pain. He felt around and said there wasn't much a massage would do, but advised me to alternate between heat and ice to keep any swelling down. Then I asked about a spot on my lower back that had been bothering me. He found a knot and worked it out until the pain became too intense.

'We'll let it rest and try again later,' he said.

Each time he finished a massage, I asked if there was anything I could do for him. Despite his being paid I felt a little guilty that he wasn't charging me anything to stay at his studio. He always brushed it off and asked if I wanted to go on a walk. I'd accompany him around Five Points while he dropped off advertising work he did for various clients. Every once in a while, after he'd been home to prepare his daughter's dinner, he'd come back to the studio to finish up some work. One evening he asked if I wanted him to try to work out the knot a little more that was still bothering my lower back.

'If you don't mind,' I said. Although I was getting used to him massaging me, I still wasn't comfortable with people touching me. Between being beaten by my father and my other experiences, I tensed and recoiled when anyone tried to hug me or lay a hand on me. Aside from Nareesha, Nick was the sole exception. His touch relaxed me as much as his presence. I felt the human touch so rarely that when he worked on me, my body sank into the mattress and I closed my eyes to lose myself in the sensation. He worked the knot out slowly and I fell into an even deeper state of relaxation, my eyes closed, unsure whether thirty minutes or three hours had passed. I felt him start to massage my shoulder blades. He went on so long that I started to drift off. I was right at that point between waking and sleep when he kissed the nape of my neck.

I froze. The muscles in my back tensed.

I didn't get up, turn over or say anything. I lay there in silence, as he started working the tension out of my shoulders again. Like a poisonous vapor, the memory of what had happened on the way back to Augusta from Albany seeped into my mind. He tried to work my shoulders out but they turned to rock.

'Should I go?' he whispered.

I didn't say anything. I still didn't turn to him. I didn't want him to go, but I was too shy to say anything, so I lay in silence, not moving or acknowledging his words. After a while he started massaging my shoulders again. Then he stopped and disappeared into the studio. I heard the sound of the lock on the front door click shut and saw the lights dim. A few minutes later he reappeared at my side with a candle, which he set on the floor. Then he worked out my shoulders again. The candle eventually burned out. My shoulders finally began to relax, then my back – I could feel the tension, the fear, the anger slowly dissipating, as he continued rubbing my back and then leaned down to kiss my ear. I concentrated on the sensation of his soft lips making contact with the sensitive skin. I worked up the courage to turn over and face him. I could barely see the outline of his face in the dark, but we stayed like that staring into each other's invisible eyes while he ran his fingers across my scalp. I remained still. I closed my eyes and let the darkness envelop me at the same moment that I felt his lips touch mine. I hadn't expected the rough razor stubble surrounding his lips and flinched, then told myself to relax, convincing myself that Nick would never harm me, that he was there to protect me as he began kissing me again.

This time I ignored the stubble, slid my hand over his shoulder and pulled him closer to me. His hands were exploring my body, at first concentrating on my chest, his fingers rubbing my nipples in a circular motion, then moving outward, over my abdomen, along my thighs. The room was pitch black, just feelings and sensations. I freed my mind of thoughts, focusing on his touch as our bodies slowly merged, blood rushing through veins, our skin warming, tiny droplets of sweat rising up through the microscopic pores, our almost silent

– but still perceptible and steadily increasing – heart rates and the breathing, most of all the breathing, the room surrounding us, the ceiling, walls and floor pressing gently inward, then retreating until our two bodies were floating in space, unconnected to anything but each other as we tightened our grip, almost violently, to stop ourselves falling through the void into which we had thrust ourselves.

Devin came by the shop on the morning of the big race up at the capitol. I hadn't seen him in weeks. He had spent spring break with his parents in Greenville. He said he had been off the bike to concentrate on his senior thesis. 'That thing's going to break me. I thought cycling was hard.'

'It's only a paper – it can't be that bad,' I said. 'Craig pushed me to almost four hundred miles a week over the last month.'

'I wish I had the luxury of riding like that.'

'Luxury? It's torture.'

'I'd trade places any day.'

'You're not hanging up your cleats, are you?'

'Hell, no. You think I want to go completely insane? Just taking some time off to get into the swing of writing, then I'll be back out there trading licks. It's going to take me a while to get my fitness back to stay with you.'

'I just want this race out of the way. Craig's so amped up about it, he's driving me crazy. Once it's done I can concentrate on the rest of the season.'

'I'll be up there tonight yelling for you. Give me six weeks to lay some base miles – we'll get something going after that.'

'Let's do that. I miss riding with you.'

The race started at seven that night. There weren't many evening races like it, but the city officials wanted to make sure that the traffic had cleared out of downtown before it started. They called it a twilight race. I went out for an easy spin to loosen up my legs and get away from the shop. I didn't want anybody else coming by and wishing me luck or congratulating me before the race started. I could only take so many people telling me they knew I was going to win before it started having a counterproductive effect. I preferred to be alone before races. Craig knew this so he had given me a key to go lie around his house and watch television for the rest of the afternoon.

The time eased by without my getting too nervous and soon I was pulling on my Lycra shorts and jersey, snugging up the strap on my helmet and rolling across town. The course was cordoned off an hour before the race. A police officer let me through the barriers and onto the course where I started doing warm-up laps with the other riders. The field was larger than I'd expected: there were several teams from New England and a big one from the Midwest – they had spent the winter in Florida, staying in shape. I had four teammates in the race with me, but they were all students and hadn't had a chance to train with me as often as I would have liked. Craig told me to try to read the other teams' tactics and piggyback off their moves, relying on my teammates only when I needed to be slingshot across a gap to reach a break that looked dangerous.

Soon we were sprinting around the half-mile four-corner course, warming up as a group at race speeds. I could hear people shouting my name at various areas around the course, some voices I recognized, others I didn't. I ignored them all and concentrated on holding the wheels of the guys in front of me. In the half-light between day and dusk, preparing for the race took on a different feeling with the large crowds gathered three and four deep around the course. I had competed in dozens of races where there were hardly any spectators and none where I was the hometown favorite. Riders who knew me from the previous season passed me and slapped me on the back. 'They're yelling for you, man. Good luck.'

As the light slipped away and the street lamps flickered to life, lighting the corners, I began to feel as if I was in a gladiatorial arena rather than at a local bike race. There was a disconnect between the riders and the crowd and for the first time I understood that they truly wanted to see us do battle, to see crashes, as always happened in the nervous early stages of a race, with riders flipping over one another and occasionally over the barricades into the crowd. That

311

was why Craig had told me to race at the front and never leave it, even if I burned more energy pulling the field around the course.

'Whatever you do, don't crash,' was his last piece of advice. 'Even if you kill yourself out front all night pulling, at least the spectators will think you're winning. It will bring me publicity and get the shop's name announced over the PA system every lap. But try to save enough in case a move goes off the front. Those guys from New England look fit.'

Next thing I knew the race was underway. We were flying at speeds usually raced in the middle of the season when everybody was peaking. I stayed up front, either pulling or in third or fourth position. Every time the field swelled around me, I pushed the pace and strung it back out into a single-file line hoping to narrow the field as the weaker riders started popping off the back and getting pulled from the race. I had fallen back to around tenth position when I heard the sound of metal scraping across the pavement behind me, riders screaming along with the distinct sound of heat-treated metal rims snapping in half, helmets and bodies thumping on the ground. I didn't look back or hesitate. To stay out of danger I went to the front and attacked as hard as I could.

When we came back around they had cleared the inside lane of the course for us to fly through – fifteen riders in the left lane were still untangling their bikes and climbing up off the ground. I didn't let off the pace. I buried myself as deep as I could go, knowing that this was my only chance to split the race up on the otherwise flat course with a single slight rise. After motoring for a lap at the front, I finally pulled off and let the next rider come through to take his turn as I glanced back to see if I had done any damage. There were only about ten riders left in the front group. The remaining field was stretched out in single file behind us, chasing, but there were enough teams represented in the break, and I saw two of my guys near the front trying to block the field, so I didn't think they'd catch us if we kept the pace high.

From that point on it felt like we had been transported back to the Middle Ages. None of the riders in the lead group spoke to each

312

other. Each went to the front and shared equally in the task of burying themselves to keep our gap as we separately began plotting our different strategies to annihilate each other and win the race. Even though we were all racing against each other, we moved like a well-practiced cavalry, flowing effortlessly by each other as we dropped down the side of the paceline after taking our pull, then reattaching ourselves to the back before rotating again to the front. Going into the final ten laps, the crowds became thicker and louder until we were racing through one continuous roar.

From there on, the break started fragmenting and the unison we had shared began to splinter as different riders took their chances attacking off the front while others chased furiously to catch up. Five or six did everything in their power to keep us in a single group leading up to the finish. Three were strong sprinters I recognized from the previous season and one was almost impossible to beat. He had won the national sprint championships years earlier on the track and was still one of the strongest sprinters on the road circuit. I begin to worry about my chances. I noticed a pain in my left knee.

I was waiting for a rider to attack and get a gap so I could join him, but none of them stayed off the front long enough for me to jump across before they were caught. With five to go, no longer confident of my chances of winning against the other sprinters, I made a split-second decision to launch an all-out suicide attack and didn't bother to consider the consequences as I came into the off-camber fourth corner and kept my hands off my brakes, knowing they would slow behind me to keep from crashing. I stood up once I'd straightened and went for it. I came through the start/finish area alone out front. I heard the name of my team blaring over the loudspeakers.

I didn't look back to see how big my gap was. It no longer mattered. If they were on me, my race was over. I had invested my final energy into the attack and had four laps left to try to maintain it. I kept hitting the corners fast, faster than we had as a group without touching my brakes, sprinting out of each corner, mashing a huge gear down the straightaways until I soon entered a state of tunnel vision. I came back through the start/finish area still by myself. The crowd noise that had been increasing with each passing lap began to sound muffled as if they were underwater and I was fighting to reach the surface before I suffocated.

I couldn't get enough air into my lungs and couldn't exhale enough carbon dioxide to clear them. The road started to feel spongy and the announcer was speaking in slow motion. I came back through the start/finish area again, glanced at the lap cards on my left and saw the number 2. Two laps to go. I was still solo, but I was drowning. My form broke down, my feet going from smooth circular strokes to desperate attempts to keep the pressure on the pedals. I felt my legs jerk over the top, down the side, along the bottom and the pain returned to my left knee but now it seared, as if a spectator had thrown a small rock and hit me directly on the kneecap.

As I came around the backside of the course, leading into the final lap, I heard something behind me. Three riders flew past in perfect form. I sprinted to latch onto the back of their break but as I did so, I almost passed out and had to sit back down and let them go. Two more riders came by chasing and I couldn't stay with them either. Knowing the remaining four or five riders would soon be coming by, I stood up once more and tried to get my speed up as fast as possible. I shifted into an easier gear and prayed I'd make it around the course one more time before the entire field caught and dropped me. Soon riders were swooshing past me on my left and right. I made one final effort on the backside of the course so that I could hide myself in a group of riders and save myself the embarrassment of finishing off the back alone.

After the race, Craig wasn't as disappointed as I thought he'd be. He actually seemed excited. My knee hurt too bad for me to ride back to the shop to cool down. I wanted off my bike. He took it and asked Janek to put it in his car. Janek bit his lip, as if to say I should have waited another lap or two before making my move. I shrugged.

He slapped my back. 'You tried.'

Craig found a chair for me. A bunch of people came by wanting to talk. Most had never seen a bike race before and asked me all kinds of questions that my mind was too numb to answer. They wanted to know why I'd given up when I was winning the race. Craig carried over a big plastic cup of beer. I gulped it down and held up the empty cup. He disappeared to get another and Janek returned with a frankfurter he had just bought from a vendor.

'That thing will make me puke.'

'It's good for recovery,' he insisted.

I took a bite and handed it back to him as Craig reappeared with another beer. I gulped it down as quickly as the first and held up the empty cup again.

'It's going to be a long night,' Janek said, as he shuffled off to get another round.

Devin appeared behind me while somebody I didn't know was asking more questions. He leaned down and murmured, 'I don't care what anybody says, that was a ballsy move. You almost pulled it off.'

I reached my hand up over my shoulder and squeezed his arm. His comment meant more to me than all the others.

Later when I stood up and turned around he was gone. I felt slightly drunk and, between the exhaustion and the alcohol, had difficulty balancing at first. Craig came by and slipped my arm over his shoulder to take the weight off my left knee, which was starting to swell. As we walked through the crowds across the capitol grounds, I saw Nick surrounded by a group. People gathered around him every chance they could. He saw me limping along with Craig and lifted his chin while carrying on the conversation he was in the middle of. I tossed him a peace sign with my free hand slung over Craig's shoulder before another throng of people obscured him from view.

For two weeks after that I didn't ride. My knee was inflamed and it hurt even to walk. Craig got me a pair of crutches to keep the pressure off and took me to a doctor, who examined it and said I had apparently torn a tiny strand of muscle where it joined the tendon. We had pushed my early-season training too hard to prepare for the first race and now I was paying for it. Other than driving back from the race in DC, I hadn't taken a single day off the bike since shortly

315

after I'd bought my Motobécane. Even when I was sick, I went for rides. There were days when rain poured in torrents and I went out for the adventure of it. Nothing kept me off my bike – but now the doctor insisted that I rest my knee, icing it every two hours and taking anti-inflammatory medication every eight. All the training we had done to reach peak fitness as the season started had been for nothing.

When I was finally able to start training again, I had to ride easier than I had ridden since I'd begun. For a month I could only spin around in an easy gear to keep from putting too much pressure on my knee. After that, I was told to build slowly unless I wanted to risk it injuring it again. It was hard to ride slowly when all I knew how to do was hammer. It would be May before I was back to my previous level, if all went well. By then the spring races I had been preparing for would be over. Being forced to forfeit goals that I had prepared for so painstakingly was difficult.

There was one advantage of being off the bike and later on such a restricted training program: new areas of my life opened that I probably wouldn't otherwise have experienced. Nick's and Craig's friends hired me for small jobs. One guy wanted me to change the oil in his sports cars when he learned I could work on engines. Another had me help him build a stereo console in a listening room – I had never seen an entire room devoted to music the way other people had libraries for reading. The odd jobs I did brought me into contact with a different class of people and made me think back to Chagrin and my grandmother's large house. I wondered what life would have been like if we had never moved away and envisioned myself in her library, studying books. I tried not to wonder if my cousins still lived there or if my mother's mother was still alive. After all, we had never been close.

The sportswriter whom Craig had gotten to write a profile on me helped me get a temporary job as a bike messenger for Associated Press on the day that Pope John Paul II came to Columbia to give a speech in the football stadium. I arrived at the stadium early that morning on my bike with a musette bag – used during long road races in the feed zones – slung over my shoulder in which I planned to carry the rolls of film AP had hired me to collect. I was taken to a press booth up near the top where a group of AP reporters were sitting around drinking coffee. The manager gave me a press pass. He then showed me a temporary darkroom they had set up in the corner where they planned to develop film I brought back from the photographers staged along the route. I was to ride alongside the Pope on the sidewalks behind the barriers, stopping at each photographer to take the film he unloaded from his camera, then racing up to the next point where another waited. The manager showed me how they developed the film, then attached whichever picture they chose to a machine with a round cylinder that spun continuously and sent it out over the wire to newspapers throughout the world. It was strange, knowing that the tiny rolls of film I was to carry across the city would appear that evening and the following morning in newspapers around the world. I had never been involved in anything that seemed so important. They were relying on me.

'Please don't lose any film,' the manager warned me.

I reviewed the course map with him one more time, then told him I'd be back with the film before the Pope climbed on-stage that afternoon. Janek had also gotten me an extra ticket to sit with him and his friends in the box seats near the stage. The AP guys had said I was free once I'd delivered the film, so I planned to run it up to the pressroom, then go down to the box seats to celebrate with the city's Polish contingent before the Pope started speaking. Pope John Paul II's birth name was Karol Józef Wojtyła and he'd been born and raised in Poland.

About an hour before the Pope was due, I rolled across town and waited near the start of the route. A large crowd had gathered. I pushed my bike through them until I was a few blocks into the five-mile route. The lead security detail eventually came through, then another, and behind them the Pope's van with a bullet-proof glass bubble protruding from a hole cut in the roof that he stood in while waving to the crowds. I made my first pickup from a photographer right after he passed, quickly caught up and rode on the sidewalk alongside him as his security detail eyed me closely. When they noticed me make several stops along the way, grabbing rolls of film from official photographers, they relaxed. The crowds eventually thinned so much that the Pope himself became aware of me shadowing him along the course. I was the only person outside his caravan traveling the route directly beside him.

We reached a two-block section where the sidewalks were void of spectators. The Pope had recently visited several Latin American countries where the crowds were never less than a million and appeared mildly baffled at the empty streets. This was the first time he had visited South Carolina. By then I was sure he was eager to finish what had to be the most anonymous tour he had ever taken, and that whoever had come up with the idea of visiting the American South would be dealt with personally when he returned to Rome. The crowds thickened near a main thoroughfare three or four deep, then thinned again.

I looked at the Pope and, without thinking, lifted my hand and waved. He glanced at me rolling along beside him. He didn't wave back, but he looked directly into my eyes and nodded to acknowledge my presence. When he did so a tiny charge of electricity shot through me. The sidewalks thickened into a mass of cheering crowds again as we neared the stadium. I cut through a side street to avoid them and raced down an alley to get ahead of the motorcade and into the stadium to deliver the film. I was in a state of elation, which was exactly how I felt when I won a race.

I reached the entrance a few minutes before the Pope, quickly locked my bike to a chain-link fence, hopped a crowd-control barrier, waved my press credentials to Security and sprinted up the steps. I drank coffee and ate cookies with the AP guys while they developed the film, clipped a picture to the machine and set it spinning in circles, disseminating it over the wire. I stayed to see which one went out so that when I purchased the newspaper the following morning I could take it into the bike shop and point out to everyone that I had delivered it.

Once the picture was spinning and they assured me that it was the only one they planned to send out from the parade route, the guy in charge paid me and I ran down the steps, checking the seat number on my ticket, and joined Janek. It took the Pope another thirty minutes after entering the stadium to appear at the podium. Janek and his buddies were ecstatic.

One evening several weeks later, while we were lying in bed in the back of the studio listening to music, I asked Nick if he considered himself gay.

'How about you?' he asked.

'I asked first.'

'I'm human.'

'Come on, we all are.'

'I thought you wanted an answer.'

'I meant a real one, not a New Age platitude.'

'I'm being serious here. I'm sexual, a sexual being. Would it make you feel more comfortable if I based my entire identity on who I have sex with?'

'I'm not saying that. I'm just asking.'

'Listen, darling, I'm as out as they come. If they insist in New York that I have to fly a flag to show my true colors then let them sew me one the color of flesh. I go up sometimes and march in parades to have a good time and see old friends, but when it comes to obnoxious behavior, proving how different we are or threatening to out other people, count me out. Don't get me wrong – I'm not in denial about the struggles we've been through, but I can't partake in self-righteous behavior that replicates the white-male power structure that most of my gay brothers grew up in. The self-appointed gate-keepers I've hung out with in San Francisco are uncomfortable that I'm comfortable in my own skin – and, believe me, I've been through it a million times. Frankly, I see their definition of gay as too narrow. Whenever I go out there, I feel stifled, not free. They try to separate themselves so much that they've become a mirror image of the culture they grew up in without realizing it. I call them born-again gays, dallying around with the same enthusiasm as Christian students at college distributing leaflets on Jesus. I don't need somebody on the coast representing me. I do a fine job representing myself right here.'

'But you've only been out there a couple times.'

'Please! I've spent enough time out there to know what I'm talking about. It's not like I've been a father forever. I'm not alone in this. I've met gays from coast to coast irritated by the way New Yorkers and San Franciscans represent us as if they're the center of the world. I'll take my ignorant provincial southern town any day over their cosmopolitan delusions. My daughter knows who I am, and I'm more proud of her accepting me than I would be of trumpeting to the world on international TV that I'm queer – and I don't pass up many opportunities for free publicity. I rule this town and don't you forget it. Who else cruises down the street with their hair dyed purple on roller skates with gold glitter?'

'What's the deal with so many straights who feel compelled to call gays "faggots" or some of your gay friends who call straight women "cunts"?'

'Their way of separating themselves. The way I see it, they've been hurt or are trying to be part of the crowd. Either way, pure ignorance.'

I thought about the bumper sticker he had designed and had his friends print up at the shop in the warehouse district. He gave it out for free and it had become something of a hit around the city, not unlike himself. It stated simply, 'Live!' As in 'to live.' It was his proclamation of tolerance and public acceptance. He kept a stack near the front door for anybody who wanted one and always carried another stack in his shoulder bag while skating around Five Points to hand out. I once saw him drop some off on an outdoor table at a café that a group of girls were studying at. He didn't stop and talk to them or explain it, he just said, 'Live!' and skated off. I saw them all over town on the cars of his gay friends, black dancers who came by the studio, jocks from the university, housewives who signed up for his morning yoga class and even businessmen he did graphics for – all of them were happy they had Nick as a friend. He sometimes

320

shouted it out for no reason, skating along the sidewalk or sitting at his desk doing graphic design work.

'Live!'

As far as I knew, it was his invention and he was proud of it.

There was one peculiar thing that I never asked him about because I didn't want to ruin it for him if I was correct. I figured it was his way of making everybody accept each other without even realizing it but it contradicted his comment about only flying a flag the color of flesh. The bumper stickers that everybody had on their cars around town were on a blue background. Each of the separate letters and the exclamation mark were in a different color, but since they were small in comparison to the background I'm not sure many people noticed that the separate colors combined made up the six colors of the gay flag – the blue background forming the first color, the four letters and punctuation mark the other five. He was devious like that. He refused to state the obvious and had no tolerance for others who felt compelled to do so – he saw such people as dense, insecure, small-minded. He was well known and respected in the gay community but he refused to be pigeonholed even as he covertly promoted it.

There were so many things I didn't know about, but sex was the one that preoccupied me most. An illness everybody called AIDS had recently appeared, but many were still in denial about it. I had lived through far too much to die from a disease, but nobody seemed sure what it was. I asked him that day about his occasional trips to New York City for dance engagements. He assured me if anything ever happened he'd use protection. We had never used or even considered it. As naïve as it might sound, I had never even seen a rubber and was too embarrassed to go into a drugstore and buy one. I knew he might find it hard to resist in certain circumstances so I asked him again, 'Are you sure? You promise?'

'Of course I promise. You're the first person I've ever let come inside me. Do you know how much courage that took? I never asked you any questions. I wouldn't put you at risk. I'm hurt you even feel the need to ask.'

321

We never discussed it again. Every day we heard new stories about people getting infected and dying. In many cases, it seemed like they were infected one day and dead the next time you heard about them. If they were lucky they survived a few years, but many died within six months. We were both frightened.

My goal of reaching the Olympic Training Center remained my primary motivation. I was eager to return to a full training regimen once my injury healed. I ended up spending a full eight weeks riding slowly before we returned to the intensity of our former training sessions when we motor-paced twice a week instead of four times and split up the other days with sprinting, intervals and hill climbing, which still allowed me two days a week for recovery rides.

Lying awake in bed one night, I created an elaborate fantasy in which I made it to the Olympic Training Center and eventually to the Olympic Games, competing in the Stars and Stripes jersey, representing my country, sprinting to victory and taking the gold medal. Afterward I climbed up on the podium and waited for the national anthem. I stood there for a few minutes with my hand over my heart, then tore open my jersey to reveal a peace sign painted in black across my chest and stomach. I had had the idea after reading about Tommie Smith and John Carlos raising their black-gloved fists at the '68 Games in Mexico City, but instead of protesting for human rights, I would protest against the use of non-political events like the Olympics to uphold global divisions, like the '36 Games in Berlin, separating people instead of bringing them together. I knew it was unlikely I'd ever win the Olympic road race, but I still wanted to make it out to the mythical castle in the Rocky Mountains. I wanted to go there for no other reason than to prove I was capable of joining the elite.

As compulsively as I had once ingested drugs, I focused on getting in good enough shape to win an invitation to Colorado Springs. Devin and I were riding together again, sprinting for the same landmarks as always. I finally pulled even with him at Brick Sling Sprint, but he had become stronger on the road, nailing it at the front, killing me to hold onto his wheel. We had so much fun training together that I convinced him to sign on with Craig's team, so we could go on the road that summer in the old VW team van and have the time of our lives. He made Craig and me promise to keep it a secret. He told his mother he was going to Wisconsin that summer for an intern program in politics. He never explained why he lied to her and I never asked. I'd promised that we'd split duties working for each other at races, giving us both a chance to win.

During my time in Columbia he was the only one really capable of making a difference at the races. The other teammates were nice, but none was as good as I'd hoped. They were either not as committed to cycling – and who could blame them? It hardly paid enough to fill the gas tank on their cars – or simply not strong enough, no matter how many hours they put in on the bike. I was riding as I always had, hoping to latch onto moves by riders with stronger teams. I sensed that with Devin it would be different. It was hard waiting for the semester to end so that we could head up to Milwaukee for our first big stage race. With him at my side, I had never ridden more confidently.

I had decided that once we hit the road I wouldn't do any partying, but for now I continued going out once a week with Janek and the crew. One night a new guy who had just arrived from Poland joined us. I recognized his mannerisms from my father and ignored his crude anti-American comments – many of which I agreed with, but which made me wonder why he had come to America at all. As the night wore on and we consumed more alcohol, he seemed to get pushy in a way none of the other guys ever had. It was my presence that seemed to bother him most. I was the only one in the crowd who couldn't speak Polish, and when he wanted to make a point to me that he didn't have the skill to express in English, he became frustrated and asked one of the others to translate. When they did, he would cut them off and say, 'No, no, not what I mean.' My only interest was passing time with some friends so I tried to ignore him but that seemed only to provoke him more. He soon started asking about my name, grilling me in a way nobody ever had – what my background was, where my parents were from, what religion I was, what religion my parents were, the sort of questions you don't walk up to a stranger and ask. Janek tried to calm him down to no avail.

The surprising thing was that when I told him my name, he said he knew other Malessas. Janek had told me about Emilia, who had helped run the Nazi resistance during the war and fought in the uprising, but the new guy – whose name I never bothered to learn – knew a family of Malessas in his hometown. I was startled because I had never met another Malessa or known anyone who had, much less a family of them. He said he had grown up with them, gone to school with them, but the main reason he kept returning to the subject was that he wanted me to know they weren't real Poles but Polish-Germans. He inverted the words from how we described ethnicities in America, but I understood his point clearly enough. When Janek came to my defense, I asked him not to bother: 'Please, Janek, no. It doesn't matter. Let's just have another drink.'

'I'll handle this,' he insisted.

He told the newcomer that I was a good guy and that he was picking a fight for no reason. Janek kept saying, 'It's not that way here in America.' I wasn't sure exactly what he meant and I didn't care. I just wanted it to end but their conversation became more heated, switching between Polish and English, sometimes rapidly in the same sentence, until the two languages seemed to fuse into a tongue they invented as they argued. Janek said something about there being plenty of Malessas in Poland who were Poles, not Germans. The other guy started saying something about Polish-Germans, then Polish-Russians and Polish-Jews, and each time Janek shouted at him, 'Same.' He shouted it so loudly that it echoed through the room. Same! Same! Same!

I had never seen Janek so angry. I couldn't grasp everything they said but I understood Janek's point that it didn't matter what they were: if they had been born and raised in Poland, they were Polish. But the other guy didn't see it that way. Finally Janek slammed his fist on the table. Some glasses tipped over and one rolled off and broke on the floor. Everyone was stunned. Now, instead of looking at the other guy, they were staring at Janek as if he'd gone mad. Then, slowly, one by one, including Mr. Grezlik, they turned and looked at me in a way they never had before.

I wanted to disappear. The man who had started it stood there defiantly, as if he had won. Janek started to say something, but I reached behind him so they couldn't see, touched the small of his back and said quietly, 'Please.'

Afterward Janek and I walked through town toward his apartment as he continued talking angrily. 'That's why I don't work with them. I love them, but I can't spend my time trying to prove we're a better country or bigger victims. I love Poland with all my heart. I would die for my country, but we're not at war. That's in the past.'

I went up with him, had another drink and stayed until he'd calmed down. Then I told him I was going back to the studio because I had to rise early the next morning to train. Before I left, I said, 'Thanks, Janek. You didn't have to do that.'

'Why not? We're friends, aren't we?'

'We're friends.' I shook his hand firmly. '*Dobranoc.*'

The streets were empty and the city silent except for the echo of my footsteps against the dark storefronts. My mind was spinning. I became so agitated that I had difficulty slipping the key into the lock when I reached the studio. I lay in bed trying to calm down, then walked out into the dark studio and sat in the middle of the dance floor, meditating, going through a series of breathing exercises that Nick had taught me, but the more I tried to quiet my mind, the louder the words became. It was as if my father was in the room with me, his voice booming off the brick walls and wooden floor. I got up and walked back behind the partition and the mirrors, but my father's voice grew ever louder: 'Our last name's Latin root, *mal*, means bad, ill, evil, abnormal. But the name isn't Italian or Spanish, or Latin, Greek or even Germanic. It's rooted in the extinct Prussian language, the fourth and final Baltic language after Estonian, Latvian and Lithuanian. The Old Prussians were the only Baltic nation forced to assimilate completely and disappear into their conqueror's culture.

325

We repelled the invading Polish Knights, but when the Poles failed, their leader Duke Konrad of Masovia invited the Teutonic Knights – fresh from battling the Palestinians in Jerusalem – into Polish territory to complete the conquest they had started but couldn't finish. The Germans quickly defeated the Old Prussians and kept the newly settled territory for themselves and stole our indigenous tribe's identity to christen their own new kingdom Prussia. Seven centuries later, the Allies abolished Prussia after the war and later unwittingly carried out Hitler's wish to create a homogenous Poland, but instead of more land for Germans to build settlements on, they took what had been for centuries an ethnically and religiously diverse nation and returned it to the insular roots of a duchy, almost entirely Polish and Catholic. They transformed a country built on inclusion into one of the most insular states on the continent.'

My mind shifted between the angry fight in the bar and my father's booming voice in my head. I thought back to my days living on the road, but even that didn't help – the only thing it reminded me of was that whenever I'd entered a homogenous neighborhood, it had seemed less tolerant than a mixed one where I'd always found places to sleep.

I clutched at the Iron Cross hanging on its string around my neck beneath my shirt. As much as I hated its national symbolism, I feared that if I threw it away I'd be even more cursed. Part of me wanted to flush it down the toilet but another part was so infuriated by the man who had ruined a good night's drinking that I clung to it even tighter than I had before. I was so angry that part of me wished I'd thrust it in his face just to prove him correct and make him shut up.

I tossed and turned all night, rose early and went for a longer ride than I had planned, doing a hundred-mile loop through the country-side to shake my father's insidious words from my head, but no matter how hard I rode I couldn't stop thinking about Poles and Prussians, Russians and Nazis. They throbbed in my mind like a bad hangover.

That evening I couldn't take it any longer and showed up at Nick's door. 'I need to talk.'

I was jittery, walking back and forth on the porch, nervous, confrontational. Nick asked what was wrong. I tried to say something but was still too wound up to speak. He suggested we take a walk. We went through Five Points and up Green Street to the university where we cut across campus to the steps of the capitol. It was already dark and nobody was around except a security guard, who watched us but didn't approach. In all the times I had passed the capitol, I had never considered walking up its steps and sitting down to relax. So close up, I was intrigued by the building. My mind calmed for the first time in twenty-four hours. I asked Nick what the large bronze stars affixed to it stood for.

'They cover pockmarks from cannon balls fired at it during the Civil War.'

'The Civil War? Right here?'

'Very much so.'

'I never thought of the war being fought here.'

'It was, all right. I'm not sure it's entirely over.'

'How so?'

'We still have a lot of work to do to settle things, especially equality.'

He was watching me gaze up at the bronze stars. 'What is it?' he asked. 'Tell me what's wrong.'

I struggled to figure out a way to answer his question. Eventually I confessed that images sometimes entered my mind of killing my father.

'Killing him?'

'With a knife. Slicing his throat and watching him bleed.'

He seemed shocked. I don't think he'd expected such words to come out of my mouth, but he maintained his composure. 'I thought you didn't even know him.'

'I knew him. I just don't know him any more. I don't know where he is.'

'What would killing him accomplish?'

'It would get him out of my life forever.'

'He's not in your life.'

'How can you say that? He lives in my mind, even after years of not seeing him.'

327

Nick sat in silence for a long time, lost in thought. I wondered if he was thinking about his own parents, his child. He suggested we get up and go over to the pillars and sit leaning against them to rest our backs. He said that my parents were no different from me.

'That's the point,' I said, becoming angry. 'I don't want to be like them.'

'Let me finish,' he said sternly. 'They weren't much older than you are right now when they fell in love and had children. They were no more mature than you, Sam. If you had children right now, rest assured they'd want to kill you too, the way you're acting. Our parents are no different than us. They make mistakes. Sometimes huge mistakes. They're not perfect. They're not even close to it. You can't hold against them the problems you've inherited. You have to grow, overcome them, become stronger than the problems they passed down.'

'But it's not only problems. It's like I'm responsible for keeping memories—' I cut myself off. I didn't want to go into it. By telling him the details, I'd be unwittingly carrying out my father's wish.

'Yes?' he probed.

'Maybe you're right. Maybe I should just forget about them.'

'I didn't say anything about forgetting them. Have you ever thought about forgiving them?'

'For what?'

'That's your area of expertise. Perhaps the things you want to murder them for.'

'I don't want to murder anybody. Sometimes I just feel like I'm going crazy.'

'You are. We all go crazy sometimes. The strong ones know how to stop it. The weak ones submit. Going crazy is easy. It's keeping from going crazy that's hard.'

I felt myself begin to cry, then stopped myself. I didn't want to look weak in front of him. He slid his arm around me and let me lay my head on his shoulder. I stared across the dark lawn and down the hill toward the river. It seemed my mind was caving in on itself, imploding.

We walked back across campus, alongside a wide water fountain holding hands. We spent the night sleeping together on the mattress in the studio.

He woke early to take his daughter to school, then returned with my favorite breakfast: thinly sliced red onions, cream cheese, salmon and bagels, with a cup of coffee brewed from freshly ground beans. That evening after I finished training, we met at Lizard's Thicket and had my favorite dinner – fried chicken livers and okra. Nick had even stopped downtown that day and bought a bag of boiled peanuts for us to share after dinner. I felt like it was my birthday. I joked that I would have confessed to wanting to kill my father earlier if I'd known how well he was going to treat me.

From then on it became our private joke. We'd be out having dinner somewhere and a mother would scream at her child and Nick would say, 'Little shit's going to murder the bitch when he grows up.'

I'd burst out laughing. 'You shouldn't talk about people like that.'

With our base miles complete and our fitness nearing its peak, Devin and I continued preparing to go on the road. With less than a month before our departure, we shifted our training from the flatlands of the swamps south of the city to the rolling hills in Fort Jackson, the sprawling army base. It covered some eighty square miles of wilderness with roads cut through the forests in all directions to provide different terrain for training. It was the largest base in the country for basic combat training or boot camp, as it was known around town. The base was too large for the small communities surrounding it to drive around so the military kept the gates open so that civilians could cut through to reach downtown Columbia from the countryside.

We often trained in the areas lying beyond the base as well. That was where our favorite climb was, Mount Zion. On long endurance days we circled the perimeter of the base, but mostly we trained inside it: the mix of terrain and road surfaces meant we could prepare for several different surfaces that we expected to encounter that summer. Sometimes we turned onto hard-packed dirt roads and raced each other for hours through the forests, often coming up on soldiers hiding behind trees. The only time we weren't allowed on certain roads was when they were firing live rounds. We kept our hair cut short like the soldiers', and I suspect that most of the new recruits and accompanying sergeants we occasionally passed mistook us for enlistees. We had even taken to saluting them. After all, we were there for the same purpose: to get in the best shape possible.

To hype ourselves up for training, we read the latest racing news coming in from Europe through an obscure periodical Devin had, *Velonews*. It was our only contact with the cycling world. We'd pass the gate entering the base, wave to the guard, then take off racing through the hills against Sean Kelly, Joop Zoetemelk, Phil Anderson, Greg LeMond, Laurent Fignon, Lucien van Impe, Stephan Roche, Pedro Delgado, Luis Herrera, Urs Zimmermann, Moreno Argentin, Giuseppe Saronni, Francesco Moser – we knew them all, and raced daily against the greats through Fort Jackson while preparing to launch our careers.

One afternoon we came upon the tail end of the 2nd Battalion, 13th Infantry Regiment in the middle of drill training strung out in two lines, marching in perfect form, continuing as far as we could see over the next rise. They marched with their arms at their sides, looking straight ahead as ordered. The soldiers at the rear heard me and Devin come up on them from behind and hit our brakes, which squealed, but they were so disciplined that even though nobody was watching them – the sergeant was at the head of the line, out of sight – they never broke formation to look back.

Devin and I put one foot on the ground and watched the two immaculate columns marching in perfect cadence and step. We rested in admiration, mesmerized by their perfection.

Typically when we came upon a regiment marching in formation we watched them briefly and turned back to avoid disrupting them, but as we clipped back into our pedals that afternoon, Devin started rolling forward instead of turning around. He looked back a couple times to make sure I was following him. I tucked into his slipstream, as he started mashing the pedals until we were going almost thirty miles per hour. He shifted into the gear he planned to hold, glanced back to make sure I was still right behind him, then leaned on the drops of his handlebars and shot up the center of the two columns, like shooting the tube of a wave on a surfboard. As we flew along between them, I heard the wind from our bikes whooshing off each soldier as we raced past hundreds on our right and left. If anyone broke file and stepped out of line we would have crashed into dozens of them before our twisted bikes came to a stop, but having observed them before we set out we were confident that nobody would break.

We continued racing up the middle, as every soldier remained looking directly ahead, our presence only coming into view as we raced past them almost touching their hands with our handlebars. We were like a single team working in perfect unison, Devin and I the motorized element coming up the center with the soldiers manning our sides. We were fully aware, as we passed each one, that he secretly relished our private act of rebellion, locked as they all were in the middle of basic combat training, which fueled us to race even faster.

We crested the next rise, looked down the slight descent and saw the head of the column with the drill sergeant, his back to the soldiers, setting an example. Devin and I went racing down the hill at full speed. We had almost made it to the front of the line before the sergeant turned around to check on the troops and saw us coming straight at him. He held up his hand for us to stop. When he realized we weren't going to slow down, he jumped out of the way at the last second.

We sailed past him out into the open, stood up in a rush of adrenaline and sprinted to the top of the next rise, where we paused briefly, turned and threw a fist into the air – a silent symbol of unity with the troops. Nobody signaled back and nobody let out a holler, but we could see from their beaming faces that we were fully in synch as the sergeant yelled at us to report back to him immediately. We waved to the troops one more time, then disappeared down the other side of the hill, racing at full speed to leave the base before he could report us to the MPs.

331

We rolled through town in a state of elation, as if we had both claimed victory in the same race, high-fiving each other at every intersection. We were jazzed and ready to take our show on the road. As we neared Five Points we came into the heavy afternoon traffic of people rushing home. We rode carefully through the streets, holding our line along the gutter of the right-hand lane to avoid upsetting the flow of cars. We reached the top of the last hill heading into Five Points and raced down the other side, shifting into big gears for one final sprint before getting off the bikes for the day. The cars were in a hurry, flying past us faster than our elevated pace. A large sedan passed, driven by an old man – I had noticed him when I glanced back to survey the traffic before we started to sprint for a street sign. When I looked up, I saw him take a hard right-hand turn in front of us without slowing or signaling. I never had a chance to scream out for Devin to hit his brakes. Everything went black.

I woke in a hospital bed. I was the only person in the room. There was an IV drip in my arm and bandages taped up the right side of my body. My mind turned immediately back to the few shattered images of the accident I retained – the car turning, Devin swerving, him going down, the sound of his steel bicycle frame snapping and myself looking down as I flew through the air above him. I glanced at the bandages covering my right side and tried to remember myself sliding down the street at high speed without my bike as the pavement ripped the skin off my body. I had been in enough crashes and lost enough skin to know the feeling but, no matter how hard I tried, I couldn't remember anything that had happened after I was airborne. I could tell from the dull pain that road rash covered my side, but I had no memory of it getting there.

A doctor soon appeared, followed by Craig. The doctor said I hadn't broken any bones, had suffered only a minor concussion and was lucky only to have road rash covering the right side of my body. He signed off on some papers and handed them to Craig. A nurse came in, removed the IV and helped me stand up. Then Craig took my arm and we walked slowly out to his car, parked directly outside the sliding glass doors.

As we were driving home I asked him about Devin. He said they were still doing tests.

'But he's okay, right?'

He didn't answer.

'Did anything happen?' I asked again, this time forcefully.

'Worry about yourself right now. We'll know as soon as they finish the tests.'

He took me back to his house on the edge of Five Points and helped me up the steps to a second bedroom that he had previously used for storage. Everything had been pushed aside and a bed set up in the corner. Aluminum foil still covered the window, blocking any light. He had placed a small table beside the bed with a lamp on it. The house, surrounded by a tall cement-block wall, faced a large park. A dog I'd never heard when I'd visited before barked incessantly nearby. After he helped me lie down, I asked, 'What about the dog?'

'You'll get used to it.'

I had no insurance, no savings, nothing. Craig had never gotten me any medical coverage. It occurred to me that this was why Craig had wanted to get me home so quickly and why the doctor had said nothing about a check-up. At least Craig had gotten a prescription for antibiotics. He pointed out another half-dozen old prescription bottles of painkillers on the bedside table that he had collected from previous accidents. 'Take one when you need it, but don't swallow a handful.' It became quickly apparent that for him bike racing and crashing were synonymous and this was simply another trial we had to endure to reach the next goal. 'At least you didn't fuck up your knees or break any bones,' he said. 'Skin heals quickly.'

A couple of hours later Janek came by to wake me and to turn me over so I didn't get bedsores from lying in one position too long. Every three hours another person from the shop, sent over by Craig, arrived to roll me into a different position. With the entire right side of my body raw, I had to switch between my stomach, left side and back or slight variations of the three.

When Craig came home that evening he ripped the bandages off my leg and hip. 'We're going to keep it exposed now,' he said. 'We can't let a scab form if you want to get back on the bike soon. The pain from tearing the new skin every time you pedal will keep you off the bikes too long.'

'But what about the hospital? They covered it with bandages.'

'They're not bike racers. You want to lie in this room for three months or be out training in less than a month?'

'What about infection?'

'Will you please shut up and let me handle this? I've been dealing with road rash for almost three decades. It's part of the trade.' He picked up a bottle of antiseptic from the floor. 'This is gonna hurt a little.'

Whatever he applied had me writhing in pain. He laughed as I clenched my teeth and held onto the bedpost.

'The sooner you get used to this, the better. I'm not going to be out there on the road nursing you when you crash up in Wisconsin or Michigan. I suggest you watch what I'm doing.'

Once the searing pain eased, I looked down. The rash along the side of my calf and quadriceps was deeper than I'd thought. I saw where gravel had scraped deep lines into my leg and a dot of exposed white bone on the small rounded knob of the fibula, which protruded slightly below the kneecap on the side of my leg. The skin along the side of my calf and up my quadriceps was gone. My right hip was raw too. He applied a thick coat of medicated Vaseline to the wound to cover it from the air so a hard scab wouldn't form and to stop infection from taking hold. He told me to bend my leg every hour and to stretch any new skin that formed to help keep my leg flexible. He had a stack of bandages called second-skin, a translucent gel-filled plastic that you could see through and into the wound, like a glass-bottomed boat floating in a clear lake, but he only applied one around my knee. 'It's too expensive to use on the rest of your leg.' I watched him work for almost thirty minutes while he completed the first prep. He said we'd have to clean the wound once a day and apply medicated Vaseline and second-skin to avoid letting air touch the wound and drying it out.

The pain was so intense for the first few days that I swallowed Demerol and Dilaudid until I didn't care about anything – life, death, making a comeback, lying in bed, even the barking dog outside the window. It would normally have driven me out of my skull but now the noise was almost comforting as I drifted in and out of consciousness, waking only when somebody came in to roll me over or clean the wounds. The intensity of the pain slowly evolved to a dull throbbing, still numbed by the painkillers. I upped the dose each day as my tolerance increased, until one morning when I reached for the nightstand and found the pills had been taken away. When Craig came by a few hours later I screamed at him to give them back.

'Yeah, yeah,' he said, 'keep up your bitching. We'd all love to be strung out on drugs and spend the rest of our life lying in bed. Time for you to stiffen up and start getting ready to ride again.'

I asked about Devin. He said they were still waiting for the results from the tests.

'What kind of tests?'

Each time I asked, he shifted to a different subject, telling me I needed to think about my own recovery. My mind was still too numb from the drugs in my system and I was in too much discomfort from the pain and mild withdrawal symptoms to focus on getting an answer out of him. I felt slightly delusional, holding my hand in front of me to watch it swell and shrink.

That afternoon Nick appeared. He said he had been by several times but that I had been sleeping each time. He peeled back the foil from the window and sun poured in. He opened it a crack and fresh air flowed into the room that offset the stink of my open wounds, which smelled of decaying flesh – somewhere between rotting compost and the faint scent of almonds. I hadn't realized that the room reeked until Nick cleared the air.

He leaned a small stack of records he had brought against the bedside table and pulled down an old record player Craig had stored on the top shelf in the closet. It looked almost exactly like the one my parents had had when I was a child. He set it on the table so that I could reach over and play the music to relax. I asked him if he had heard anything about Devin's test results. He gave me a peculiar look, so I asked again, 'Have you heard anything?'

'Craig hasn't told you?'

'Told me what?'

He paused for a few seconds and sighed.

'What's wrong?'

'Maybe I shouldn't—'

'Shouldn't what? Don't be like Craig. I trust you. Tell me what's going on!'

He paused, as if he didn't want to articulate the words, waited longer, then said it, 'Devin's paralyzed.'

'What do you mean he's paralyzed?'

'He can't move his legs. He can move his arms slightly but he doesn't have control of his fingers.'

'Are you sure?'

'Yeah, I'm sure. We've all been by the hospital to see him more than once. One doctor said people sometimes heal and regain use of their hands but it doesn't look good.'

My vision blurred, then Nick came back into view. I was breathing heavily. Thoughts flashed through my mind. What if it had been me? Why hadn't it killed him? Why had it happened to him and not me? Maybe it was a mistake – maybe they had misdiagnosed him. Maybe it was a cruel joke. They were replaced by a heavy sensation in the pit of my stomach that I imagined must be the way someone feels when they begin to die. I couldn't open my mouth or form a complete word. My breathing eventually slowed enough for me to speak, but the weight in my stomach remained. The sunlight pouring into the room took on a different aspect, shifting from warmth to a clinical brightness, illuminating every detail in the room right down to the trails of dust floating in the air.

'Help me out of bed and take me there.'

'It's not visiting hours right now.'

336

'Goddamn take me there right now, unless you want me to walk.'

I was already climbing out of bed. I could feel the tiny membranes of the new skin growing over the wound ripping open as I bent my leg but I ignored the pain.

'Okay okay, I'll get you there. We need to find you something to wear.'

'They've seen people in robes before. It's a hospital. Help me get this on and tape the side open so it doesn't fall over the wound on my leg.'

We taped the bottom of the robe open and to my leg so it wouldn't stick to the Vaseline, then walked to his car and drove across town. I told him to take me directly to Devin's room and not to stop by the nurse station. I didn't want interference. We made our way down a long hallway, until we neared a door where Nick told me to stop so he could check if anyone was in the room with Devin.

'Don't break up in there,' he said. 'He needs our strength right now.'

As soon as he said it, I felt myself breaking up. He turned me around and walked me back up the hallway until I was calm again. Then we went back to the room. Nick went inside briefly, came back out and waved me in.

Devin was sitting up in bed when I entered. He didn't look bad. Less road rash covered his body than mine. The only visible injury was a small bruise up near his left eye where his head must have hit the car. There was another person in the bed beside him watching television at low volume. Devin turned to Nick and nodded at the curtain. Nick pulled it to give us privacy. I went over to the bed, stood beside him and put my hand on his shoulder. He looked at the open wound covering the side of my leg.

'That looks nasty,' he said. Then he glanced at the robe taped to my leg. 'Who's your fashion advisor?'

I laughed a little at his joke but he could see that I had no idea what to say. Nick waited for me to speak, and when he realized I couldn't, he broke the awkward silence by asking Devin how the food was.

'It sucks, but at least there's a cute nurse who helps feed me.'

We stood there for a while longer. Finally I said, 'I don't know what happened. I glanced back and when I looked around he was already turning in front of us.'

'He had two drinks at lunch,' he said.

'How do you know that?'

'They tested him. He'd been out with friends.'

My mind went blank again. I grabbed for the first words that came into my mind. 'What are the doctors saying?'

'Different things.'

'Did they say how long you'll be here?'

'They want to do more X-rays and tests. I have no feeling in my legs.'

I looked down at them. Their muscular tone was clearly defined through the thin sheet resting on them.

'We're not sure,' he continued. 'I think I'm going to have to go back up to Greenville to my parents' place for a while.'

He waited for me to say something, and when I didn't he looked down at his legs for a long time. Eventually he took a deep breath and said, 'I want you to do something for me.'

'What's that?'

'Go on the road like we planned as soon as you heal and tear those races up. You have to promise and come back this winter and tell me all about it.'

At that second I couldn't hold it any more and I collapsed on the bed beside him and held him. 'It wasn't supposed to happen like this.' I felt his chest heave against mine. Nick, who had been standing with us the entire time, stepped quietly over to the curtain, pulled it the rest of the way closed and went out into the hallway. 'I don't know what to say, man. I'm sorry, but I just do not know what to say.' We sat together like that for maybe fifteen or twenty minutes without speaking. I kept reaching out and squeezing his hand and nervously running my fingers through his hair, letting him feel my touch wherever I thought he could. The tense muscles in his neck relaxed. It wasn't until we heard somebody outside talking to Nick that I sat up and wiped our faces. A few seconds later his mother was standing at his bedside.

'You must be Sam,' she said, reaching out to shake my hand. I could see immediately where Devin got his strength. 'Devin's told us a lot about you.'

I felt awkward again and still couldn't think of anything to say. Nick came in and rescued me, telling Devin's mother that he needed to get me back home and into bed.

'Why didn't you tell me? Why the fuck didn't you tell me?'

A customer who had been standing near the register quietly slipped out the door without finishing her purchase.

'Man, you gotta calm down – you're freaking people out in here,' Craig said. He took me into his office. 'Devin didn't want me to tell you. He wanted us to wait until you could come down and see him. He said he had something he wanted to tell you.'

'That doesn't matter. You should have told me. You know you should.'

'What good would it have done? You were too high on painkillers to hear me anyway.'

'Don't fuck with me.'

'You're fucking with yourself. You need to start worrying about yourself. It's not going to get you anywhere worrying about him now.'

I knew he was trying to desensitize me to Devin's accident. I didn't want to be desensitized. I was aware that the hypersensitivity I had acquired from being beaten as a child had destroyed me little by little ever since, but I didn't want to lose the capacity to feel another's pain. It had happened to my father when he was young and had driven him to things I'd never wanted to know about. I felt my mind shutting down again. More information was flowing through me than I could process. I tried to stand up but felt dizzy and sat down again. Craig came around the desk and took hold of my arm. I slapped his hand away. When I tried to stand again and started to lose my balance, he grabbed my arm, but when I slapped it this time he ignored me and tightened his grip while sliding the other hand around my waist.

339

'Let me and Nick take you back to the house and put you in bed. We can talk about this later.'

I walked out into the middle of the shop with Craig. My robe was still taped to my leg. Janek kept his eyes on the bike stand, working, instead of acknowledging me. I knew it made him uncomfortable to see me weak, screaming uncontrollably. Nick held the door open and they walked me out to his car and set me in the front seat. Then Nick slipped into the driver's seat – Craig ducked into the back – and drove me the few blocks to his house.

As we were climbing the front stairs, Craig said, 'I want to show you something.'

He took me into the dining room, where the table had been pushed to the side and a couple of rubber mats had been laid on the floor on top of which stood a stationary trainer with a new racing bike attached to it. Beside it was another stationary trainer with his bike attached to it.

'That's your new bike. You're going to do your first training today. Nick'll help you into a pair of riding shorts while I run back to the store for a few minutes to get mine and we'll spin an easy thirty minutes to loosen your legs up – it'll help get you going again, clear your head. We'll do it every day for a couple of weeks. Then you can get back out on the road.'

Riding that afternoon was harder than I thought it would be. It was difficult just sitting on the stationary trainer. Craig turned up the stereo and blasted some pop-rock through the speakers. It was numbing to listen to but helped set a rhythm. My entire body was stiff from the crash and in my short time off the bike I had already started to lose fitness. Maybe I hadn't been drinking enough liquids since I had been bedridden, but after fifteen minutes I was so tired I had to stop. He helped me back upstairs to clean up and get into bed.

That became our routine for the next two weeks. I lay in bed all day and all night, except to get up long enough with Craig to do a short ride on the indoor trainer, increasing the length of the ride by five or ten minutes each day. Craig brought me a couple of cases of liquid protein drink that he said had enough nutrition to get me through until I recovered and was able to make my own meals. Janek came by a few times with kielbasa and Nick made some fresh pesto that he mixed with pasta and delivered to me in Tupperware so I could crack it open and eat whenever I felt hungry. I spent most of the following two weeks in the room by myself, listening to music. I thought a lot about Devin and about him asking me to promise I'd go out on the road, a promise I had never responded to that day. I thought briefly about the Olympic Training Center and the Peace Race that Janek had competed in when he was younger. I thought about the last time he and I had gone out to meet his friends and wondered whether I would ever see any of them again. But mostly my mind returned to the road. Not the road of a professional bike racer but that of a wanderer. I missed moving from place to place. I had been in Columbia for almost a year. I liked it more than anyplace I had ever lived before – I liked living in a big city, liked being near the university. I liked living in a section of town where all the storeowners knew one another, and I enjoyed the camaraderie that I had found there. But even with all that it still felt like it was time to move on.

I wasn't sure why I felt so compelled to move on. Perhaps if I had grown up more stable, I wouldn't have felt the desire to drift from one place to the next, but whatever it was I couldn't ignore it. I was sure Janek and I would stay close friends but I didn't want to harm his relationship with his other friends any more than my presence already had. It hurt every time I thought about Devin. Even if Craig sponsored me for another year or two, I couldn't see what benefit I'd be to him after that. I loved Nick but he was almost twenty years older than me, he had a child, he had been to New York City and San Francisco, he owned a business and people looked up to and relied on him. For as long as we stayed together, people would see me only as his partner, not as an individual chasing and fulfilling my own dreams. Besides, his view of things like San Francisco was jaded. I wanted to see it for myself and make my own decisions without him imprinting his views on me any deeper than he already

341

had. I wanted to see and experience the world on my own terms, not anybody else's. I had seen the Pope. I had seen two presidents. I had seen the underbelly of America and experienced things nobody wanted to discuss and would probably refuse to believe anyway. I didn't owe anyone anything. I just wanted to try to break the spell of everything going wrong every time I was sure I was about to achieve something. I wondered if everybody went through the same thing and whether it was true that only the strong eventually emerged or whether some people, no matter how hard they tried, never got anywhere while others who invested little succeeded. I felt as if I had been through three or four lifetimes already but each time I found a path that I was sure would lead somewhere I came to a dead end.

My mind shifted to California. I remembered my parents talking briefly about meeting there before going back to Ohio to have me. My older brother had been born in Santa Monica, but my mother never spoke fondly of it. I remembered a convict, released from state prison into the custody of Relativity, with whom I'd sat up late one night in the dorm when we couldn't sleep. I'd listened to him whisper about hitchhiking one summer up the California coast and spending the winter camping on the hillside in a small redwood forest alongside Strawberry Creek overlooking the bay near a town he had called Berzerkeley. I never forgot the strange-sounding name or the idea of camping on the hillside in a forest overlooking the ocean. I'd listened to Nick's stories and looked through his photo albums, but the thing that illuminated my imagination most were two records Nick had left that I spun on the turntable day and night for a full two weeks. I even told Craig I wanted to listen to them on the stereo downstairs each day while we completed our indoor training sessions. When he saw them, he rolled his eyes and wanted to know if I planned on wearing love beads while we trained. 'I should have known Nick would turn you into a Joni convert,' he said.

But I could tell by the way he gazed at the covers that he had his own set of memories attached to the music and remembered that he had been out to California to race a decade or so earlier and had talked about eating fresh avocados and oranges off trees. *Blue* used

342

nothing more than an acoustic guitar, a dulcimer and an occasional piano alongside soft drumming on a couple tracks. The mournful innocence of the music wrapped its arms around me and wouldn't let go. When I lay in bed late at night unable to sleep the words held me. Only one song mentioned California directly but something about the music seemed saturated in the place. It was *Hejira* whose dark sounds convinced me I needed to go back on the road. I sensed that Joni Mitchell hadn't simply invented songs about a person lost on the road or who felt at home there: they were based on her own experiences, for the moods seemed too close to my own to be made up. At four in the morning, my leg throbbing, I lay perfectly still until dawn, listening to the bass player's fingers sliding across a smooth Fender fretboard, producing sounds like a small boy weeping juxtaposed against her voice singing about a strange boy, comfort in melancholy, a ragged black crow flying from tree to tree, and a blue motel room. I put the record on auto-repeat to play over and over while I lay there in sheer exhaustion, my mind unraveling, lost in a world I couldn't understand, accompanied by music that I heard more as release than self-pity – the loss, the pain, the frustration, my failures and self-exile circling endlessly in my mind until finally, exhausted, I fell asleep at the first rays of dawn.

I didn't see Devin again that summer. His parents transferred him to a hospital in Greenville without notifying us. I learned later that his mother had disapproved of his cycling on public roads. He had apparently told her that he only trained on Fort Jackson. Now her worst fears had become reality. I remembered him saying he had told her he had gotten an internship up in Wisconsin to explain our planned road trip there. I called him, though, and made the promise.

When I finally started riding on public roads again, it was strange going out to Fort Jackson or to the swamps past Brick Sling Sprint alone. I couldn't bring myself to sprint for the broken branch any more and sometimes it was hard just finishing the training ride, but I knew the bike provided the only means for me to leave Columbia, other than putting on a backpack and hitchhiking out of town. The memories of the last time I had done that still haunted me more than the fear of being run over by a car.

Slowly my form returned. I got faster every week, confirmed by the time splits I recorded on my stopwatch doing loops out on the base. I didn't focus much on sprinting any more. Without Devin around I knew I'd never be much of a sprinter. I didn't have the natural speed required to win races in field sprints and had only gotten lucky the previous year through mistakes made by other riders and Devin whipping me into shape before my only victory the previous fall. But even without the talent to win sprints, I was strong. I could climb fast for my size and felt certain that, in a moment of hesitation by other riders, I could jump away near the finish line and claim a win for Devin. Once I returned to my previous level of fitness, it didn't plateau as it had in the past: I became stronger and stronger. Whenever I thought about Devin lying in bed unable to move, I rode harder until I thought I might push myself too hard and injure my knee again.

By then I knew I was ready to leave. I didn't want to travel with anybody else now that Devin couldn't make the journey. I didn't care about having a teammate. Fortunately Craig understood and let me pack the VW van with my belongings alone. We parked it behind his house and carried old pieces of lumber out of his garage and used a circular saw to build a makeshift bed frame in the back that I secured by drilling holes through the steel floor and inserting massive nuts and bolts. Craig dragged the mattress I had recovered on down the stairs and into the van. He took an old cooler from the joists in his garage and slid it under the bed. He lifted a five-gallon water tank off his workbench and helped me build a holder for it near the sliding door, so I'd have water to prepare meals with and shower in rest areas. He took his old Coleman stove out of a storage closet, bought new gas canisters and loaded it into the van. He used all of his knowledge from living on the road as a professional cyclist and passed it on to me. He taught me how to massage my quadriceps after races. He gave me a big jar of vitamin B-12 and told me to take them before important races. He told me never to be embarrassed at being a bike racer or living in a car.

He was convinced we were laying the foundation for what would become a great American sport and told me not to dismiss the fact that it was possible somebody would be the first American to win the Tour de France and it might be me. When he mentioned the Tour de France, I thought of the Peace Race behind the Iron Curtain but I didn't mention it.

He helped me weld a couple of old hubs with quick-release skewers to the gutter on the rear of the van to attach my bike to while I was traveling so I'd have more room inside. He told me to buy bananas and fig bars to carry in my jersey pockets for fuel during long road races and to mix my water bottles with fifty percent Coke – after shaking up the can and releasing the carbonation – and showed me how to take an old toe-strap and slip it under the rails of my seat to attach another water bottle to my bike in case I needed more than the two stored in the cages in the main triangle. He taught me every old racer trick in the book, then unexpectedly told me he didn't care if I didn't win a race for him that fall as long as I returned to town without the long face I'd worn since Devin's accident.

'It won't bother me if you don't win a race, but I know you will.'

One night when Nick and I were sitting up together in the back of the dance studio a few days before I left, I asked him if he believed in God. I needed something besides the bike to carry me, and I hoped that the profound philosophies of monks, priests or rabbis who had spent generations gathering knowledge might guide me to a more purposeful life. When I was running through the woods to escape and burying myself in leaves I hadn't done it with the arrogance of an atheist. I had difficulty accepting that atheists existed among the world's poor: atheism seemed to belong to the wealthy, who never had to worry about their next meal.

The little I had read about agnosticism made sense in that it was impossible to know whether or not there was a God. Or as Bertrand

Russell stated, 'If not impossible, at least impossible at the present time.' I had never been to church but my mother had taught me how to pray. Our prayers weren't so much religious as a way for us to spend a warm, private moment together with our eyes closed thanking God that we had each other, a warm house and food. I waited in bed for her to share a prayer before sleep with more anticipation, warmth and love than any human contact I'd experienced since. In a sense those prayers formed my emotional foundation.

Nick knew that I was leaving for the Midwest to race, but I hadn't told him I might not come back and, besides, now that I had promised Devin, I had to return and tell him all the stories about going on the road. Nick had never mentioned his religious background and I'd never asked, but he had said he didn't believe in an exclusive God. He said any godlike entity was too powerful to belong to one group. He spoke for a long time about something he called a godhead. Most of what he said was too esoteric for me to understand, but he had clearly studied and given it a great deal of thought. I understood for the first time why so many people sought him out for spiritual consultation. We had previously avoided such discussions in our own relationship but on that day, with my departure imminent, he shared his views with me.

He said it was impossible to know if there was a God, but the universe was infinite and its creator one and the same. He said that God manifests himself to us at all points of being, through intellect, emotions, persistence, contemplation, mercy, understanding, strength, knowledge and our physical presence. He said that the soul had three attributes: the first makes up our physical appearance and our inherent behavior; we develop the second throughout life – our moral nature and ability to differentiate good from evil; the third separates us as individuals from other life forms. In essence we were emanations of God, yet independent and able to choose our own paths through life.

Praying for success, he insisted, was useless – God would not assist us in achieving it because success was a human desire that did not figure in the laws of the universe. Life's journey, he said, was along

346

a dark path whose end never fully revealed itself until we were in the final stages, at which point the real journey began. He refused to indulge my questions about whether there was an afterlife. He didn't dismiss it but it didn't matter, he said. 'You only have enough energy for the physical journey.' He didn't believe in redemption but he did believe we were ultimately held responsible for our actions, but those actions paled in comparison with the mental suffering humans faced. It was the mental suffering that broke us, he said, not physical limitations or roads not reached, but areas in our mind that we failed to penetrate and use that had been available to us all along. With enough patience and perseverance, he believed, it was possible to crack our internal code through contemplation and meditation, slowly unlocking the secrets that God, or whatever, had programmed. But he was insistent that the code didn't supersede free will for there were so many variants that the outcome became infinite depending on how the code was cracked. The sadness of it all, he said, was that humans had such a limited life span and took so long to develop that it was almost impossible to unlock more than a few of those possibilities.

I asked him what I should do when I experienced a moment of weakness.

'We pray for and to ourselves,' he said. 'God exists in every place of worship, so if you feel the need while searching, stop wherever you're drawn. But don't expect answers to reveal themselves in relation to how or with whom you pray. The answers lie within.'

I awoke early after spending the previous day visiting with Janek at the bike shop, talking about racing strategies, and left before dawn. I took the few hundred dollars Craig had given me to reach the first races in Wisconsin and instead drove up the eastern seaboard to compete in New England. I was scared Craig might not let me use the van if he knew I wasn't going to Wisconsin. I no longer wanted to go to the Midwest since Devin and I were supposed to go there together and it was too close to Ohio. I didn't want to be tempted to revisit the place of my birth. I was going on the road to free myself, not confuse myself further.

I drove through the first day until I reached the outskirts of Richmond, Virginia, where I pulled off the interstate and slept alongside a road leading up to what looked like a plantation house – it was bigger than any I had ever seen in the Deep South. I was awoken early the following morning by a state patrol rapping on the window with his flashlight. He wanted to see my driver's license and registration. He radioed it in. Once the dispatcher cleared me, he asked me to open up the back of the van so he could see inside. 'You belong to some sort of traveling circus with bikes?'

'No, sir. I'm a bike racer.'

'I advise you to move on and don't stop until you've crossed the state line.'

'Yes, sir.'

I was relieved he hadn't ticketed me. I hardly had enough money to get to the races and eat, much less to pay fines. For all Craig's generosity in saying he didn't care if I won a race, my financial resources were so slim that if I didn't place in the top ten I wouldn't have money for gas or food. He had his ways of getting results.

I traveled along the interstate the entire day, passing through Newark and miles of what I assumed was government housing in the middle of the biggest city I had ever seen. I tried to imagine how anyone could feel anything but lost among such immense anonymity. Every time my own life started to feel overwhelming, I came across situations that made me seem fortunate. And for all the roads that had led nowhere, at least none had taken me to prison. I entered a tunnel leading into New York City feeling more confident than I had before I entered Newark and later, in Connecticut, I felt prepared to test myself against the New England riders on their home turf.

I eventually crossed the border into Massachusetts, parked my van between two other VWs somewhere outside a small college town and fell into a deep sleep. When I woke, I cooked breakfast by the roadside on the Coleman stove, pumped up the tires on my bike and headed into the rolling hills for a long training ride. Partway through

I came upon a small pack of local riders and latched onto their group. They seemed mildly irritated that I wouldn't drop off the back. When their team leader attacked over a hard climb to get rid of me and I was the only one who could hold his wheel, I knew I was ready.

The races turned out to be much tougher than I'd expected. I didn't know any of the riders so I didn't know who to watch or what breaks were dangerous. After failing to crack the top twenty in the first two races, I focused on winning primes – lap prizes – in the following races so I'd have enough money to stay on the road. Those were actually quite easy to win because they didn't know me, either. When I headed off on a suicide mission early in the race, they let me go and I stayed out long enough to collect enough lap prizes to equal the pay of breaking the top ten, then pulled out of the race to recover for the next.

I was stronger than I had ever been, but the races were more competitive and the strategies more complex. I finally managed a top-ten result, and then a fifth place at a criterium in Fitchburg. Slowly, over six weeks, the riders got to know me. I discovered my main talent up there – time trialing: the race against the clock. Since it was only the rider against the clock, going off at one-minute intervals, you didn't have to worry about team tactics or strategies, you just went all out. I finally claimed my first victory in a prologue time-trial at a three-day stage race. I rolled off the starting ramp and raced at full speed, thinking about Devin the entire way. Still, I was surprised when I saw my name atop the results page that afternoon. I was awarded the leader's jersey going into the first stage, but five laps into that race I rolled a tire in a corner and slammed onto the ground.

The following week I entered a smaller road race in Vermont whose course rolled through the Green Mountains. I escaped with five miles to go and held it to the line. No matter how small the race, the rush of victory was the same, but it would have been all the more intense winning with Devin at my side. Two victories were more than I had expected that fall. They gave me a trophy at the road race that I planned to take back to Devin. I had collected the results I had come after. I spent a week camping in my van near Stowe, Vermont, training

349

on the roads outside town for a race down in Central Park the following weekend.

In Manhattan I claimed sixth place and considered that my breakout performance. Several Europeans had showed up and three national champions were in attendance, two of whom I beat that day. But my real reason for coming to New York was to find the location of the original Madison Square Gardens to see the spot where bicycle racing had reigned as one of the greatest sports in America before motorized vehicles had become popular. The site had since become one of the most famous landmarks for concerts – few knew its origin as a velodrome, a banked, circular, bike-racing track.

The following weekend, I entered my final competition for the year, a criterium in Atlantic City. After warming up in the big field, I waited until everybody was lined up, then rode backward around the course and approached the starting line, stopped, turned my bike around and pushed my way into the first row, ignoring the riders in the second and third rows screaming at me to go to the back of the field. I knew it was an important race and even though it was hard to ignore the social pressure, I followed the advice Craig had given me shortly before I left: 'If you don't have the balls to push your way into the first row at the start of the race, you ain't got the balls to come over the line first at the end.' The guy beside me seemed irritated, but he pulled his bike to the side and gave me room to squeeze in.

The announcer introduced several riders present that day. He went through the names of several national champions who had been in Central Park, then introduced as the highlight a rider named Eric Heiden. Leaning down on my bike I looked up at the man standing next to me, waving to the crowd. He had won five consecutive gold medals in speed skating at Lake Placid in the 1980 Winter Olympics. He had been on the cover of *Time* and *Sports Illustrated* and was one of the most popular athletes in Europe where speed skating was revered. He had since transitioned into bicycle racing since it used similar muscle groups as speed skating. I felt like a moron – I'd asked him to move aside so I could push my way in. The amazing thing was he had done so and I was standing shoulder to shoulder with one of the world's great athletes, preparing to compete.

When the referee fired the starting pistol, I followed him through the pack. I wanted to know if I could match his pace, see who he chased down and when he waited. I had been given a chance to study the racing habits of one of the world's best and I wasn't about to pass it up – at least, not until halfway through the race when he glanced back and noticed me shadowing his wheel and gave me a subtle hand gesture to take a pull at the front and do my share of the work. I went ahead, even though it benefited me in no way whatsoever. I finished the race eighteenth, but I felt as if I had just won the world championships.

Instead of driving directly back to South Carolina, I got off the interstate and took a secondary highway into North Carolina, then drove west across the state to the Tennessee border. Along the way I stopped in Asheville and bought a used backpack at a thrift store and a disposable camera at a drugstore. I had always dreamed of climbing to the top of a mountain and, without the pressure of any more races or the necessity to keep my form at the end of the season, this was my chance. I had studied my road atlas while camping in New England and settled on the Smoky Mountains. I liked the name and knew of an area there called Rocky Top from an old country song my mother sometimes played by Lynn Anderson. Back then I had dreamed of hiking along the Appalachian Trail that meandered through the wilderness and along mountaintops from Georgia to Maine, crossing the Smokies on the way. I went to a ranger office to get trail maps, drove out to a trailhead, packed enough gear to spend a few nights in the woods and set out.

I climbed through dense forest until I approached a large stream flowing down the mountainside. The trail crossed it, so I sat down, took off my shoes and carefully balanced my way across the fast-rushing current. At the other side, I put my shoes and socks back on, then continued up the trail until it switched back and crossed

351

the stream again. I sat down a second time, repeated the process and climbed further up the mountain under the dense canopy until the trail switched back yet again and stopped at the creek. After two or three more crossings, I kept my shoes on and waded through the current each time. A couple of hours later, in soggy shoes and socks, I entered the stream for the twelfth time. Instead of being irritated, I was delighted by the challenge. I hadn't expected the hike up the mountain to require me to ford a stream so many times – it brought back memories of my brother. I remembered a line from the song of two strangers climbing to Rocky Top, looking for a moonshine still.

If I could have disappeared into that forest forever and been able to survive, I wouldn't have thought twice about it. There was no tension in the trees, no pollution, no traffic noise, nobody screaming, no cars honking. Other than the gurgling stream running down the mountainside and an occasional rustle of leaves from a breeze blowing through the forest, there were no sounds. It was a weekday, late in the fall, and I didn't pass a single person along the trail. I came to a spring below the ridgeline and walked up unexpectedly behind a black bear, startling us both. I looked down at the ground to avoid eye contact, a sign of aggression, as the ranger had told me, and didn't run, which might have triggered him into chasing me. After a few minutes the bear slowly ambled into the brush. The ranger had said several bears lived near the ridgeline, though I hadn't expected to see one. Before he disappeared I snapped a picture of him crossing the creek, for Devin.

The path eventually intersected with the Appalachian Trail at the ridgeline, where I came out on a bald – a wide, treeless meadow covering the ridge – and the view opened up in all directions. A panorama of rolling green mountains spread before me. I sat down, drank some water and caught my breath after the long climb. My eyes followed the trail along the ridgeline. I tried to imagine what it would be like to have enough freedom to leave everything behind and hike all the way to Maine. I followed the Appalachian Trail upward across the tops of mountains and eventually reached Rocky

Top, a small area of exposed sandstone boulders. Looking across the endless vista, my mind returned to my brother, and then to my mother. My entire family seemed to have disintegrated. I wanted nothing more than to be free and unconnected to the past, but at certain moments I wondered where they had disappeared to. We seemed to be on separate journeys away from one another, traveling as far and wide as we could, as though to avoid the possibility of accidentally crossing paths.

I was aware of the mistakes I had made but I wondered what else about my personality had driven my parents away. I couldn't imagine severing contact with any child of mine, the living form I had brought into the world, influenced, taught, nurtured. I realized then that one reason I liked training and racing so much was that it kept me in an elongated state of pain in which I could think of little besides pushing through its barrier and trying to reach the next level.

I continued to the summit of Thunderhead Mountain. When I reached the top I looked into the distance, at Tennessee on one side and North Carolina on the other. Rhododendron and mountain laurel grew all around me, straddling the ridgeline, the razor's edge between stability, success and complete mental breakdown. I had so far avoided letting myself fall into the abyss, but standing there so far out in the wilderness, so far away from society, I wondered whether I had found peace or if I was simply ignoring the insistent buzz of insecurity that corralled me in an invisible barbed-wire fence. At the same time I knew the outposts were in my mind and that I was the only one capable of defeating myself after all I had stood through. I had to tell myself that, to repeat it over and over and believe it: there was no other option. The only other route led to a place that I didn't want to confront any more than I already had, a place below the earth's surface that I could not bring myself to acknowledge. I would never descend to it even if I had to stand alone atop the mountain for the rest of my life.

Devin's parents' house was located on the edge of Greenville near the base of Paris Mountain. He insisted that I spend the night and

353

climb the mountain on my bike first thing in the morning. 'I always wanted to bring you up here to climb it.'

He was as strong as he had been in the hospital. At first I interpreted it as a false confidence, a way to avoid thinking about his life, which had been turned upside-down. I could see that his mother was still adjusting to the radical change. She knew Devin liked my company and she wanted to see him happy. When I gave him the trophy, he asked me to set it on the windowsill, then tell him every detail of the race. I spent the night lying on the floor of his bedroom and we talked until sunrise. He wanted to hear what New England had been like, every move in each race, Central Park, Madison Square Gardens, and especially how it had felt to race against Eric Heiden.

The following morning, at first light, Devin said, 'Go get your bike out of the van and climb Paris Mountain.'

'We haven't slept.'

'I'll get some rest for you while you're gone.' He laughed. 'I want to know how the climb is at this time of year. I was always in school right now.'

I went out before his mother woke, got on my bike and rolled away. I didn't want to upset her any more than my presence already had and thought I should probably leave that afternoon and complete the short drive back to Columbia. The ascent wasn't as long as I'd expected from Devin's description, but it was a hard climb, the hardest I had ever done in South Carolina and more so since I felt as though I were seeing it through his eyes. It was painful being with Devin. He maintained his optimism in the worst of circumstances, an optimism that I barely managed when things were good. He refused to get lost in the dark.

When I returned to the house, his mother was helping him read a letter the university had sent him. 'There's a program for handicapped students,' he said. 'I might be able to finish up my degree. Mom's going to check for me and see if anyone's representing the handicapped in the state capitol.'

A smile spread across my face. He was already plotting out his career back into politics.

When his mother had left the room, I said, 'I can't even get into school and you're going to take a degree and make it to the capitol?'

'This is serious stuff,' he said. 'As a congressman or even senator I'd be caught up in politics as usual. As a voice for the handicapped, I can make a difference. I can make a real difference.'

'You've already made a difference, Devin. Every time we're together I come away looking at things differently. You have a gift, man.'

'I appreciate hearing that, coming from you. My body's down, but I can't let my mind waste away over it. That's the amazing thing this has taught me. Your mind is bottomless. Do you realize how much power you have when all your energy is focused exclusively on your mind? I can't even begin to explain.'

Driving back to Columbia, I thought a lot about what he'd said. I wondered if there was any way I could tap into the same places he had been since the accident. He had such an amazing outlook. He refused to pity himself. I had been mourning my own life since almost the day I was born and here he was, unable to move, but he wasn't about to let it stymie him. Even if privately he sometimes fell into depression, he persistently sought to find opportunities that hadn't been available to him before the accident. His brief presence filled me with optimism.

To make some money that winter, I found a job as a cook at a Mexican restaurant in Five Points. I started out prepping in the morning, but when another guy was fired they moved me up to the cooking line at night. With no races coming up I wanted a steady income. Work at the shop slowed through the winter. Between Craig, Janek and a cashier who subbed as a mechanic, there wasn't enough work to keep me busy and I wanted more independence anyway.

I asked Janek how to apply to the winter training camp in Colorado that started at the beginning of January.

'You need to make a resumé.'

'How do I do that?'

'Write your results on paper.'

'That's it? On a regular piece of paper?'

'No, use newspaper and crayon.'

'Be serious.'

He handed me a pen from his workbench.

'Just handwrite it?' I asked.

'You have secretary?'

'Okay, okay. I'm just asking.'

I worked on it all afternoon. When he finally approved it, I rewrote it as neatly as possible on a piece of paper I'd torn out of a spiral notebook, then used scissors to trim off the jagged edge, sealed it up and took it to the post office.

Nick was remodeling the back of the studio, building offices to rent to dance majors at the university to bring in more money, so I moved back into the bike shop. I set a bedroll on the floor in the storeroom, the same place I had slept when I first arrived in town. I was comfortable there. Craig said I could take the spare bedroom at his house, but I didn't want to be reminded of the accident and I liked the independence of having a key to the shop and being there alone late at night. It was my place of solace. I preferred the Spartan surroundings of the storeroom. For me it emphasized my sacrifice to reach a higher goal, instead of enjoying comfort I hadn't earned. I maneuvered several bike boxes and built a tiny private room in the rear corner like a little fort.

The job at the restaurant was a challenge. I showed up at five in the afternoon to set up my station, warm up the grill and then stood around visiting coworkers until the dinner rush hit. From then until closing it was like racing the hardest time-trial ever. The waitresses stood in front of our line glaring at us whenever we got an order wrong or if we didn't bring them out fast enough. We were like a conveyor-belt, relying on each other. We hit a three- or four-hour period each night when it was hard to keep up with the orders. I flipped meat on the grill with one hand and garnished plates with the other, experiencing an unexpected sense of accomplishment.

Cleaning the grease out of the vent above the grill, scrubbing the

356

burners and mopping the floor until midnight was no fun, but we cranked up music on the stereo after the customers left and danced around the kitchen while we worked, making the best of a dirty job. The owner occasionally broke out a bottle of tequila after locking up and threw a private after-hours party for the employees from midnight to three in the morning. One night the waitresses piled their tips into a big stack of money on a table at the center of the room and paid us to do a striptease on the bar. I played it to the hilt, with my shaved legs and muscles from the racing season, eyeballing the stack of money as I shook my ass and executed dance moves I hadn't known I was capable of performing. By the end of the night, I won the stack of money but ended up splitting it with the other cooks.

Through it all, I still meditated on the freedom of being on the road, living from place to place, but Colorado was occupying my mind most. As I worked nights I was able to maintain my daily training sessions, and with the extra money I had from work, I drove down to the coast on days off, putting the bike in the back of the van and going to places like Beaufort to ride along the waterways.

I was sleeping between the long, narrow bike boxes in the windowless storage room when Craig walked in and turned on the bright florescent lights. 'Wake your lazy ass up.' He dropped an envelope on the floor in front of me. I squinted in the bright light to adjust my eyes. 'Hurry up. Some of us work for a living.'

I looked at the envelope. In the top left-hand corner, in official lettering: 'United States Cycling Federation.' The next line down: 'Olympic Training Center.' Below that: 'Colorado Springs, Colorado.' I stared at it in disbelief, until Craig asked, 'What are you waiting for? They're probably telling you to fuck off. You plan on opening it or staring at it all day?'

I tore open the envelope and unfolded the page. 'After reviewing your results, the coaches invite you to attend . . .'

'Are you in or not?'

I held up the letter. He snatched it out of my hand and read it. I clearly wasn't the first rider he had worked with to receive an invitation. He made it clear that he wasn't interested in savoring the moment.

'Congratulations, but this doesn't mean much. You'll have three weeks to prove yourself once you arrive. You'll be right back here sleeping on this floor in less than a month if you don't make the cut in the first camp. Of forty, all get cut but five. Then they start over again, through three camps. Whoever's left standing at the end of the last camp goes on the road with them. I suggest you get the hell up, pump your tires and mine and get ready to ride. I'll fill the bottles and ask Janek to watch the shop while we're out.'

I rubbed my eyes again and picked up the letter he had dropped onto the floor in front of me. I was required to arrive in Colorado at the beginning of January, exactly two weeks away. I leaned up and sat for a minute, stretching my arms and rereading the short invitation. I felt like I was floating. Finally something good had happened. A dream I had focused on to the exclusion of all else had been realized. Once I arrived in Colorado, no matter what happened, I would belong permanently to that select group of athletes who had been invited to live at the training facilities in Colorado.

Before leaving the shop to ride with Craig, I went over to Janek. 'Did you have anything to do with this?'

He looked at the invitation, shrugged his shoulders and smiled. 'Congratulations.'

'Is that a yes or a no?'

'You earned it. You're fast now. Chance to go to the Peace Race, no?'

'I just want to make it through the camp. If you had anything to do with this, I don't know how I can repay you.'

'You earned it yourself. We all need friends.'

Later that afternoon, I called Wade. I asked him if he could take the day off work tomorrow, ride over to Aiken and meet me.

'What's it about?'

358

'I'll tell you there.'

'Why don't you come over to Augusta? We miss you.'

'I can't come to Georgia right now. But I can meet in Aiken.'

The following day I set out for the long ride through the South Carolina countryside to Aiken, a town near the border famous for horse breeding. The round trip was longer than I normally trained at that time of year, but I wanted to arrive in Colorado in the best shape possible. We met near the center of town around noon and had lunch. Instead of telling him, I set the letter on the table in front of him. He knew its contents without reading it because he let it sit there and just smiled. 'You did it.'

'I wanted to keep my promise. Took a little longer than planned, but I'm going. Not sure whether I'll come back or not, regardless of what happens there.'

'I'm proud of you. You never dropped the ball. After your knee injury, after your accident, you stood back up each time. Most people would have folded.'

'It's because of you. I wouldn't even be racing if it wasn't for you. I didn't even know people raced bicycles. I didn't want to disappoint you.'

'You wouldn't have disappointed me, but this makes me happy. Happier than you can imagine. Makes me feel like I'm heading out on the road again myself.'

'I wish there was some way I could show my thanks.'

'This is my thanks. Nothing against Craig, but I didn't want to see you get stuck over there. Life is better here in Augusta than Columbia – at least, for me it is.'

'I miss it sometimes. But I don't know. Lot of hard memories.'

'It's not perfect for everyone, but it helped get you back on track. I expect you to come through and see us some time during the year if you make it back down south to race. You've always got a place to stay. Janet misses you keeping me busy.'

The last week in Columbia before my departure was kind of sad. Everybody wanted to know my plans for the spring, after the training camp finished, but I remained vague. I would already be halfway to

California by the time the training camp ended in Colorado. It didn't make any sense for me to drive all the way back to South Carolina, but I couldn't tell anyone that. Craig could see that last summer's accident had changed me and had become more of a friend than a sponsor, but I still didn't have the guts to tell him I wasn't coming back. It was hard and selfish keeping it from the people who had become my family but I knew if I told them they'd try to talk me out of it.

I waited until a few nights before I left to tell my manager at the restaurant the news. I wanted to make as much money as I could before I went and feared that, if he knew I wasn't going to be around much longer, he'd cut my hours back and give them to somebody else. When I did share the news with him, his only response was 'You can't leave like that. You have to give at least two weeks' notice.'

'I just got accepted into the Olympic Training Center. What would you do? You expect me to stay here out of grace and pass it up?'

He wouldn't give in. Instead of wishing me luck, he seemed intent on bringing me back down to earth. I worked my shift that night so the guys in the kitchen wouldn't be left short-handed and so I could say goodbye to everybody, but on the way out after clean-up, I told the manager I wouldn't be back tomorrow. He muttered something about my final paycheck, which included that night and the hours I had worked the previous two nights.

I'm not sure what made me do it but, uncharacteristically, I said, 'Take the money and shove it up your ass. And thanks for all your encouragement. I didn't think you'd jump up and down, but I wasn't expecting you to make me feel like I'm obligated to stay here, either.'

Being around Nick was difficult. We'd spent a lot of time together those last couple of weeks, mostly hanging out at the studio or preparing dinner at his house, but he was quiet and it didn't help that I remained silent myself. Instead of celebrating the last days together, he moped around and ate dinner either without looking at me or glancing at me with an expression of resignation. I hadn't

360

expected it from him, especially after all the times we'd shared. Now I could potentially accomplish something larger than I had ever thought myself capable of and, instead of encouraging me, he seemed more interested in keeping me where I was. It showed me how hard it really is to break free: it wasn't only my mind that could hold me back but those I loved most.

Nick was proud of my achievements. He had helped to develop my leg muscles with deep tissue massages, and I felt indebted to him for it, but not enough to give up my dreams and stay in Columbia. I can't be sure but I think the day I packed my van and left town, without announcing plans to return, I broke his heart.

Driving to Colorado, I stopped the first night at Devin's. I had already called him and told him the news, but since I wasn't sure when I'd see him again I wanted to spend one last night visiting. Of all the people who should have been bitter, he seemed the happiest. I doubted I would ever be able to tap into the place he found his energy, but whenever we visited, the future possibilities seemed limitless. If I could take with me a grain of his optimism and strength I knew I'd go far.

He told me that to keep his mind active he often went back through each training ride, remembering the details, including many things he claimed he hadn't consciously noticed when we rode, like the smell of the fall leaves, the scent of freshly cut grass, the sound of crickets returning late in the evening on summer rides. We had always ridden too hard to pay attention to the small details along the way, but his mind had recorded them.

The drive west was monotonous. I kept my mind busy reminiscing about bike races but for some reason it kept returning to one of my earliest memories – the sound of a telephone ringing in the front room of the lake house in Indiana. The house had a small antechamber constructed from rocks hauled out of the lake and cemented together, through which you entered the exterior door into the vestibule, then an interior door to the main house.

In the antechamber there was a small table with a heavy black telephone. Its bell was nearly as loud as the one that rang at the end of the day in the first elementary school I attended. Since we only stayed at the lake during the summer, the heavy exterior door remained open. I often sat in the shallow water at the lakeside, playing with buckets and shovels. The phone rarely rang but when somebody did call from Chagrin it rang sometimes for as long as five or ten minutes – the caller aware that reaching it often took considerable time. If I were upstairs in bed, resting during the afternoon, it echoed loudly through the house and often, instead of racing to answer it, I'd just listen to it ringing, comforted by the sound. Most of all, I loved hearing its ring when I was sitting on the lawn out front with the hot summer sun beating down on me. The phone was on an old party line, and when you eventually picked it up and started talking, a neighbor sometimes tried to make a call, then apologized for interrupting. It was a time of innocence when I was still unaware that so much conflict existed in the world, a time when anything seemed possible and each day brought hundreds of new experiences, along with the security of knowing that, with the telephone, I was connected to the wider world.

The appearance of a snowcapped peak on the horizon distracted my thoughts. For the entire day I had driven across a windswept plain, surrounded in every direction by tabletop farmlands, dormant in the cold. I had just crossed the border from Kansas into Colorado and knew it was still more than a hundred miles to Colorado Springs where the Front Range of the Rockies rose. I never imagined that I would see a peak looming from so far out, but as I continued across the plain toward my goal more peaks appeared until soon one unbroken line of mountains stretched from south to north. I had never seen mountains so immense or peaks jutting so dramatically out of the earth. They were at least twice as tall as the Appalachians, and I was reminded of my family's move from Ohio to Georgia. The line dividing the East from the West, marked by the mountains before me, was even clearer than the division between the North and the South. In their presence I sensed myself slowly transforming inside, preparing for another journey into uncharted territory.

BOOK VII

Refuge of the Road

Entering Colorado Springs and stopping at a gas station to get directions, it became evident that the training center was no castle at the end of a winding mountain road. The attendant referred to it as 'the old airforce base.' I drove into the center of the busy city until I reached a compound surrounded by tall barbed-wire fences and a guarded entrance with several cars backed up, waiting for permission to drive in. The buildings inside the compound were stark and industrial, but gaining entry for the first time seemed the equivalent to getting inside Buckingham Palace.

'May I see your identification?' a security guard asked.

'I just have this letter.'

He unfolded it and read the contents. 'ID, please.'

I showed him my driver's license.

'First time here?'

'Yes, sir.'

He handed me a card and told me to place it on the top of my dashboard, visible through the front window. 'You may pass.'

I had never lived anyplace protected by armed guards. It was like an inverted return to Relativity – instead of guarding us to hold us in, they were guarding us to hold others out. I pulled up to the administration building to go inside for an ID card. A woman behind the desk took my invitation, looked at my driver's license, asked me to step behind a line, took my picture, laminated it and handed me the card. 'Welcome to OTC,' she said.

I repeated it to myself as I left the building: OTC – the informality was part of being on the inside. Walking back to my van, staring down at my freshly minted ID, I felt as if I had just won a gold medal. To that point I had dreamed only of getting there. I knew if I planned on making it through the first camp, I'd better set myself another goal right away.

I settled into a dorm that I shared with a rider from Long Beach, California, named Ronnie and another from the Bronx named Max. Ronnie was soft-spoken and Max more direct, but both had racing palmarès that far exceeded my own and both had been at the camp the previous year. They seemed unimpressed by their surroundings. They settled quickly into the room while I went out exploring the hallways.

That evening all the riders were called to a camp meeting and the rules were laid down. Lights off at ten p.m., rise at seven a.m. sharp, gather in front of the dorm and walk as a group to the cafeteria for breakfast, stopping on the running track to do calisthenics on the way. The hours were almost the same as at Relativity and the daily regimen similarly structured, though we were given a large block of free time in the evening, 'recovery time,' as the head coach – nicknamed Tommy K. by the riders – referred to it.

He was the best-known coach in American cycling, having delivered the U.S. cycling team its first gold medals in nearly a century during the previous year at the LA Games. His real name was Tomasz Kionski. The two assistant coaches, also from Poland, Pawel and Boryslaw, were known as Paul and Bobby. I felt stupid calling the head coach Tommy K., but it would have been even more awkward if I had been the only one to call him Tomasz. There were two national-caliber riders named Tom and another Tommy, which was why the head coach was Tommy K. The three Poles had defected in the mid-seventies and come to America seeking political asylum. All had long histories as riders and later coaches with the Polish national team.

Aside from established national team members – split into the A team (who mostly skipped the camp to follow their own programs), the B team and a more nebulous third group called the national development team – we all vied subtly for their attention to get noticed. On my second day there, I left the dorm in the afternoon and walked over to the bike rack where we kept our unlocked bikes in front of the dorm, then rolled across to the cafeteria for a snack. Halfway there I decided to take off my jacket and tie it around my waist. The sun had come out. I didn't bother stopping. I had taken it off hundreds of times before, riding along with no hands. As I came around the corner of a building I saw Tommy K. walking back to the Cycling Federation offices. Remembering Craig's advice that I would be sent home unless I stood out at the first camp, I wanted to make an impression, especially now that he was alone. He looked up when he heard me rolling toward him. I was tying my jacket around my waist when one of the arms dropped down between the fork and the front wheel, wrapping itself around the axle and into the spokes. Before I could brake, the bike flipped over and I slammed onto the pavement. He set down his drink and sandwich and leaned over to help me up.

'A klutz until the day I die,' I muttered under my breath, so he wouldn't hear me.

'Are you okay?' he asked. He looked carefully at a minor scrape on my forearm.

'My jacket slipped,' I said, stating the obvious. What else could I say? The only thing he'd remember was that I was a hazard to the team he had been training for years. I prayed he wouldn't ask my name.

'What's your name?'

'I don't know what happened,' I said. 'All the times I've taken my jacket off, I've never crashed before. I've only crashed a couple of times since I first started racing.'

He glanced at the fresh scar still covering my right forearm from the accident the previous summer and raised his eyebrows slightly.

It's no use, I thought. 'Sam Malessa from South Carolina.'

'Friend of Janek?'

'Yes, good friend.'

'I miss him,' he said, and smiled. 'We rode together in Poland.'

Then, switching subjects, he added, 'We like to ride fast here and keep our boys safe. I expect you to stay upright when we head out tomorrow. I'll be keeping my eye on you.'

Each morning before we left on a group ride Tommy K. stressed that it was early in the season and we were simply there to get a little conditioning before the real season started, especially those of us who had arrived from snow-covered states and couldn't train on the open road. But by the end of the first ride it became clear that he said this only to relieve us of the pressure that we were heading out for a daily race in which we'd be watched closely and notes recorded in the follow-vehicles by the coaches whenever we fell off the pace, when we attacked, who was in the breaks that went up the road and so forth. Never once did he pull up beside us in the middle of the training ride after we'd hit the desolate roads on the plains east of the city and opened it up into a full-blown unspoken race and tell us to slow down.

They were training rides in name only. I had never raced as hard and been attacked as relentlessly as on those cold winter rides. And unless there was an ice storm, weather – in Tommy K.'s view – was no reason to avoid training. There were only three weeks, now two and a half, for him to observe our abilities and for us to impress him. For all practical purposes they were selection races, as Craig had said, and anyone hoping to make the national team had to make the front group every day or have a damn good reason for going out the back door. Small icicles hanging off the downtube of your frame and freezing water spraying in your face from the rider ahead's rear tire, or brakes so completely frozen that they no longer worked, were not good enough reasons to back off if the coach was anywhere near your group.

I had never ridden on icy roads before but I quickly learned to handle my bike in all conditions, and whatever I lacked in strength I made up for by ruthlessly attacking anyone I rode with, including my roommate Max right after he had taken a hard pull at the front

370

and was trying to get back on my wheel for a rest. If you planned on making it to the next camp, you had no real friends – more like forty enemies of whom you needed to eliminate thirty-five. My only immediate goal was to make the next camp. If I didn't slam it every day I'd be back in the South as fast as butter melted in warm grits.

Well-established riders, who had won national championships and Olympic medals, riders we idolized from reading *Velonews*, arrived at camp every few days. They'd occasionally join us on the group rides while Tommy K. gave them their training schedules, then departed afterward to sunnier places while we were left in icy Colorado to battle it out as they had done during previous winters. I realized that if I hoped to come close to achieving their success, I'd have to attack every ride as if it were my last.

I headed out with the group the following morning, a wool cycling cap pulled down tightly over my head, a bandana covering my face from the icy wind, gloves, wool tights covered with Lycra, rainproof booties over my shoes, but no matter how warmly I dressed, my fingers and toes went numb immediately. Once we cleared the city limit, I tucked into the first echelon, pulling away from the rest of the group as we moved like a conveyor-belt, trading positions, spread out across the road from gutter to gutter, sliding down the back of the double echelon, temporarily shielded from the biting cold air. Aside from the sound of a dozen thin tires slicing across the wet pavement, the air was filled with snapping sounds as everyone clicked their brake levers constantly to keep them from freezing solid. Soon we were winding out our gears, clocking twenty-five miles per hour into the wind, flying, everybody smooth, fit and well oiled, as if it were the middle of July.

Coming across the front of the echelon I hit the wind. For twenty strokes I powered the group against its stiff resistance into the onslaught of freezing air. As I finished my pull, dropped back and began rotating for the next, I felt my rear wheel go flat and looked down to see the rim beating against the pavement.

Fuck, I thought, I'm in the lead group. I'll never catch back on. I drifted out of the back and pulled to the side of the road. As I did so a station wagon with flashing yellow lights affixed to its roof and the words 'U.S. Cycling Team, Olympic Training Center' on the doors screeched to a halt. Bobby jumped out and screamed something at me in Polish. Still straddling my bike, I held up the back end of the machine by grabbing the seat as he ran over, wheel in hand, popped the quick-release, yanked the flatted wheel from the drop-outs, slammed a new one in place and began running beside me, pushing me back up to speed.

Soon I was back on the road, sprinting alone into the wind. After a short distance, I began to crack under the effort. I glanced back and saw the group behind me, still too far away to stop and wait and the lead group still far ahead and pulling farther away. I hung between them in no man's land, slowly dying, but still attempted to bridge back to the front group to impress Tommy K., before faltering in the middle all alone.

It's over, I told myself, preparing to give in and wait for the riders behind me.

I shifted up to the fifteen-tooth cog, then sixteen and back to the fifteen. I couldn't find the right gear. My legs weren't smooth like before. The follow-vehicle suddenly appeared at my side, driven by Tommy K. He hung his arm out the window, beat his open palm against the side of the car and looked at me. He saw me dying. Disgust flashed across his face, sending a jolt of adrenaline through my system. Then he barked an order: 'Get on!'

I looked back at the next group, still almost a minute down, and did as told, dropping in behind the car and ducking into its draft. The cold wind suddenly disappeared, as the station wagon pulled me along in the vortex of air directly behind it. The coach waited for me to adjust to the car's pace, giving me a short time to recover, and then slowly increased the speed. We quickly returned to twenty-five miles per hour. Then thirty, thirty-five, forty. Leaning down over my bike, staying in the draft, I could see through the rear window and into the warm car where the coaches were laughing about something, and beyond them, through the front window, I saw the front group still ahead of us, fighting into the wind. One slight error by

372

myself or Tommy K. and I'd hit the pavement and break countless bones or worse, but he appeared unconcerned, continuing to laugh with Bobby, looking up the road at the front group occasionally and glancing in the rear-view mirror at me to make sure I was still tucked in the draft.

I concentrated intensely, my front wheel within inches of the car's rear bumper as I stayed as close as possible without touching it, in a relationship of supreme trust, coach and athlete operating as one. No tapping brakes. No swerving. I continued sprinting to hold my place within the vacuum of the car. Lactic acid seared my legs. My heart pumped enough blood to keep a small family alive. I leaned down closer to the stem and handlebars, glanced through the rear window and out of the front windshield. We were closing on the lead echelon.

I leaned up slightly to stretch my back. I saw the flashing orange lights on top of the car that warned approaching traffic to pull to the edge of the narrow farm road until we'd passed. I glanced to my left and saw the Front Range of the Rockies jutting out of the earth, their giant snowcapped peaks lining the west, then looked ahead across the barren overcast plains spreading eastward to the horizon. Tommy K. kept increasing the pace little by little, testing me, seeing if I'd come off, until we were ripping along so fast I was too scared to look at my speedometer.

Snowflakes were whipping over the top of the car. Flurries at first and then a steady white stream, zipping past my head as we raced toward the echelon, the orange lights flashing, round and round like an emergency vehicle racing toward its destination. The coach tapped the horn – signaling me to pull out into the wind and bridge the final gap to the front group solo. I came around the car and the air hit me like a wall. I leaned down as far as possible to cut through it and held my pace, passing the car as Tommy K. let his foot off the gas, and noticed the large emblem again in my peripheral vision as I flew past: 'U.S. Cycling Team.' It's snowing, I thought. I'm in the middle of Colorado and coaches from OTC are towing me to the lead group. I felt like I was dreaming, but it was reality, bending my

373

mind harder than any drug. The coaches dropped in behind me. As I raced forward to make contact with the group, a couple of riders at the back turned and saw me coming.

When I neared them, instead of dropping smoothly into the rear of the echelon per protocol, I went hard left and attacked up the gutter of the road so nobody could hold my draft. The group fragmented. I knew it was underhanded after I'd been paced back to them, but I didn't care. I'm not going back to Carolina, I thought. No way am I going back to Georgia. The stronger riders bridged across and joined me, one of them screaming, 'Get your dumb ass out of the gutter so we can draft.'

I glanced over and noticed it was a rider who had won the road nationals two years earlier. I ignored him and stayed in the gutter until the group split cleanly in two, then pulled into the center of the road so they could draft, and started rotating as the five riders still with me fell into formation. I dropped in behind them to recover and glanced back to make sure the rest of the group wouldn't reconnect. The same guy was yelling at me again: 'Go back to wherever you came from and learn how to ride a bike.' I glanced around once more, trying to ignore his verbal attacks, and saw the coach laughing in the car. It was still snowing. We were racing. Racing to nowhere.

I started laughing under my breath. I was free. My legs and lungs burned. I'm not going back. I'm never going back. When it was my turn to take another pull right after the national champion pulled off the front, I attacked again because I couldn't stand the prick screaming in my ear, telling me to go back to where I'd come from.

Two riders swiftly crossed the gap, including one who had taken a gold medal at the LA Games the previous summer and had been silent all the while. As he came up to my side with another rider in tow, he looked up at me, and yelled, 'Drop in.' I obeyed and fell in behind him as he sailed past and took a monster pull, the hardest pull I had ever seen a rider take, opening a tremendous gap on the group he had just dropped. After his superhuman effort at front, he flashed his right hand resting on the brakehood without looking back, signaling me to pull through and take my turn at the front.

I did exactly as instructed. We started trading off smoothly, taking pulls at the front, no longer three individual riders, but a single rotating unit racing into the icy wind.

After that I didn't worry as much about making the cut into the next camp. Whenever I saw Tommy K. or Bobby around camp and I was on my own, they called me Little Janek. They rarely called me Sam, except when they addressed me in the meeting room with the other cyclists. I learned later that Bobby had raced with Janek, as well as Tommy K., and that Janek had always been a ruthless competitor. I continued riding consistently near the front, but I felt confident that I didn't need to show myself again so aggressively. I let the other guys fight it out while I tried to hang onto their wheels so they never got too far ahead.

During the following week the coaches began subjecting the riders to a battery of physiological tests that ultimately formed the core of the training camp, though it wasn't until well after leaving the center that I understood what they meant. Like most riders, I paid attention only to our daily training sessions. During the week of testing, the coaches scheduled riders individually, working through eight each day, four before lunch and four after. I never saw them that week other than during my own tests. The national team mechanics drove the station wagons and led us on training rides.

The primary tests were a VO_2 max, a load test and a recovery test. All three were performed on a stationary bicycle, called an ergometer, mounted in the Federation offices. We called it the torture chamber. A large plate-glass window faced an interior office behind which the coaches sat at a desk, drinking coffee and making notes. They rarely looked you in the eye. When you were finished, they gave no indication as to your results.

In the first test, a physiologist entered the room and strapped a gas-mask-like apparatus to my face with a long tube attached to a machine that recorded lung capacity and the concentration of oxygen and carbon dioxide. The physiologist slowly but steadily increased

375

the workload until the level of oxygen consumed no longer increased. By that point I was close to cracking. We were more frightened of entering that room alone than facing the most competitive ride. Something about being forced to push ourselves to the maximum under the clinical observation of the coaches on the opposite side of the glass unnerved even the strongest riders.

The calculation the coaches were most interested in was the maximum rate of milliliters of oxygen per kilogram used per minute in relation to our bodyweight. They wanted to know how much oxygen we processed during a given minute to utilize for power – or, more simply put, how big our engine was.

The load test was completed on the same ergometer but this time no equipment was attached to our body. It was a test of brute strength as delivered through the pedals of a bicycle. In this case an assistant stood beside me while the coaches remained on the other side of the glass. I was permitted to warm up, then the assistant slowly started increasing the workload, but unlike the previous test, they didn't care when our oxygen consumption maxed out. By the time we hit that point, we still had several excruciatingly painful minutes to go, the load increasing little by little until we finally cracked. And every rider cracked eventually, whether world champion or weekend warrior: no human rode an ergometer with a steadily increasing workload indefinitely. For each of us, competing against the machine was humiliating – the machine broke you and left you panting for air like a ninety-year-old climbing a flight of stairs. It was impossible to finish the test with any dignity, and no matter how long you stayed on the machine, you felt certain that if you had dug a little deeper you could have stayed on a little longer and scored higher when it was over.

The recovery test consisted of nothing more than the assistant placing his index and middle finger on your jugular to measure your heart rate after you had been humiliated by the ergometer. The coaches were less interested in maximum heart rate than in how quickly it dropped after a maximum effort, measured at thirty-second, minute and two-minute intervals. And that was it.

At the end of the week, they posted a chart on the wall of the office showing everybody's results, so that you could see where you stood compared to other riders, including those who had won silver and gold medals. My scores were squarely in the middle – they weren't the lowest, but they were nowhere near the highest.

The first camp was due to end in less than a week. I had done well enough in the selection races not to worry about being selected for the next camp, but when I saw the physiological results, I was concerned that they weren't high enough to secure me a spot. Almost everybody present would soon be given walking papers and none of us knew for sure who'd be staying. I was so worried that when I went to my dorm that night I wrote a note to the head coach, saying I had nobody left to push me in South Carolina and that in order for the organism to grow it must be stressed. I ended by saying simply, 'I don't want to go back.' For anyone coming from behind the Iron Curtain, whether my father as a young man from East Germany or Tomasz defecting from Poland, I knew it would strike a chord. I had never met a single person who had left the Communist East and wanted to return. I don't know if he read my note or not, but when the list was posted naming those invited to the following camp, my name was there.

The next training camp was much easier for the simple fact that I wasn't required to undergo the battery of physiological tests again since they already had my data recorded. It allowed me to focus exclusively on training and figuring out what my next goal would be, beyond making the third and final camp. The answer soon arrived through an older national team member who told me that the opening stage race on the calendar, and one of only two international races then held in the U.S., was the Tour of Texas. Unlike most stage races, it didn't run over consecutive days but, rather, every few days as a race series during March. Riders came from all over the world to compete alongside several domestic trade teams and national development teams selected during the camps by the coaching staff.

From the moment I learned that, I aimed for a berth on a team heading for the Tour of Texas. Riders were to be chosen during the final winter camp through a series of selection races in which we were awarded points according to our result in each race. Those with the most points went with the team to Texas. Depending on your results in Texas, the coaches then selected teams to go to Europe for stage races. At that moment, all I wanted to do was make the team going to Texas to discover what it was like to compete in an international race. I redoubled my training efforts, going out some afternoons after we had already completed our training rides that day to put in more miles.

By the time I made the cut for the third training camp, I had become friends with a rider named Alex Danziger from Wisconsin. When he learned about Texas he became as fixated as I was on making it there. He was older than me, and I learned he had enlisted in the military straight out of high school. He had been discharged for a medical condition he didn't reveal, then enrolled in university, but had taken the semester off after he had received his invitation that winter to OTC. He said he wanted to go to law school once he'd graduated but not before he'd found out how far he could go in cycling. One afternoon while I was waiting for him near the running track, he came down and said, 'Look at that.'

I squinted up at the peak looming above the training center that I had first seen out near the Kansas border driving to OTC. 'What about it?'

'Pikes Peak. Tallest easternmost peak in the country.'

'How do you know that?'

'What do you mean, how do I know? I'm sharing something with you. You think I'm making it up?'

I had been conditioned to be on the defensive for so much of my life that it was often hard for me to take people at face value. But Alex, cooler than most, put me at ease. He was different than the other riders I met that winter. Maybe he was simply more secure, but he had a calm, humble demeanor at odds with the arrogant streak that ran through most of the other riders. There were exceptions, of course, including some who had won major events, but in my limited experience, they were exceptions and not the rule. And the longer I hung around riders there, the clearer it became that it wasn't limited to arrogance: it stretched into subtle racism.

Apart from Alex and one or two others, elite road racers in general were not a friendly, accommodating bunch. Most came from families rich enough that they could afford to buy them expensive racing bikes. Cycling wasn't basketball or football where all you needed was a ball to demonstrate your skills. You needed an array of expensive equipment, money to maintain it, a car to drive it to races, money to fill the car with gas and so on. There were people of limited means among the crowd but you could count them on one hand. I didn't see anybody who might have struggled, except Alex, who had grown up working on his grandfather's farm.

At such moments I wished that American cycling was more like its European counterpart where many riders came from the underclass. Nearly every farm boy in France and Italy had stood by the road as a race zoomed past his house, wishing he could join them to get off the farm and see the world. Cycling was intense physical labor, perfectly suited for a farm worker, but the racers I competed against from my very first race were anything but blue-collar athletes. The experience made me perceive whites in a way I had not seen them before. They had a sense of entitlement. Arrogant. Condescending. Patronizing.

That winter, while I was living at the training center, I began to dislike whites even more than I had after listening to my brother. And everyone there was lily-white. No black person had ever competed in the Tour de France and they called it the greatest sporting spectacle in the world. It was impossible for me to deny: my chosen sport was elitist. It prided itself on endurance, yet the majority of the world's population, including the best endurance athletes in Africa, were excluded from competing. Maybe that's how it was in every profession once you reached the top – arrogant and insular. But it didn't make it easier to swallow. Especially when you knew the playing field wasn't level and you had got there all the easier as a result. That was the one thing that disappointed me about OTC. The sport seemed less pure after I'd been there a couple of months – or perhaps a little too pure. Back in South Carolina, cycling had been my temple. I would never deny the ways in which it had helped me grow, but it was still a disappointment, like learning that the Church had a history of molesting children. I was forced to find a way to embrace cycling, even if it excluded others, for it had welcomed me when nobody else would. Besides, there were people like Alex and Devin, who were fair, balanced, humble individuals, and Alex was the only person I really liked at OTC outside of the coaching staff.

One day, a pack of teenagers approached me after I had placed third in one of the selection races for Texas. They were juniors – riders under eighteen – who had lived at OTC since they were fifteen and trained separately from us. They swaggered around the center as if they owned it. The biggest one wanted to know how old I was.

'Twenty-two.'

'You're too old.'

'For what?'

'You can't start racing at twenty-two. You have to start young.'

'What difference does it make?'

'You're wasting space. Somebody younger could be here. Ask Tommy K. If you want to go anywhere you have to start by sixteen at the latest to develop.'

'Listen, you little shit, I'll ride your ass into the ground right now and do it again when you're twenty-two.'

'That won't happen.'

'I know it won't. You won't even by cycling by then. You'll be burned out, talking about your glory days as a junior at OTC. Get the fuck out of my face.'

But his words wormed their way into my brain. Maybe I was too old. Maybe I was wasting my time. I tried to shake what he'd said out of my head, but it rang in there for the rest of the night. It bothered me how easily another's words cast self-doubt, as though their goal was to create insecurity.

* * *

Part of our time in camp was devoted to finding ways to occupy ourselves in the afternoons and evenings after the training day had ended. Alex was still in the habit of studying, even though he was out of school that semester. When he learned that I had never attended high school or college, he said, 'Let's hit the bookstores. Bunch of learning to do out there and time's wasting.'

It was his way of encouraging me without embarrassing me. He was more educated than I was, yet he pointed out that it didn't necessarily make him smarter. To prepare for his law career, he researched different subjects whenever he got a chance, working away through a subject like shoveling dirt to get to the bottom of a hole. When we stopped at the front gate one afternoon to ask a guard if he knew any good climbs in the mountains that stayed clear in the winter, he suggested Norad Road.

'Norad?' Alex asked.

'That's the one,' the guard said.

'As in N-O-R-A-D?'

'That would be it.'

'No shit,' Alex said. 'I had no idea NORAD was in Colorado Springs.'

'It's not exactly in the Springs,' the guard said. 'It's deep in the mountain.'

When we rode away, I asked Alex, 'What is it?'

'The North American Aerospace Defense Command. The command center to warn of nuclear attacks on the country.'

We rode up the climb and to the high-security entrance of a tunnel that led into the mountain. Alex rolled up to the guard and asked him some questions.

When he came back to where I was resting on the curb, I asked, 'What did he say?'

'Not much. He can't talk. Let's hit those bookstores over in Manitou Springs that I mentioned.'

He dug around the shelves for any military titles he could find with information in their appendix relating to Colorado Springs, NORAD or the airforce base that had become OTC. He taught me how to cross-reference and how to use a bibliography to find more information. He reminded me of my father, but instead of focusing on one subject he took a wider approach to knowledge, ingesting anything that piqued his interest. He also did a lot of informal asking around town for more information and that was how he learned that the former base we lived on had used the Petersen Field for its runway. That was the answer to the riddle that had puzzled him of how OTC could have been an airforce base without a landing strip. But that didn't come close to satisfying his curiosity and pretty soon he had me caught up in it too, searching through any books we could find at OTC and going over to Colorado College in the evenings to look through what they had. By the time he was done, I was dazzled at how much he had learned about the place we lived and the surrounding area.

I had never given OTC or Colorado Springs much thought beyond getting into shape there, but with a little sleuthing Alex had brought the city to life and made me look at it in a more comprehensive way that helped me understand how research illuminated its subject. He made me realize that digging up little-known facts about the past wasn't always bad.

The facility we lived at had been the Ent Airforce Base, named after General Uzal Ent, the man who had summoned Lieutenant Colonel Paul Tibbets to Colorado Springs forty years earlier and ordered him to fly a secret mission to drop the first atom bomb on Hiroshima. After the war, the facility we lived in had housed NORAD until its superiors became concerned that its location at the center of the city left it exposed to nuclear attack. In 1957 the Soviet launch of Sputnik demonstrated the enemy's ability to launch intercontinental nuclear warheads and hastened the airforce to develop a new facility to monitor possible attacks. A granite mountain above the city was chosen as the new site. Engineers bored a tunnel nearly a mile long into its solid granite core and chiseled large rooms in the center of the mountain. Once it was complete, they transferred the command center to its new accommodation.

'Do you realize the legacy of this place?' Alex asked. 'It's gone from first-line nuclear defense to training athletes to defeat other countries in international competition.'

He looked more excited with his conclusions than he did after doing well in a training race. To have learned this when we did was doubly ironic because the Soviet boxing team had arrived earlier that week to spend the rest of the month as part of an international athlete exchange program in which participating countries, including some from the Eastern Bloc, sent their athletes to different places around the world to train and ease international relations through mutual understanding. Early that evening we recruited Cam, a rider with a rudimentary understanding of Russian – his parents were from the Ukraine – to come with us to the dorm where the Russian boxers were staying. We had seen them training in the gym, but they were so well guarded we were too intimidated to approach them. With the information we'd uncovered about the history of the training center, Alex was desperate to greet them. We weren't interested in telling them the origin of the facilities they were presently living in, just wanted to put a real face on the enemy we had been taught to fear and who were now living in the next dorms.

We loaded our pockets with U.S.A. pins from the front office at OTC, a few cassettes of American rock bands, the little money we were able to raise between us, and Cam grabbed a *Playboy* magazine and shoved it down his pants. The dorms they were staying in were off limits to us during their stay. Heading over there under the cover of darkness, we felt as if we were sneaking across the Berlin Wall. We waited in the cold for nearly thirty minutes before one of their guards stepped away from the exterior door, then slipped in and ran upstairs to the third floor where they were staying. We peeked through the small glass window on the door sealing off the staircase. Another guard was sitting in a chair outside their room. After waiting thirty minutes, we realized he wasn't going anywhere. Alex gave Cam a twenty-dollar bill and urged him to go and tell him some fellow athletes simply wanted to meet the boxers. We watched through the window until, after a short discussion, Cam waved us in. 'He'll give us fifteen minutes.'

The guard let us slip inside the boxers' room. They were surprised and delighted to see us. As soon as we began dumping our small surplus of U.S.A. Olympic pins on their bed, they immediately dug through their suitcases and pulled out C.C.C.P. Olympic pins, the Cyrillic Russian initials for the U.S.S.R. All along they had been waiting to meet some American athletes to exchange souvenirs. They stared at the cassette tapes in wonder and tried to say the names of the bands. One guy broke out a bottle of Russian vodka and insisted we all do a shot. They flipped when Cam pulled *Playboy* out of his pants and howled so loud that the guy guarding the door looked in to see what the commotion was about.

'American girls!' one shouted. 'They bring us American girls!'

Once our fifteen minutes was up, they said, '*Spasiba*,' so many times that I finally asked Cam, 'What are they saying?'

'They're thanking us.'

We shook hands and left the building elated. We knew in our hearts the Cold War would thaw sooner or later, especially with Russian boxers thanking American cyclists for *Playboy*.

After my third-place result in the first selection race for the Tour of Texas, I approached the remaining two races with more tranquility than I had ever ridden. During the days leading up to the races I didn't fret about my form. For one of the first times in my life I was entirely comfortable. I lived among my fellow racers but for the most part I didn't feel like one of them. And, with the exception of Alex and one or two national team members, they didn't extend themselves to me. I never consciously tried separating myself from them – on the contrary: I had tried to join their fraternity, but there were so many different cliques, and each one seemed to have its own unique behavior, that I gave up trying. Besides, it was easier that way. Instead of worrying about making friends or maintaining relationships, I got on with what I had come there to do and was happy enough that Alex had befriended me. It was probably partly my fault anyway. I hadn't been raised in the same schools and backgrounds

384

they came from. The vast majority seemed to have no apparent ethnic identity, which allowed them to integrate among themselves easily and made me wonder if class ultimately superseded ethnicity.

Alex and I often warmed up together before races. To take his mind off the race, he'd stop at lights and practice rolling in reverse or remaining motionless – a 'track stand,' in racing parlance – without touching his feet to the ground. He was quite talented.

'You should have taken up gymnastics.'

'Right,' he said, patting his stomach to bring attention to his short, stout figure. 'Could you see me up on the parallel bars? I'd look like a construction worker trying to rip them off the frame.'

One of the coaches would say that riders should be shaped like a tree, not a V – meaning we should be built solid from the trunk up, not developed like a weightlifter, with broad shoulders and chest and a thin waist. Alex fitted this model to a T. He was an all-rounder, probably most gifted as a sprinter, but not a pure sprinter and a bit too heavy to climb with the goats – the mountain goats, as we called the pure climbers. In the selection races we fed off each other – we had to, we were both outsiders – and in doing so we fueled each other. There were no major upsets, but by the end we had both taken two top-three finishes and one top five and put a lock on our positions on the long team heading for Texas.

We celebrated the night of the final race by eating two extra yogurts in the cafeteria, watching a movie, then waking early the following morning and taking a leisurely ride out to the Garden of the Gods near the edge of the city, a geological formation of deposits – reddish and white sediment standing in vertical shafts made from conglomerates of limestone and sandstone that had once been at the bottom of an ancient sea. We tooled along the road, crossing former beaches, sand dunes and alluvial fans until we reached the Tower of Babel, a massive protrusion of rock sticking out of the earth. We stood in wonderment, our celebration forgotten.

Riding back through town and approaching the training center, we saw cars parked along the curbside, a mob of reporters moving feverishly about and the local police and OTC guards setting up barriers to keep the entry gate clear. As we neared the gate, the reporters swarmed around us. Before they had a chance to ask any questions, one of the U.S. Cycling Team station wagons pulled up to the gate driven by Tommy K. and they rushed toward him. The guards blocked them from getting in front of his car and the coach kept his window rolled up, but he noticed us pushing through to the gate. He put his forefinger and thumb to his mouth and squeezed his lips together, then drove through the gate and disappeared among the labyrinth of buildings. The guard recognized us and let us pass without showing IDs.

'These guys will chew your head off if you let them,' he said, as we rolled past.

Once inside we learned they were covering a news story that had just broken about members of the Olympic team in LA using a controversial practice known as blood doping to win medals. During a meeting that afternoon in the conference room, the coach commented briefly about the reporters swarming out front. 'It's a free country,' he said, 'so feel free to talk to whoever you want to. Just be ready to pack your bags after exercising your constitutional rights, because you won't be coming back here.'

I wondered how different it would have been to sit in the same room listening to lieutenant colonels lecture on classified information off limits to the general public. Over the following days, countless different newspapers and periodicals, including *Sports Illustrated* and *Rolling Stone*, were passed around the riders, including one magazine with a large Olympic gold medal pictured on the cover and 'TARNISHED?'

Many of us now knew the details of blood doping: blood was drawn from a rider or another source weeks before a competition and placed in a centrifuge device where the red blood cells were spun out and saved in a concentrated form to put back into the rider's body through transfusion shortly before the competition. By increasing his red blood cells, he enhanced his ability to carry oxygen to the muscles and thereby boosted his natural power. When the story broke, the procedure wasn't technically illegal. The Olympic

Committee had never dealt with it before and it had never been prohibited. Rumors of other doping methods also circulated among the riders – antihistamines to open your lungs and caffeine suppositories to amp you up for short races.

The information posed a massive dilemma. If I were to achieve the heights of my fellow team members, who had indulged in such practices, I would have to confront the notion of using substances to reach those same goals. Cycling represented, for me, a way to escape relying on drugs. Cycling was my drug. Riding helped me cope. If I used drugs to achieve my cycling dream, succeeding would be less a dream accomplished than the illusion of it, no different from angel dust. I became increasingly determined that if I achieved anything in cycling it would be through my own power and natural abilities. And if I failed, I would do so as a result of my own shortcomings. If I were beaten by others because they were doping, well, they could reap the hollow Faustian glory of their success.

Ever since my arrival at the training center, I had had a series of dreams that became increasingly vivid. I didn't dare discuss them with anyone, even Alex, for fear of being ridiculed. After the blood-doping story broke and it became impossible to leave the facility without journalists following us, my dreams intensified: I saw flesh and machine merge until it was impossible to tell where flesh ended and machine began. I still couldn't accept my brother's vision of whites being subjected and ruled by those not, but in my dreams I had begun to see a world in which man himself became subject to and ruled by the synthetic life forms that emerged from his initial experiments and designs. When I fell asleep I began to see whites and nonwhites uniting against an enemy far more potent than the earlier European conquest of various places around the globe.

The day finally arrived for us to go to Texas. I left my vehicle in the parking lot near the dorms and loaded my bag into one of two huge U.S. Cycling Team vans, painted red, white and blue, with the Stars and Stripes. Twenty state-of-the-art racing bikes were clamped to the roof rack. Alex and I piled into the van with a group of other riders. Somebody slipped a Red Hot Chili Peppers cassette into the stereo and cranked it up as we rolled down the Front Range of the Rockies to Pueblo and then east across the Colorado plains, through the Oklahoma panhandle and into Texas. We felt like a rock band going on tour. Whenever we passed cars, kids waved and told their parents to honk the horn. When we pulled into a fast-food restaurant and ordered burgers, the manager came out and said, 'This one's on us. Keep up the good work. We want to see you win.'

We reached Austin and settled into an apartment complex. The coaches handed out our monthly stipend the day after we arrived, making us professionals who were retaining our amateur status strictly for international racing purposes. They also gave us meal cards for the cafeteria at a nearby dorm of the University of Texas. For once everything in my life was falling into place. I was part of the national team and had access to the University of Texas as though I were a legitimate student. I had finally made it into a part of the world I had always fantasized about – I was almost as excited about taking my three meals every day with students at the university as I was riding for the national team.

When we went to the race presentation to collect our race bibles, the heavy hitters I had read about for the last couple of years were present, including American powerhouses like Davis Phinney, whose three hundred career victories eclipsed those of any other U.S. rider, his teammate Andy Hampsten, their Canadian nemesis Steve Bauer standing on the other side of the room, and the diminutive self-described Irish leprechaun Alan McCormick, who frequently trounced competition, despite a slender frame that gave no hint of its inherent power. Various national teams were also on hand, including world champions, Olympians and riders who would go on to win stages in the Tour de France and the Tour of Italy overall. The most prestigious races were still in Europe, but with the exception of Greg LeMond who had just become the first American to win the world professional road-race championships and had finished on the podium in Paris the previous year, you couldn't have assembled a more elite group of racers on American soil.

The competition was different than anything I'd experienced. They started off so fast that it seemed we were approaching the final sprint in the first lap. After getting ground and spat out the back of the first two races, like a branch being shredded in a wood chipper, the coach came to me and said, 'Just concentrate on finishing the race, Sam. That's all we expect of you in your first year here.' Following his advice, I did just that. I gave up any notion of trying to secure results. We traveled to Houston, Dallas-Fort Worth, San Antonio, out into the hill country surrounding Austin and every place in between, racing at the centers of the big cities packed with large crowds to the desolate countryside where the only spectators were lizards and armadillos crossing the road. But no matter where we raced, the speed was ferocious and it was a full-time job simply to stay in the middle of the pack and hang on for dear life. I finally adjusted to the speed and occasionally moved up front to see the action there. It felt as if we were racing at a hundred miles per hour when I saw a rider from Denmark, Jesper Skibby, go solo off the front and disappear up the road. The rider beside me yelled, 'I want whatever he had for breakfast.'

The month passed in a blur. Most nights I was too tired to do anything more than lie in bed after a massage and study the race bible, which contained detailed course descriptions of each stage with elevation charts, mileage marks and any unusual features of the upcoming race. The coaches housed us with riders we didn't know to try to integrate the team. I was put up in a two-bedroom apartment with one new rider and some older ones. Most of the time we were too fried from racing to carry on much of a conversation. The only time I saw Alex was in the middle of races where I'd find him hiding in the middle of the pack hanging on as best he could. We were amazed that big-name riders finished directly beside and behind us.

With four races to go we made a pact when we bumped into each other at the starting line to attack off the front that day so we could

389

at least say we'd tried and have our race numbers come up on the radios in the race caravan so the coaches would know we'd done more than finish the races. After the pack finally settled down, the feed zone approached: bags of food were passed to us, but Alex and I skipped lunch and went on the attack instead. Our glory was short-lived when Jesper Skibby zipped out of the field and straight up to us like a motorcycle cop out on a Sunday cruise and informed us in a thick Danish accent that it was bad etiquette to attack in a feed zone. We played dumb Americans and thanked him for clueing us in. Bad manners or no, we had gotten out front of the field and shown our colors. Other than the first two races, I finished all of the others until the penultimate stage: I went down in a crash that took out half of the field. Fortunately I didn't break any bones or get too scraped up, but I did pull a groin muscle that made it painful to walk for the next two days. Tommy K. told me to skip the final race and let it heal.

'You've gotten your feet wet,' he said. 'We heard your name on the race radio the other day and knew what you and Alex were up to. Go out there this season, get some good results and come back next year knowing what to expect.'

I left Texas without glory, but I had achieved my dream of becoming a resident of OTC and made the national development team. I wasn't leaving with great results but I had experienced the inner workings of what it meant to reach the top. More importantly, I had found my next goal: to come back to the first winter training camp next year, make the cut to Texas and achieve enough results the next time around to get on the team heading for Europe. I wanted to compete in the Peace Race – I wanted it now as badly as I had originally wanted to go to OTC. I wanted to go to Poland nearly as much as I wanted to race. Just as I had used my bike to get out of Augusta and Columbia, I'd also let it take me to Poland and the Peace Race the following spring. I felt freer of the past than I ever had and was sure that if I could make it to Poland, I could finally shed it forever. I had no idea what I'd find there, but I had to go. I had a year to bring my level of fitness up enough to make the cut. I promised myself I wouldn't cloud my mind with anything that might deter me from my goal.

The mechanic who drove me back to Colorado Springs to get my van mentioned the Tour of Baja in Mexico, another international stage race that took place the following month.

'Do you think I can get in?'

'You gotta find a team, but you're fast enough. The competition won't be quite as deep down there. You'd do okay, probably better than in Texas.'

'How do I find a team?'

'Go out to California. There's a bunch of teams out there getting ready to go. I'm sure a couple of them have spots open for capable riders.'

My next stop had been to go to California to race anyway and now, with the information he had given me, I decided to head straight out and start searching for a team in need of an extra rider. With Texas behind me, I had a big multiday race under my belt, but I needed to do better, especially if I planned to make good on my goal. The Tour of Baja would be the perfect way to start my resumé that year. I was fitter than I'd ever been in my life, even if my results in Texas didn't show it. I had gone from competing in regional races last fall to racing against the world's best that spring. I had been little more than a pack-filler in Texas, but I was flying and knew if I played my hand right I'd rack up some victories that season in harder races than I'd won in the past.

My decision to go to Mexico marked the first leg of a journey that took me all over the country. The previous month, before leaving Colorado Springs for Texas, I had called Craig and told him that I'd made the team to Texas. When we talked, I had also told him I wouldn't be coming back. I never did call him or anyone else again, not Nick, Devin, Janek, Wade, no one. After Texas, I disappeared into the roads stretching across the plains, climbing over mountains, through deserts, along the coast, journeying more miles in one year than I had traveled in my entire life, doing my best to lose myself in the vastness of the country of my birth. If the month in Texas was a blur, the remainder of the year was a shadowy haze. I became a wanderer. A professional drifter.

I drove out to California on Interstate 15, passing through Las Vegas. While refilling at the last stop in Nevada before entering California, I studied the atlas and noticed a remote back road through the Mojave Desert between the interstate and Palm Springs. It wasn't quite as straight as the freeway, but it still led to Los Angeles. I decided to take it so I could stop and train along the way and sleep out in the desert away from the noise of civilization for a few nights. The traffic was bumper-to-bumper leaving Las Vegas, a veritable traffic jam flowing at seventy miles per hour. I questioned my idea of taking the back roads, assuming that many others had had the same idea. If so, traffic on the two-lane blacktop would be slower than staying on the freeway. But as I neared the mountain pass, frustrated with aggressive drivers riding my bumper, I decided to chance it, knowing I could get back on the interstate easily enough. Within two miles of leaving the freeway behind I was in utter isolation. There wasn't a single car traveling in either direction through the vast arid forest of strange mutated joshua trees. Entering California was the most unsettling shift I'd ever experienced. I might have landed on a different planet.

The terrain of the desert was so stark and unforgiving, the land so vast, that all my preconceived ideas about the state melted away. I had come to California envisioning it as a population center, not a desolate wilderness of deformed trees and sun-baked earth littered with scattered boulders. I drove cautiously onward, wondering why nobody else had taken the same route to LA. I wondered if it was safe out in the endless wasteland. I pulled over to decide whether I should turn back to the freeway and as I did so my tires sank into the sand on the shoulder of the road. I gunned the engine and plowed my way out. Once back on the pavement, my heart was pounding. After that I didn't risk turning on the narrow road for fear I might get stuck. I drove onward following the road toward a place with the peculiar name of 29 Palms.

Over the next hour, I never passed another car in either direction. Eventually I reached a crossroads where a deserted train station stood. I had no idea what it was doing out in the middle of nowhere – there was no town, no sign of water, nothing but a set of tracks passing through the middle of the desert. I parked to rest. Another hour passed without any cars appearing. I decided to sleep that night in the van beside the station to give me a chance to figure out where to go in California and to train that day without the danger of passing traffic. I suited up, filled my water bottles from the cooler Craig had mounted in the van and headed off for a two-hour ride. After returning, I cleaned up with a damp towel and stood naked beside my van for the few minutes it took the sun to evaporate the moisture from my body. I pulled out the cooking stove, set it on the ground, fired it up and made dinner.

Sitting in the back of the van after I'd eaten, with the doors ajar, I enjoyed the serenity of the open space and the beauty of the barren landscape. A bank of clouds rolled in over the desert, the cumulus thicker and taller than any I'd ever seen, forming and reforming into different shapes. Numerous species of cacti grew in the surrounding desert and the longer I sat in silence, the more the desert came to life – birds appeared that I hadn't seen before, a large nest protected by the thorns of a cactus that they entered and exited without caution. Lizards scurried past. Ants rummaged. At dusk a jackrabbit sprinted by and an owl swooped past. The sun set behind a mountain range. A coyote somewhere out in the dark let out a short yapping noise, followed by another in the opposite direction. Before long the sounds erupted into a chorus, sending a slight chill down my spine. I pulled the doors closed and settled in for the night. A strong wind picked up, its force increasing as the hours passed, the van shuddering under its pressure.

Tired from the long drive and training ride, I fell asleep. I dreamed somebody was standing outside, lurking behind the joshua trees, sneaking up to the van and ducking each time I looked out of the window, taunting me like a cat playing with a mouse before the kill. I tried to wake myself, certain it was only a dream, but the harder I tried to force my eyes open, the heavier the lids became, pushing me deeper into the dream.

The van was shaking violently. I jerked up in bed, sweating, and the blast of a horn pierced the air as a freight train roared by only feet away. I had parked almost on the tracks, assuming that, like the station, they, too, had been abandoned. The van shook so violently that I held onto the bed until the train had passed and the sound of its clanking cars died. I got up, started the engine and pulled away from the tracks.

As I waited to fall back to sleep, I heard something plinking against the metal roof. I was too scared to get out and investigate – it was pitch black outside, no moon and thick cloud. The sound grew heavier until I realized it was raining, at first a light sprinkle, then a cloudburst pounding against the roof, the air thick with moisture, water seeping through the cracked rubber seals around the windows.

It rained hard for a long time, and when it started dying away, I heard a rushing sound. I climbed up front, turned on the headlights and saw a stream of water growing in size. I started the van and backed up to the higher ground of the train station's platform that I had pulled away from earlier and sat watching the stream in front of me grow into a small river, pulling with it dead joshua limbs and small boulders. I had read about flash floods in the desert, the earth too hard and dry to soak up any water as it rushed along. Roaring rivers appeared one minute and were gone the next but I had never seen anything remotely like it until now. The area surrounding the van was flooded with fast-moving water and I knew why nobody had taken the back road. The desert was impossible to tame. A streak of lightning flashed near the mountains, then another, and a small electrical storm followed, arcing down against the range across the valley floor.

I woke the next morning, squinting at the glare of the sun shining through the windows. There wasn't a cloud in the sky. I found a pair of sunglasses in the glovebox and put them on, then looked out at the road where the river had appeared the night before. The water was gone but the ground was still damp and steam rose in places.

394

Debris carried by the water was scattered about. Across the valley I saw smoke rising in a thin column. I tried to make out whether somebody was over there burning something, then realized it was a small fire ignited by the lightning. I decided to move on, instead of relaxing and making breakfast, scared the weather might change rapidly again. I drove at half the speed of the previous day, swerving between rocks and pieces of cacti that had been ripped from the desert floor. Dips in the road formed natural washes in which patches of sand had covered the pavement.

Eventually I came to another crossroads and turned right onto a wider, better-maintained road and drove into a town called Amboy – also deserted, but at least there were ruined houses and a derelict gas station that I pulled into so that I could look at my map again. I discovered the road was Route 66, the original transcontinental highway that had once crossed the country from Chicago to Los Angeles, now a shadow of its former self. A volcanic cone rose out of the desert floor at the edge of town and a lava field, vast beds of porous rock, flowed up to the roadside. I continued until I reached an area of parched earth, the bottom of an ancient lake bed encrusted with thick slabs of borax and salt. I pulled cautiously to the edge of the road, to make sure the crust was hard enough to bear my wheels, stepped out of the van and walked into the lake of crystalline whiteness.

Since I'd entered California, every physical thing had taken on so many different shapes and aspects from what I was used to that I had difficulty comprehending my new environment. Forty or fifty miles on I came to the first inhabited structure I had seen since leaving the interstate near the Nevada border the previous day. I was still way out in the desert, but several cars were parked in front so I pulled over, went inside and discovered a bar with a handful of people sitting at tables, their weathered skin creased so deeply that it seemed their faces might crack if they smiled – but nobody smiled. They huddled over their drinks, protecting them, as if they had just walked in from a nuclear winter, glancing suspiciously at my clean jeans and red Adidas warm-up jacket.

'Is the proprietor around?' I asked, to break the silent tension.

The room looked unchanged since the first homesteaders had come out into the desert to claim their land.

An old man sitting at the table nearest me, said, 'Eye, yi.'

'Can I use the bathroom, sir?'

'I don't know. Can you?'

The room erupted in laughter, much too loud and out of proportion with the clichéd joke, reminding me of my time at Relativity. He pointed toward a door at the back of the room and scratched his neck. I used the restroom and left the bar, driving onward. In all my travels, I had never seen a place as desperate. On the edge of 29 Palms, small single-room shell cabins lined the roadside, with no water and many with no electricity. When I finally reached the town the heat was so intense that the fig bars I had bought in Colorado to snack on had liquefied in the package and the sticky remnants oozed out onto the passenger seat. The thermometer at a gas station read 109 degrees. I went inside and asked the owner if it was correct.

'I wish it wasn't,' he said.

I drove farther into town to find something to eat, stopping at a small Mexican restaurant. The place was packed with soldiers – marines I soon learned, dressed in desert camouflage, various shades of tan and black splotched together. As I ate, the plate-glass window facing the street occasionally rattled and the ground rumbled like a small earthquake, eliciting laughter among the young soldiers. I asked a guy sitting near me what the noise was from.

'They're bombing.'

'Bombing?'

'Yeah, dropping bombs on base, training new recruits. You don't want the people responsible for protecting your country to be gun-shy when a bomb explodes near them, do you?'

Another bomb rumbled and the windows rattled again. The soldier told me 29 Palms was the largest marine base in the world. 'Bigger than Rhode Island.'

I tried to imagine the immensity of a place whose sole purpose was to practice war as I paid my bill and drove up the highway through a one-horse town named Joshua Tree and into Yucca Valley. I wondered who would settle their family in such an unforgiving place. Later I descended a mountain pass through a ravine into the lower desert where a massive snow-covered mountain peak rose from the desert floor directly in front of me. I drove across the flat, arid valley, crossing the top of the San Andreas Fault, marked by a sign, and finally reached Palm Springs.

Driving down South Palm Canyon, I felt relieved to be back in civilization and stopped for coffee. Entering the café was almost as disorienting as it had been entering California. Many of the patrons were openly gay, sitting at tables, laughing, holding hands. Other than a small bar Nick had taken me to called Trax in Columbia, I had never seen a gay establishment in the center of a city where people sat in the middle of the day holding hands. I nursed my coffee as my body loosened up and my mind continued adjusting to its new environment.

A man wearing neatly pressed slacks and expensive leather shoes approached my table and asked if he could sit. He introduced himself as Aaron. After an hour or so of small talk, when he had learned that I was a cyclist and had come out to California to race with no real idea of where I would stay, he invited me to his house. 'You're welcomed to stay until you figure things out. Plenty of room.'

He lived in a large modern house made from glass and concrete blocks. He had recently built a swimming-pool in the backyard. Directly outside the glass bedroom wall there was a hot tub. As I was unpacking, Aaron came into the bedroom with two drinks, set them on the table and made a pass at me. I was taken aback. In my exhaustion, it hadn't occurred to me why he might have extended the invitation. I abruptly pulled back. Not knowing what else to say and not wanting to offend him, I said, 'I just got out of a relationship. I came out here alone on a journey, looking for freedom.'

I was surprised that something so simple affected him so deeply, but it struck a chord and he apologized. He told me he had come out to California two decades earlier on a journey of his own. I ended up staying almost two weeks, but I still wasn't interested in being tied to anyone, emotionally or physically. What I had had with Nick had been special, but I still didn't know if I wanted to spend the rest of my life with a man, a woman, alone or in some other relationship beyond my present experiences. My time there gave me the opportunity to continue my training and to drive around to different bike shops until the owner of one, in Rancho Mirage, gave me a contact number for the manager of a team in San Diego who needed one more rider before heading for the Tour of Baja.

While I was packing my van to drive, Aaron came out and said, 'I have a place up in Humboldt County, a remote ranch, a retreat deep in the forest. You're welcome to come up and stay. There's a bunch of small cabins on the property that are usually empty.'

'Where's Humboldt County?'

'Up near the Oregon border. I'm leaving next month to go up there. You can make a little money helping out, if you want.'

'The racing season doesn't end until late September or October.'

'I plan on staying until early November. Come by later in the year if you have time. Let me get you directions before you take off.'

When he came back out, I thanked him for letting me stay.

'That's what we're here for,' he said. 'Good luck on your journey.'

In San Diego the team manager let me sleep on the couch in his living room the night before we crossed the border. The team was composed of six riders – two Mexican-Americans, three Mexican nationals and me. They all had relatives in the different cities the race stopped in – Tijuana, Tecate, Mexicali, Ensenada – who would put us up between stages to save the expense of hotels. The manager had secured a car dealership in Tijuana as the team's sponsor and handed me a jersey that bore its logo. I never asked for any money. I was lucky enough to have found a team willing to take me and was glad of the experience. My teammates playfully nicknamed me El Gringo. Their relatives prepared food for us each night. I learned just enough Spanish during the week to show appreciation to our hosts.

Each morning before starting the race, I joined my teammates for a quick prayer, crossing myself after the team manager said, 'Vaya con Dios.' They welcomed and respected me, and in turn I respected them. I was comfortable. The two Mexican-American riders seemed almost more American than I was. They talked about American TV shows – I hadn't watched television since I was a child; they joked about things they had heard on the news – I rarely read newspapers; and they talked about college courses and girls at San Diego State University – I had never attended high school, much less college. Conversely, the Mexican riders reminded me a bit of my father, eating food like cow's tongue that most Americans – including the two others on the team – didn't touch but that I ate with as much relish as the Mexicans. Regardless of our similarities and differences, we all got along great.

After the prologue time-trial, the first stage departed Tijuana and passed through Tecate before cresting a mountain pass – La Rumorosa – and descending eighteen miles of switchbacks. Cresting the summit on that first day, the world fell away four thousand feet to the desert below, the most beautiful and frightening view I'd ever seen – a hundred and fifty racers strung out in single file, inches from the wheel in front of them, vertical cliffs dropping away to the left side of the road with no guardrails to save us, death awaiting anyone who made a minor error. Without batting an eye, we tucked together in consummate trust and followed one another through hairpin turns at breakneck speeds to the desert floor. Small, brightly painted handmade crosses with fresh flowers flashed by on the road-side, memorials built for family members who had gone over the side. I saw the crumbled chassis of cars and trucks littering the rocks below, vehicles that had gone too fast to make the turn and sailed out into thin air.

Approaching Mexicali, I led my teammate out in the sprint racing into town and he took second place. We had wanted to make sure he placed as high as possible since his family was waiting at the finish. After spending the night in Mexicali, we started at the same place the race had finished the day before and followed the previous day's racecourse in reverse, racing toward the new finish line in Tecate. Instead of descending eighteen miles, we now had to climb.

La Rumarosa, looming in front of us, was legendary among the Mexican racers as the climb on which Raúl Alcalá had raced away from his American competitors to earn a contract to race professionally. He had gone on to win a stage in the Tour de France, asserting himself as the greatest bike racer in Mexico. Nobody raced ahead of the pack that morning. Riding across the desert after breakfast, we took our time warming up, reserving our energy for the climb, four times longer than anything I had ever done. As we crossed the desert floor I felt intimidated by what lay ahead. I was decent on shorter climbs – a mile or two long – but I was nowhere near as small as my two Mexican teammates. Weight was my enemy. Fortunately, my teammate Manuel was intent on making it to the top with the first group in hopes of winning in Tecate, so all I had to do that morning was ride ahead of him on the flats, protecting him from the wind leading up to the climb. The race opened up when we hit the lower slopes. Another teammate and I paced Manuel up within spitting distance of the leaders, and when we hit our limit he rocketed forward and caught them. Our work was done for the day. Now all we had to do was make it to the finish. We settled into a big group that came by and struggled over the climb, saving our energy to fight another day. When we finally rolled into Tecate long after the leaders, Manuel was ecstatic. He had won the stage. We celebrated that night drinking the town's eponymous beer.

While I was lying in bed, at my teammate's grandmother's house, trying to fall asleep, I thought about my mother. It had been a long time since I'd thought about her and it was painful. My intention had never been to cut contact with her, but after the way she had behaved toward me when we'd moved to Georgia and again when I showed up at the house after running away from Relativity, I was sure she hadn't wanted me around. Even though I had faced other traumas, I knew of no pain greater than being rejected by those who had brought me into the world, first by my father disappearing and then her. Since I'd returned to Augusta, to find her gone with no forwarding address, I hadn't known what to think. Part of me wanted to find her and show her what I had made of myself. At the same time I had achieved my lifelong goal of freedom and was scared that she might reject me again, or shackle me with guilt, or take me down in a way that only your family can, knowing your every weakness, your every pain.

I lay awake for part of the night, when I should have been recovering to make it through the next stage. As I fell asleep, I decided I couldn't risk finding her. I was free at last, traveling through the world on my own with no obligations, duties or responsibilities. I didn't want anything to sidetrack me from achieving my goal of going to Poland and competing in the Peace Race. I was sure that if I made it to Eastern Europe, I could free myself from all the pain of the past once and for all and that afterward I would have the strength to face anyone in the world. But until then, I had to move with caution, keep my focus and confidence, my sense of security and place.

I was caught off guard the following morning as we raced toward the finish that day in Ensenada. We rode through a shantytown near the edge of Tijuana, a vast network of hovels made from cardboard, plywood, aluminum siding, anything the occupants could gather to make shelter, built against one another in a flat area saturated with mud. When the children who lived there saw me they came running up to the side of the road, yelling, 'Hola, hola, Americano.'

During my years of poverty, I had never seen anything that came close to the level of destitution I saw that morning. I took my new water bottles and tossed them to the children standing alongside the road, then started unloading the food stuffed in my jersey pockets and tossing it to them. Manuel rode up beside me. 'What are you doing, man? You need that food for later today.'

'They need it more.'

'They'll get food. Coming down here to race brings attention to Mexico. You're doing your part. Don't throw away any more food. Now we got to find some more water bottles and food for you so you don't get left behind on the road to Ensenada,' he said, a hint of irritation in his voice.

401

That evening we had our final meal together in Ensenada, a big feast at a restaurant near the beach, with crab and all kinds of seafood I had never tasted before.

'It's cheap,' Manuel said, pointing at a boat in the marina near the restaurant.

I didn't have much appetite and it wasn't only because I had seen the hungry children along the roadside that morning. That was part of it, but for days I had been noticing that while competing in stage races you burned so many calories every day that you had to eat constantly and eventually you got tired of chewing. I had never been a big eater, but I had to make sure I got enough calories into my body to recover and have enough energy for the next day. My body didn't want to process any more food. It was processing more than it had ever processed and I was still losing weight, so I forced it down anyway. I wanted to make a good showing on the final day.

My teammates had scored one win, a second placing and two thirds that week. All the other riders were watching them now, so on the final stage they decided to use me as their secret weapon. Nobody knew me and I had spent the week working anonymously for my teammates without going for any results, just happy to be part of the team and gaining more racing experience. The route traveled from Ensenada back up to Tijuana, but instead of following the road along the coast, like the race south yesterday, it cut inland through rolling hills and short mountains.

'Hey, Gringo, you can climb, can't you?'

'Yeah, I can. Just not La Rumorosa.'

'You better be able to if we're going to work for you.' They started laughing. 'Can you believe it? We're going to work for El Gringo. Nobody in the race will even know what we're doing until it's too late.' They were laughing again. 'You'd better not disappoint us, Gringo. We don't want to lose our sponsor next year.'

I didn't like the pressure, but I'd been dying to race hard all week, holding back to satisfy my duties as a domestique, working for them. Besides, the year was ticking past and if I intended to make it to the Peace Race I had to get some results. I was tucked comfortably in

402

the middle of the pack as we rolled out of Ensenada. Going over the climbs and rollers the race broke apart, but my teammates kept going to the front and pulling it back together. It went that way all afternoon until we finally reached the outskirts of Tijuana where Manuel dropped back and said, 'Don't disappoint us, Gringo.'

Our strategy was to draw the attention of the field to our other teammates as they launched a series of attacks coming into the city that all the other racers would immediately respond to after their high results throughout the week and then, at the last moment, as the field came back together before the final I was to counterattack.

'Nobody will follow the Gringo up the road,' they had said that morning at breakfast. 'He hasn't placed high all week.'

The hope was that the field would let me go, too tired from reeling in dangerous riders, and that by the time they realized I might hold it to the line, it would be too late. When my teammates started launching attacks, one after the other, I was nervous. Riders in the pack were screaming in Spanish. I had no idea what they were saying, but I knew it wasn't good. They kept pulling them back, then another of my teammates would go. This continued until we had only one teammate left to go on the attack and then it would be my turn. When he went, he didn't get very far. They were ready for him, but I could see they were tired of repeatedly bringing the field back together. As they closed in on him, we passed through the same shantytown we had ridden through the day before and what appeared to be the same children were lining the muddy roadside. The sight of them brought on a feeling of sadness, then anger at the massive chasm that existed between classes, between people. At that moment, my teammate was swallowed by the field and I heard Manuel at my side hissing, '¡Ahora mismo! ¡Ahora mismo!'

I launched myself off the front so hard that I had trouble swerving around a traffic island after escaping the field. I looked back to make sure I had a sufficient gap, then put my head down and thought about only two things: the children who had been standing by the roadside and making it onto the national team heading for the Peace Race next year. I mashed my pedals like a pneumatic jack-hammer and opened the gap, glancing back only once more before concentrating on the road between me and the finish. As we entered a busy road near the center of the city, two Federalis riding big Harley-Davidsons with blaring sirens came up beside me and formed a motorcade, while another went out front, signaling traffic to pull over to the curb as I came racing solo through the rush-hour streets following the lead motorcycle to the finish. It was the sort of treatment President Reagan had been accorded when he was driven up Washington Road in Augusta. Now I was in a foreign land being treated like a dignitary. I had no idea if the field were about to catch me or whether I was gaining ground, I just kept my head down and concentrated on churning the pedals, amid the thunderous sound of the Harley-Davidsons surrounding me and the blare of sirens. We came around a corner and I saw the finish line less than a quarter-mile away. I glanced back. I didn't see anyone behind me. I rode in as hard as I could and crossed the finish line, still thinking about the children I had passed at the roadside. I didn't thrust my fist in the air that day or signal number one. Winning the biggest race of my career, my first international victory, I felt very small in contrast to the city surrounding me.

Driving north after the Tour of Baja, I spent a night sleeping in the van on the outskirts of Los Angeles and raced a criterium the following morning. Then I continued up Interstate 5 through the Central Valley, reaching San Francisco that evening where I had a troubled night's sleep in my van, woken several times by the police telling me to move on, before I found a parking place near Haight where they left me alone for a few hours. Early the following morning, I rode my bike across the Golden Gate Bridge looking across the bay to the hills in the east. I had come all the way to the edge of the continent, suspended above the water, the Marin headlands pushing out into the sea, the skyscrapers behind me piercing the low-lying clouds.

That afternoon I continued driving north to another race called Tour of the Unknown Coast. I drove for five or six hours without stopping, past Santa Rosa, past Ukiah and into a land as uninhabited as the Mojave Desert but the polar opposite – verdant green hillsides, ferns sprouting up along the roadside, rivers and creeks, the earth curving steeply up and down as the road meandered between peaks and summits, twisting about in its search for the path of least resistance. Eventually I reached a small town named Rio Dell where I pulled off for the night to sleep.

I got up the following morning and went for a training ride along a road called Monument that climbed straight up, a near-vertical path into the clouds, before turning to dirt and crossing several pastures along the ridgeline with a lone bull in each field. I turned right at a sign indicating that I had just crossed Bear River Ridge and descended another road called Wildcat that dropped into a tiny Victorian village surrounded by dairy farms that reminded me of Ohio. I followed Blue Slide Road back through a strand of redwoods to Rio Dell. For the next week I parked my car on the south jetty of Humboldt Bay in a caravan of other cars and trailers that belonged to people who lived there – homeless save their vehicles and the beautiful, desolate beach we lived on. I rode my bike each day into the towns of Eureka and Arcata – the latter appeared lost in the sixties, college-aged kids with long hair, dreadlocks, colorful shirts decorated with peace signs, ecology flags and various symbols of unity, bell-bottom pants, leather sandals and the smell of patchouli drifting out of stores that sold bongs and water pipes.

The difference was striking after Los Angeles where there was a mix of cultures everywhere I looked. Even Georgia was more diverse. On the plaza in Arcata, every single person was white. It struck me as odd that so many people were wearing clothes symbolizing peace and unity when only a single group was present. I tried to make conversation several times but, with my hair cut short like a marine's and wearing the national team jersey the coaches had given me in Texas, they weren't interested in talking much with me.

The older men who sat around the diner where I bought lunch each day a few blocks from the plaza were more sociable. They worked at the lumber mill on the north jetty. When they saw me walk in the first day wearing Lycra clothing that clung to my skin, one said, 'We got a fruit loop here.'

They were a sarcastic bunch, but keen to debate with me the pros and cons of logging. 'Listen,' another told me, 'I'd love to hang out on the plaza all day and make people aware of the spotted owl but until they pay me to do so I'm stuck pulling green chain at the mill. You think I like the work? Do I look stupid? It pays the bills and helps put my own kids through college.'

'Do they go here?'

'Hell, no. My son's enrolled in Sacramento State. Humboldt State's full of kids from San Francisco and Los Angeles. I figure if they're going to send their kids up here to ruin my town, I'll send mine down there to give them hell. Next time you're down on the plaza and they're spouting off about logging, ask them why they aren't demonstrating in support of the Yuroks instead.'

He said he was part Yurok, a local indigenous tribe he claimed to be the largest in California, inhabiting a reservation in the mountains. The following day, out of curiosity and in need of endurance miles, I went on a long training ride and eventually found my way to the reservation he had described. I stopped in a store to buy a soft drink and see what a full-blooded American looked like. In my entire life, as far as I knew, I had never seen a real Indian. When I asked the man selling the soft drink if he was an Indian, he laughed and said, 'Would you like to see me do a rain dance?'

'I've never been on a reservation before.'

'You've been on a reservation all right,' he said. 'You've been on a reservation for white people.'

He wore a T-shirt that read: INJUN WARRIOR: RED-BLOODED AND PROUD. As far back as Chagrin I had been taught the word was a racial insult but he wore it with pride. He reminded me slightly of the logger who had given me directions there and seemed similarly trustworthy. I was embarrassed but concerned enough to ask, 'Am I safe out here?'

He looked at my bicycle and my racing clothes. 'Long as you aren't carrying a tomahawk you are.' He laughed at his joke, then said,

406

'You'll be okay. Tell them you know Old Man Parker if anyone bothers you.'

The region's beauty was undeniable – steep ridges covered with redwood and Douglas fir, a wide bay with Arcata snuggled against its northern edge and Eureka along the southern side. The race the following weekend took us through the center of an ancient rain forest with the tallest trees on earth, which had sprouted as seedlings at the same time that the Egyptian pyramids were being built – redwoods that towered above the surrounding forests, the dead tips of snags with eagle nests atop and ferns as tall as me growing along the roadside we raced down. I knew I'd be back after the season ended to stay again, but I avoided visiting Aaron's place deep in the wilderness. I wanted to see the area on my own first. I also wanted to see what the coast and towns were like before I was isolated at a remote ranch where I wouldn't likely see anybody at all.

As I drove across the Oregon border, continuing north toward Portland, an owl swooped off a fencepost, the underside of its wings illuminated by my headlights. The state I had left behind was larger and more complex than I had ever imagined. It was difficult to think about it as a single state. My teammates in Baja California had made it clear that the state was historically Spanish and more recently Mexican territory. What most Americans considered California – where Los Angeles and San Francisco stood – was the same place that my Mexican teammates in Baja called Alta California and had been taken from Mexico in the Mexican-American War.

I found it equally confusing that people in San Francisco differentiated themselves from those in LA by printing 'Welcome to Northern California' on the travel brochures I had picked up when it was actually in the middle of the state. It had taken me six hours to drive from Los Angeles to San Francisco and another six to drive from San Francisco to Humboldt County. San Francisco had more in common with Los Angeles than any part of true Northern California, a lightly populated area of ancient forested mountains inhabited by the Yuroks and other tribes, like the Wiyots, Karuks and Hupas, who lived in the neighboring hills. I had no reason not to

407

believe Old Man Parker who had said that most of his tribe lived without electricity or telephones. I was quickly learning that California as a singular place, and perhaps the idea of America itself, was more a consensual hope than an easily demarcated and defended fact.

Instead of eating big meals as I traveled from state to state and race to race, I snacked as I drove. I didn't want to stop and break out the Coleman stove every time I got the hunger knocks. I kept my Campy peanut butter wrench up on the dashboard to make sandwiches. Peanut butter was inexpensive, loaded with protein and enough fat that I didn't get hungry immediately after eating, while jelly provided plenty of sugar. The wrench was made by Campagnolo for tightening the crank-arm bolts. Craig had told me to double-check the bolts at least once a month to keep my pedals from falling off in the middle of a race and to avoid damaging the expensive equipment. The handle had smooth edges and a rounded tip like a thick butter knife, which made it perfect for sandwich-spreading.

After racing in Portland, I headed back to Colorado and spent a month competing in different towns – Durango, Vail, Copper Mountain, Steamboat Springs, Denver, Boulder, Fort Collins – then moved on to races in Nebraska, Iowa, Missouri, Illinois, scoring enough results to get invited back to OTC and making enough money to continue my journey. Once I felt confident that I had enough results, I started hiring myself out in the summer as a mercenary, secretly paid in cash by teams looking for hometown victories who hired me before races to attack from the starting line and go up the road on suicide missions in an attempt to blow up the field and set up their team leader for a win. It never ceased to surprise me how the field responded to my attacks, since I often pulled out of the race once my work was over – it taught me that if you attacked there was always somebody willing to try to take you down even though their reaction usually destroyed their own chances of victory.

The road passing outside the window of my van that year became the only constant in my life. The hypnotizing, never-ending broken yellow line at the center became my most steadfast guide, leading me on into the heartland. The screaming crowds that gathered around racecourses, the whooshing air inside the pack, the smell of asphalt, of burning rubber from racers skidding in front of me to avoid a crash, the feel of my smoothly shaved legs and the cool water of the creeks my feet rested in after shaving them – each sensation, sound and experience blended together from place to place.

After one race a father and his son approached me to talk about the sport. I said, 'Kansas City is a great place to race.'

The father seemed confused, then said, 'Never been there. I'll have to make it over there one day.'

I realized I was in Des Moines. Cities and states blurred together after you'd traveled through enough of them, and unless there was some highly unusual landmark or architectural feature to distinguish them, they soon became one. Traveling without companionship was lonely but serene. The peace of loneliness was more rewarding than the confusion and demands of too many friends. I had only to answer to myself.

By July I eventually made my way to Wisconsin for Superweek, where Devin and I had planned to race the previous summer. The name of the race was a misnomer: it was a month-long series of races that sat squarely in the middle of the race calendar and the country, bringing together the best fields at mid-season. The organizers put me up at the dorms of the University of Wisconsin in Milwaukee. My sixth-floor room looked out over Lake Michigan. I kept the window cracked so that a light breeze blew in and freshened the air.

I was able to ride my bike directly from the dorm to the starting line of numerous races – the Schlitz Park Challenge, the Great Downer Avenue Race and the Lake Front Road Race, my favorite because it ran up and down tree-lined streets through neighborhoods bordering the lake and downtown. Others, like the Tour of Holy Hill Road Race, the Proving Grounds Road Race, the Carl Zach and Otto Grunski Classics, required driving around the state to places like Waukesha, Menasha, Sheboygan, Kenosha and a half-dozen more.

My roommate was a member of the Canadian national team.

When he learned that I had raced with the national team in Texas he started talking about the Polish coaching staff that the U.S. Cycling Federation had hired to help elevate our international results. 'Every one of those guys came up in Eastern Europe under an athletic system based on the Soviet model,' he said. 'Your government encourages every kind of coach from behind the Iron Curtain to defect and apply for political asylum.'

'Why would they do that?'

'To win. Why else? We've all been getting our ass kicked by the Soviet Bloc, but your country is more desperate than mine to prove that it's stronger than the U.S.S.R. The Soviets have refined their tests so well that they can reach their decision within minutes on the potential of a child to become a world-class athlete. They send teams of physiologists around the Soviet Union testing schoolchildren to see who's worth developing at the national institute.'

He had a small stack of books on genetics stacked up on the desk in his corner of the room that he often read during the days off between races. He had finished his undergraduate degree and wanted to become an exercise physiologist for his national team after he retired from competitive cycling. With nothing better to do on days off, I started reading his books and asking him questions about sections I didn't understand. He also introduced me to new methods of training, such as riding at your lactate threshold. One section that caught my attention was the claim that oxygen uptake could be improved by only 15 percent through training, but it stated that 'Most people who have the opportunity to undergo expensive testing have already trained extensively and will likely see little future change in additional tests.'

I had never considered the concept of genetics before he brought it to my attention. I was interested only in riding my bike, in racing, not in studying scientific data related to results. For me it seemed so far removed from the original reasons that I'd gotten into sports that I questioned the validity of placing so much emphasis on it. It took the soul out of the thing I had fallen in love with and explained away the beauty of humans competing against each other by boiling it down to complex mathematical formulas that didn't seem related

410

to what we did once we clicked our cleats into our pedals at the starting line of each race.

The more cities and states I traveled through, and the more people I came into contact with, the more I learned. Knowledge seemed infinite. No matter how well accepted the preconceived notions we had of certain data, there always seemed another angle or more information that expanded previously held beliefs. Even something as seemingly uninteresting as the city of Milwaukee was a new experience for me. It was the first city I ever saw where people with German ancestry, which appeared to be the majority, didn't try to hide it. If anything, they flaunted it. During the street festivals that were staged at the same time as many of our races to draw bigger crowds, they sold bratwurst on every corner and sauerkraut was easier to find than pickles. I even saw one guy wandering around in Lederhosen – it wasn't a Halloween costume and no one was laughing at him. After exploring the library archives at the university and learning some unsettling details, I was never compelled to investigate Wisconsin's German culture any closer, but I did bump into Alex from OTC at a race up in Green Bay.

'What are you doing up here?' he asked.

'Pedaling my bike, trying to make a dollar to go another round at OTC. Peace Race or bust for me next spring. How about you?'

'I live an hour from here. Where are you staying?'

'Milwaukee. At the university.'

'You got to get out of that place and see the real Wisconsin.'

'I've seen a lot already. I've raced in more towns here than in any other state.'

'I just came back from New England where I competed in a short stage race. I know most of the guys here, so I wanted to race against some other riders to get more experience.'

'Pretty much the same reason I'm here. I did New England last fall. Beautiful place, too.'

'Come and stay at my grandfather's farm for a couple weeks before you take off. We can train together.'

Once Superweek concluded, I took up his offer. He lived in a room

411

his grandfather had helped him build above the garage. He reminded me of Devin with his boundless energy and enthusiasm. He insisted that we shed our training schedule and instead load up some gear on our bikes and take off for a two-week tour through the Northern Highland Lake District, a forested region with thousands of lakes where glaciers had once passed, carving the bedrock and leaving small pockets in its wake.

'I don't want to mess up my form,' I said.

'We've been racing all year. We can stay fit touring to get a break from the grind of racing. We'll put in more miles riding around the lakes every day than we would training anyway and we can sleep out in the woods each night.'

He made it sound better than staying at the farm, doing intervals and sprint training.

'You're going to pay for this if it screws up the rest of my season. I'm serious about making the national team to Europe next spring.'

'You're not the only one, but you can have Poland. I'm signing on for the Belgium trip. What's the big deal with Poland anyway?'

'The coaches say the best races are behind the Iron Curtain.'

'You can still keep it. I'd rather go down to Paris after Belgium and cruise along the Seine River.'

'If we don't keep our form, neither of us is going anywhere.'

Touring turned out to be exactly what I needed to keep a fresh outlook for the rest of the season. After living in the back of my van that spring and summer, focusing on race after race, rarely paying attention to the peripheral world, it provided me with a chance to recover from constant competition without losing any fitness. He took me around lakes, down back roads, through forests and briefly across the border into the Upper Peninsula of Michigan. It reminded me of the year after I left Relativity and wandered, but I was more confident now and my life had direction. I had missed the fresh scents of the forest that you only experience when you're sleeping on the ground, and the sound of crickets in the evening. He carried a small telescoping fishing rod in one of his panniers. Each day I dug up earthworms for bait, we caught dinner and ate on the shore.

During that trip I decided that when I eventually retired from cycling I'd return to the wilderness I had passed through traveling across the country and hike in the mountains, like I'd done at the end of last season in Tennessee. There were so many things I still wanted to do, but unless I found success in cycling I knew such goals would be difficult to achieve. I didn't want to get trapped back into the life of a transient laborer. I had paid my dues. I liked my new line of work and intended to take it as far as possible.

In August I drove west along the northern border of the country to Seattle, where I took Interstate 5 north and crossed into Canada to compete in the Gastown Grand Prix in downtown Vancouver. Then I slowly worked my way down the west coast, competing in small backwoods races in Washington, stayed a few days in Portland and the following week raced near Crater Lake in southern Oregon. Eventually I made my way back to Humboldt County as the racing season came to a close. In Humboldt I trained with local riders on climbs outside Arcata – Kneeland, Fickle Hill, Old Lord Ellis, Butler Creek, Panther Gap – before finally heading out to Aaron's retreat deep in the wilderness, up dirt roads cutting through the dense forest. He hadn't left a phone number and the deeper I drove into the forest, following his detailed directions, the more apparent it became that he didn't have one. I eventually reached a gate blocking the road with a sign warning: 'No Trespassing. Violators Will Be Prosecuted.'

On his directions, he had warned me about the gate and told me to park off to the left and hike in. I didn't want to leave my van or bike behind. I hadn't passed any other cars, but if somebody stole either it would be impossible to make a living or pursue my dream. Neither did I feel secure climbing the gate and hiking up the dirt road deep into the wilderness, unsure of what lay ahead. But I liked the remoteness of the property – even more remote than anything Alex and I had cycled through in Wisconsin. I wondered if anyone had ever hiked all the peaks and ravines surrounding me. I walked up a short, steep hill. A mile up the road, I heard a faint cracking sound that grew louder the further I hiked. I had trouble figuring out what it was. It sounded similar to the small snapping sound of a .22 rifle being used for target practice, but as I neared its origin, the sound stopped. I hid behind a tree. Soon the sound returned and I came out of my hiding place and walked in its direction. I eventually came to a bend in the road where a clearing opened up and I saw a man splitting wood with an ax.

I drew his attention by letting out a loud whistle. He turned, looked at me for a second, then called in Spanish for Aaron, who appeared on the porch of a cabin at the edge of the clearing. When he recognized me, he said, 'What a pleasant surprise. Let me show you around.'

'What about my van?'

'We'll get it before dark. Nobody ever comes up that road.'

He introduced the man splitting wood. When it became apparent that he spoke no English, I said, '¡Mucho gusto!'

'El gusto es mío. ¿Habla Espanol?'

'No,' I said. 'Un poco. Mi Espanol es muy mal. Forgive me.'

Aaron gave him some instructions, then led me down a path through the woods to another clearing with a pond in the middle. Along the way he told me the worker's name was Yaxché. 'I call him Ché. He's from Guatemala. He worked on my property in Palm Springs last winter. He works harder than Americans at half the price.'

I had done enough similar work that I wasn't interested in learning how much money Aaron saved in hiring him. It made me think of bosses I had worked for.

'The pond's stocked with trout,' he said. He picked up a bag of feed stored in a wooden box and flung it out into the water. The surface came to life, fish splashing to get the morsels of food. Then he showed me another clearing with a small orchard that he had planted and fenced off so the deer didn't eat the seedlings. Afterward, we walked down a ravine lined with five-inch pipe that led to the small hydroelectric generator that powered the property. 'I run twelve-volt appliances in the cabins, but there's an inverter in the main cabin to step it up to 110.' The system was gravity fed, the pipe originating at the pond near the top of the hill and running down the slope to the hydro-generator a quarter-mile downstream. I had never seen anything like it. The entire property was self-contained, or 'off the grid,' as he called it, flush with fresh water, hydroelectric generators, food in the form of fish, fruit and a vegetable garden. I was unaware that people still lived like this, especially people with as much money as Aaron. I didn't want to pry at first, but later that night, after drinking some wine, I asked him how he'd paid for it all.

'I made a lot of money in advertising down in LA. I wanted to find a way to give some of it back.'

'Give it back? In the middle of the woods?'

'I built this place to help keep people safe.'

'From what?' I asked.

'The city. Civil unrest. This place is ready to go.'

'What kind of civil unrest?'

'Who knows? Economic, political or just overpopulation. You get too many people in one place and they become like rats crawling on top of each other. Sooner or later it explodes. Almost every city in the world that's been around a few hundred years has experienced it. It's only a matter of time.'

His paranoia reminded me of my father, but at least my father had seen cities disintegrate with his own eyes. Aaron had told me he was born and raised in Denver. To my knowledge that city had never exploded, but as the night wore on and he shared more of his life, it became clear that it had shaped his view of the future. He had been raised Seventh Day Adventist and educated from grade school through university at institutions run by Adventists. He explained in detail, without my asking, that they emphasized diet and health and ran hospitals and schools around the world. They also believed in something he called a 'time of trouble,' which he described as a test of sorts that would occur before Jesus reappeared on earth.

To change the subject, I asked about his parents.

He became visibly angry. 'We don't speak. They don't approve.'

'Of living out here?'

'Of being gay. I built this retreat for people raised in conservative families and brainwashed by their religion into believing there's

415

something wrong with them. Those thoughts don't easily disappear, no matter how successful you are. I want to be able to help protect them too, in case anything should happen.'

He proceeded to explain that, in the 'time of trouble,' he believed gays would be persecuted. 'You can't trust a world that teaches you to hate yourself growing up. I'm convinced something will happen.'

I thought about my brother and wondered again where he was. I had traveled thousands of miles and now, on the other side of the country, I was in an uncomfortable position, similar to the one I had been in with him. I tried to be gracious. 'When do you expect it to happen?'

'Who knows? I've set up a trust. They'll eventually appreciate what I've done. Even the gays in Palm Springs call me crazy, but it hasn't stopped me completing this place.'

In one way his views were progressive, in another extreme. They didn't seem realistic, but he had pointed out that Yaxché had left Guatemala because of a revolution. The United States seemed too big, too stable, too secure for such a complete breakdown, but then again Aaron was more successful, better educated and obviously smarter than I was, as demonstrated by the way he had used a bull-dozer to dig the ponds, figured out how to line the bottom to stop the water seeping back into the earth, piped water in from streams to fill them, then stocked them with fish, planted and irrigated orchards and generated hydroelectricity. I had little more to show for myself than a bicycle a sponsor had given me.

The first few nights were peaceful, but then I started having night-mares about men dressed in camouflage, carrying M-16s, sneaking through the forest, climbing to the highest points of the property that Aaron had driven me to in his four-wheel-drive Jeep, showing me how to secure the area. He had thought out every detail to the point that his ideas seemed creepy and were oozing into my mind whenever I fell asleep. Less than a week after arriving, I packed my van, thanked him for inviting me and left.

* * *

416

I drove to San Francisco and put up in an inexpensive room at a boarding house on O'Farrell in the Tenderloin for a week so that I could walk around the city to convince myself that society wasn't breaking down and that gays weren't at risk of being persecuted in the violent ways Aaron envisioned. I felt more relaxed walking up Turk Street at midnight being approached by drug-dealers than I had falling asleep deep in the wilderness and having nightmares about society collapsing. I liked the way the city was laid out and everything so centrally located. The only decent long training rides, though, were across the bridge into the Marin headlands and I had to fight constant traffic riding through the city to get there.

When I moved out of the boarding house and back into my van to save money, I was constantly hassled by the police prowling around the streets. It was almost impossible to sleep in the van there. I finally moved farther down the coast, driving along Highway 1 through Monterey and Big Sur. Eventually I reached Isla Vista, a densely populated student ghetto adjacent to a university and Santa Barbara.

Several cycling teams were based in the area and I joined them on training rides into the mountains and slept in my van each night, parking in front of different houses and dorms. Unfortunately the section of town was small enough that, when a cop saw me climbing out of my van one morning, every police officer in the neighborhood became aware of my presence. There was a law on the books that stated a person could not live in their car. After two warnings I moved on, first to Ventura, then to San Clemente where Kevin – a rider I had roomed with in Texas and who had medaled at the LA Games – had casually invited me to stay if I were ever in the area.

From his expression when I knocked on his door, I doubt he'd ever expected me to show up, but he let me shower in his house after rides and included me in a select training group of five riders he had put together to maintain fitness over the winter. They had nick-named themselves Kevin's Krew and officially accepted me as a member once it was clear that Kevin approved. I still had good form from the season, and training regularly with them helped bring my fitness up another notch. I paid for a post-office box to receive mail, and one afternoon while I was sitting on the pier watching the locals fish, I wrote out my results from the previous season and mailed it to OTC. I spent the rest of November and early December waiting for my invitation to arrive so I could drive back to Colorado Springs and settle comfortably into the dorms for a couple of months before the season started again.

Each Wednesday and Sunday Kevin's Krew went out on an eight-hour training ride that covered a 120-mile loop to keep our endurance up and avoid putting on extra weight. We met for coffee and pastries at a bakery in San Juan Capistrano, then headed out along Ortega Highway to a long climb over the Santa Ana Mountains, racing each other to the summit, where we regrouped and gazed down at Lake Elsinore below. Then we sailed down the twisting descent and rode out through farms, orchards and vineyards to Temecula, where we took the remote Pala Temecula Road out to a tiny Indian reservation that had a single store near the crossroads of Highway 76. There, a man hung out every Wednesday, waiting for our arrival, and when he saw us approaching, he ran into the middle of the road and put his hands in the air to indicate the finish line. We sprinted, then sat out front with him for twenty minutes, drinking sodas and eating cookies, before riding Highway 76 to Oceanside, where we encountered heavy and often dangerous traffic, especially near the coast at the end of the workday.

From there we turned north on a frontage road skirting the beach, up through a narrow state park hugging the coast on the ocean side of Camp Pendleton, another marine base, and past the San Onofre Nuclear Plant, racing north toward the old wooden pier jutting out into the ocean at San Clemente.

It was easier living in my van there than it had been anyplace else I had stayed. The police dismissed me as another surfer waiting for waves down at Trestles. During my free time I rode up the coast. There was a state park in Dana Point that I occasionally camped at, and Laguna Beach turned out to be an equally good place to live in my car, with showers on the main beach. Whenever I slept in my van in the residential neighborhoods in Laguna, I rose early and walked down to Zinc Café. They served cappuccino in ceramic bowls and attracted a diverse clientele, from businessmen to musicians to eccentric individuals – a wealthy woman showed up each morning carrying a pink poodle wearing a diamond-encrusted collar with its name, Phrizzy, neatly outlined in gold lettering.

I sat, with my cappuccino, in the middle of the crowd, dressed in a warm-up suit the national team had given me. I felt as much a part of it as anyone and there weren't many places where I felt part of a crowd. I lived all winter long in various communities along the south coast with as much comfort and more freedom than most of the permanent residents. There was an openness about the culture there that I hadn't found elsewhere. Perhaps it was because everyone was used to hanging out in the sun on the beach all day, and as the winter wore on I felt free of Ohio, Georgia, South Carolina, the countless places I'd lived on the road and the things that had happened there. I rarely thought about my brother's or Aaron's apocalyptic visions and usually avoided thinking about Germans or what had become of my parents.

I no longer saw the road as a means to an end but as an end in itself, a place where I could travel in ever widening circles, as I had all those years, going repeatedly through many of the same places without passing the same police officer twice. I had little reason to fear the police, but after my conditioning as a teenager, I still avoided them. I knew my journey would soon be complete. I had found the peace and solitude I had been searching for. The only goal I had left was to make the Peace Race and travel back to the southern part of the territory my father had come from in Poland. I hoped for a chance to glance across the bay to the Russian oblast Kaliningrad and the peninsula I had been named after. But even if I didn't get to do that, going to Poland, I hoped, would finally free me. Those weeks in November were one of the few times I relaxed enough to let myself feel the pleasure of my recent accomplishments. I was finally going someplace positive and nothing in the world could hold me back.

* * *

Twice a week I went to my post-office box in San Clemente to see if the invitation had arrived. Nobody else had my address so I didn't bother checking it every day. By the beginning of December nothing had appeared, so I started checking it every other day. By the fifteenth I still hadn't received a letter with the familiar USCF logo. I wouldn't have worried except that a half-dozen riders who showed up for a training race around the Ziggurat building in Laguna Niguel every Tuesday evening had already received their invitations to the first camp, riders with fewer results and less experience than I had.

Nothing. No response. Not even rejection.

I waited until the end of the week, then called the training center. Perhaps there had been a mistake. I wanted to catch them before they closed for the week over Christmas. I went to the bank, got a ten-dollar roll of quarters and found a payphone in a quiet location on a side street off Forest Avenue in Laguna and called. The secretary answered, checked the roster and said my name wasn't on the list.

I asked to speak to the coach.

'He's busy. I'll have him call you back.'

I gave her the number of the payphone and waited for two hours. It never rang. I called back.

'He's gone.'

I called again the next day.

'He just stepped out. He won't be back until after lunch.'

After lunch he was in a meeting.

I waited two days, then called so many times that she finally put me through so I'd stop calling.

'May I help you?' It was Tommy K.'s assistant, Boryslaw.

I asked him if there was a mistake. 'I have better results than most of the riders I've met that you invited.'

'The spots are tighter this year. More applications.'

'But I got the results. They didn't. I did exactly what you guys told me to do after Texas.'

'I'm sorry, Sam.'

'Sorry about what? My results are better than half the people you're inviting. I can outride them.'

420

'We use different criteria – not only results.'

'What kind of criteria?'

'Everything.'

'I competed internationally. I won a race in Mexico. My time-trial results are as fast as some of the guys who went to the LA Games. What more can I do?'

He told me he had to go. I was still talking when he hung up. I called back. I was livid. When the secretary wouldn't put me through again, I called repeatedly until finally the head coach, Tommy K., came on the line. 'Is there a problem, Sam?'

'You tell me. I spent a year doing exactly what you told me to do and now you're filling up the spots at camp with guys I beat consistently. I don't understand.'

He didn't respond immediately. I interpreted the silence more as irritation than contemplation. 'Let me look at the camp lists,' he said eventually. 'Can I call you back?'

'I don't have a phone. I'm living in my car. I'm calling from a payphone.'

I heard him rustling impatiently through papers. 'How about the third camp? Can you make it out in the middle of February?'

The third camp, I thought. They're not even interested in the riders by then. But what could I do? 'Yeah, yeah, I can make it out.' I tried to sound appreciative, but it came out sounding reluctant.

'Be here by February fifteenth sharp, or I'll have to give your spot away. You know the rules.'

'Yeah, I know the rules. I'll be there. Thanks for giving me a break.'

I hung up feeling partly vindicated, partly defeated. My place in the final camp had been secured by little more than my being pushy and persistent. But I had earned it with sweat and sacrifice. He had given all the spots in the first and second camps to riders who had never won a race, never competed internationally. I felt almost certain that if Janek hadn't called him the previous winter to put in a good word for me, he probably wouldn't have taken my call, even with my persistence. It was part social obligation that had helped me get in, as much

421

as my pushiness. The only thing he knew about my background was that Janek and I were close and that I spoke a few words of Polish. And, like Janek, Tommy K. knew that my father had come from *Prusy Wschodnie* – East Prussia. He had asked where my father was from when he saw my last name. I'd told him. But I never told him about my German past. I never mentioned that my father was raised in the Hitler Youth. I wasn't duplicitous or dishonest. I just wasn't stupid for once in my life. I had answered every question he had asked me last year with complete honesty. He had made his own assumptions – the world seemed to turn on its axis fueled by assumptions.

I started thinking about my roommate from the Canadian national team in Milwaukee last summer, what he had said about the USCF recruiting its new coaching staff from Eastern Bloc countries. All the information he had shared with me and the books on genetics that I had read over the summer coalesced at once. It was my numbers. My test scores. They were deficient by Soviet Union sporting standards. I had seen the numbers the Soviet athletes required to receive state assistance printed in black ink in one of those books, and mine didn't cut it. At the time I'd read them, I'd thought how lucky I was to have been born in America where I didn't have to deal with such regimented criteria. I had been lucky to have coaches select me on my past results, my savvy, my motivation, my ability to crash hard in a race, jump back on my bike and catch the pack afterward. They had seen me. They knew how I raced when I was motivated.

But I had been mistaken. There was a vast pool of untested athletes out there in America. They didn't care how much you had competed or if you had won a race: they were looking for that uncut diamond, the individual with superior hidden genetics. I was genetically inferior. It wasn't a matter of insecurity or low self-esteem: it was the factual data that the coaches had stored in my profile at OTC. They were being clinical in their decision, not emotional. It didn't matter that my genetic ability was above average: it was below elite, and even if I improved by 15 percent, my numbers still wouldn't match those of the *crème de la crème*. I was already in prime shape, so at best I'd see a five percent improvement in them over the next few years if I were lucky. My race results were good, even superior for my limited experience, but the numbers OTC had filed away on my physiology were not. It didn't mean I couldn't win races and, with enough panache, even big races, but I would never win consistently, as far as they were concerned, and they would never trust me to win against the world's best. Instead of developing me farther, they would go on sifting data, sampling more untested riders, searching for the next hidden vein of gold.

Sports presented themselves to society as the one area in which individuals, regardless of circumstances, were equal. But if meritocracy were defined as 'society rewarding those who show talent and competence as demonstrated by past actions or by competition,' most failed to understand that the chief requirement to join the athletic elite lay more firmly in an undiscovered nepotism – family connections – than success demonstrated by past actions. Like being born into a wealthy family and having privileges few experience, achieving a legendary status in sports was a birthright no matter how poor your family. If your parents did not carry the right genetic coding, it was impossible to become the best. Without the genetic gift that only parents could provide, such immortality was impossible, regardless of how much you dedicated yourself, how much you trained or who coached you. It was true that many with superior genetics failed to achieve greatness, but no one achieved greatness without the right genetic coding.

The governments of the Eastern Bloc countries had attempted to reduce the odds of unknown nobility escaping them during the years when gold medals at the Olympics were politically valuable: they had sent genetic screeners to every city, town and village in each state, province and oblast. The screeners had little interest in encouraging young children but a great deal in locating those able to perform a series of rote physical tests with agility, speed and power. The idea that somebody from a poverty-stricken background could achieve fame and wealth by dedicating themselves to a sport – as an untold number of children watching TV believed – was a fraud. Their dedi-

423

cation and discipline would never result in anything if their genes lacked the coding of a champion. Even the second- and third-tier athletes, the teammates and workers of champions, were genetically superior to most of humanity.

I was incensed and enraged by all this information that, in a moment of clarity, made sense. I couldn't shut my mind, no matter how hard I tried to calm myself. Maybe the cliché was true: ignorance is bliss. Having too much information seemed only to break you down. It had been a mistake for me to delve so deeply into my roommate's books. It had awakened the same curiosity I'd had as a child and had led me to spend afternoons in the dusty vaults of the library at the university in Milwaukee reading books few people checked out, using the research skills Alex had taught me. Down in the archives of the University of Wisconsin, I had become more curious about possible American influences on Nazi Germany than the German influences on America that my father had pushed on me. Perhaps it was my way of rejecting him for good, my personal rebellion, but whatever had pushed me into those archives, it still pained me to acknowledge the information I had found. My mind felt like a live wire, jumping from one place to the next. I had never imagined that trying to make the national team again would throw me into such turmoil. I felt as if I had been thrust into Nazi Germany where they had relied on laboratory results to find the perfect human being.

My mind returned to several unsettling books I had found on eugenics, a movement that sought to evolve the human species by eliminating people with certain genetic traits while increasing the procreation of people with allegedly positive genes in an attempt to achieve racial purity resulting in supremacy. In the 1920s, the programs became so popular in the United States that proponents like Henry Ford, the Carnegie Institution and the Rockefeller Foundation encouraged enquiry, the latter two spending millions to promote and research possibilities through German scientists, some of whom would eventually work for the Nazi Party, including Hitler's raceologist, Otmar Verschuer. I also learned that Ford, under an affiliate, had published truckloads of anti-Semitic tracts in Dearborn, Michigan, virtually reprinting the notoriously fraudulent *Protocols* to distribute to an American audience. Many copies had made their way to Germany and were translated and republished there. At the Nuremberg trials, one Nazi said that Henry Ford's anti-Semitic publications had made a profound impression on him: 'We saw in Henry Ford the representative of success, also the exponent of progressive social policy. In the poverty-stricken and wretched Germany of the time, youth looked toward America . . .' Hitler himself once stated, 'I regard Ford as my inspiration.' Ford also admired Hitler – he accepted the highest honor Nazi Germany granted to foreigners: the Grand Cross of the German Eagle.

I wandered through the neighborhood and lay down in my van, still reeling, unable to shut off the flow of information I had read. Few people were interested in the influence that Ford, the Carnegie Institution and the Rockefeller Foundation had had on the development of Nazi ideology in eugenics. Their actions were well documented and never denied, but they remained ignored by a society unwilling to tarnish the reputation of institutions that funded research and development both privately and through universities. Nobody wanted to lose their funding.

So much adrenaline flooded my body that I felt as if I was going to snap. I tried to calm down by reminding myself that it was during the final camp that the coaches held the races to select the long team for the Tour of Texas based on points awarded according to your final placing in each of three races. They couldn't take those numbers away from me. If you won one of the races, you were given an automatic berth. If I earned enough points, they couldn't deny me a spot to Texas even if my VO$_2$ was that of a chain-smoking couch potato. I'd arrive ripped and ready to roll.

Once I was in Texas, where the teams going to Europe would be appointed, it would be the same. I wouldn't let them take from me the numbers I won in races. I still had a chance to achieve my ultimate goal. If I accomplished it I wasn't even sure I wanted to continue

425

racing full time afterward. I couldn't live in my van for the rest of my life – but if I could make it to Europe on my bike, I would have enough confidence to move into the professional world, join society and rid my head of the very thoughts that made me despise the mainstream. I wanted to finish what I had set out to do and end on a positive note. I had no idea what the future held, but I wanted to achieve my early dream. I didn't need to be world champion or make the Olympics. My goals were reasonable, I told myself. It was only a matter of staying calm and keeping my head on straight.

The following day my mind was still spinning. I needed to talk to someone. Someone who would understand and not tell me it was all in my head. I couldn't let it kill my self-esteem and drag me down. I knew I could make the team going to Texas. I felt sure I could make the team going to Poland, if I stayed calm. But I desperately needed somebody to talk with. Nick was the only person I was close to who could put his emotions aside at a time of need. It had been a year since I had heard his voice. I knew he'd be upset, but I also knew he'd forgive me once I'd called. It was part of having a true friend, even when they disappeared or insulted you: you let it pass. He knew better than anyone that I'd needed to develop after I'd left Columbia and I was already partway there. I could finally share some of my experiences with him and his advice would soothe my frayed nerves.

I called his studio. An automated message stated that his line had been disconnected. I dialed his home and got the same message. I couldn't remember him telling me he had any plans for the following winter, but we hadn't talked much in the time leading up to my departure. I called Information to find out if his number had been changed. The operator gave me several different ones, but none connected me to Nick. I didn't want to call Craig right then. Where Nick would help calm me, I worried that Craig would tear into me for not being in touch, but I finally broke down and called anyway. I wanted to find out where Nick was and didn't know whom else to call.

As usual, he answered on the second ring. 'Sam here,' I said. 'Calling to check in. I know it's been a while.'

It took him only a second or two to pull his thoughts together and respond sarcastically, 'It has been a little while, now that you mention it.'

'Sorry about that. I had to hit out on my own, like you did when you first left home.'

'Well, I hope you found what you were looking for.'

'It's there, it's getting there,' I said.

'Where are you anyway?'

'California. I leave to go back to Colorado in a few weeks. I'll bring you up to speed when I get back there. Hey, man, I tried calling Nick. What's up with his phone? I keep getting a disconnect signal.'

'Yeah, it's disconnected.'

'What's going on with him?'

'You've been gone a year now. Nobody knew how to contact you. Call me later tonight, and we'll catch up.'

'What gives? Tell me what's going on. I'll call again tonight, but don't leave me hanging like this. Just give me his number and I'll call you after work.'

He was silent. I didn't like the way he paused. It reminded me of how he'd acted after Devin's accident. I could literally hear my heart beating in the silence, the phone pressed firmly against my ear to block out the noise of passing traffic. I waited and grew impatient. 'Is something wrong? Just give me his number. Don't be a dick.'

'He doesn't have a number.'

'What do you mean he doesn't have a number?'

'He's not here any more.'

'Where did he move to?'

'He didn't move anywhere, Sam.'

'Don't fuck with me on this, Craig. Tell me what's going on.'

'I'm not fucking with you.' He paused again. Before I could say anything, he said, 'He died, Sam. He passed away less than a month ago.'

Twenty-four hours ago it hadn't seemed possible that life could get harder. 'What happened?' I asked frantically.

427

'Meningitis.'

'What's that?'

'Inflammation of the spinal cord.'

'How could that kill him? I saw him less than twelve months ago.'

'Complications.'

'What kind of complications?'

He paused again. I couldn't bear the silence.

'Complications of what?' I shouted into the phone.

'AIDS.'

The word slid through me as if a dull iron rod had been rammed into my chest. I dropped my head. I stood there for a time, staring at the passing traffic. 'He's dead?' I asked.

'He's dead, Sam. Nobody knew how to reach you. Nick didn't want to see anyone anyway. He was with somebody new, who took care of him up to the end. The last time I saw him he was ghostly thin. He didn't want anyone to see him like that – and I'm not sure he would have wanted to see you anyway.'

'I have to go. I'll call back.'

I dropped the phone. I was devastated. All my concerns about not being invited to the first camp, about having inferior numbers, seemed unimportant now. A wave of guilt swept over me for not staying in touch. Why had I neglected him? It would have been so easy to pick up the phone. Now it was too late. It was less than two months since I'd stayed in San Francisco. I'd thought a lot about Nick while I was there. One night, walking up Market Street to the Castro, I'd remembered the story he had told me in detail about being in a friend's house up on Twin Peaks overlooking the city when his friend had put on a copy of the recently released *As Falls Wichita, So Falls Wichita Falls* – an electronic instrumental recording that had provided a soundtrack to the unfamiliar skyline he was peering at as a bank of fog rolled in from the ocean, swallowed the Golden Gate Bridge and crawled over the city, eventually engulfing the Bay Bridge and rising above the skyscrapers until only the tip of the Transamerica Pyramid protruded through it, illumined by a full moon in the clear sky above. The fog had continued rising to the window where he was sitting until everything disappeared into the white mist.

I had never contacted him while I was there because I wanted to understand the city on my own. I had already heard his opinions, and respected them, but I'd wanted to form my own view so that when I eventually returned to Columbia I could share it with him in person. Now I would never have a chance to tell him what I had finally seen with my own eyes. The man who had opened up so many positive things for me was gone. I had broken our tie and now it could never be repaired. It was only with his death that I realized I had lost the most important person in my life.

I spent the following two weeks in a daze. I left the south coast and drove up to the west LA beaches of Santa Monica, Hermosa, Manhattan and Redondo, training with the South Bay Wheelmen, going on their doughnut ride and the grind up over the Palos Verde grade. I rode to retain my sanity but wanted to do so anonymously, not with Kevin and the other riders in San Clemente who would see the pain I was in. I wanted to be left alone. I didn't think they would understand. They hardly knew me. And I was in no position to start explaining my past. Neither did I want to tell them I'd had to fight my way into the training camp – the only thing they would be interested in discussing. There was no dignity in pushing yourself someplace you hadn't been invited. I spent long days alone, riding up the coast through Malibu and continuing north on the desolate highway, bordered by tall sand cliffs on my right, the expanse of the ocean and vacant untouched beaches on my left, until I reached Oxnard, where I turned around and headed back south into the city. In the midst of accomplishing my dream, I was lost.

If I were to remain stable, I knew I had to focus on following through with the goal I had set for myself – it was the only thing I had now. Last year I had loved being free of all connections and had felt more relaxed than at any other time in my life, but through it all I had known that one day Nick and I would reunite, even if

429

only as friends, and I had imagined that we would remain so until the day we died. It had never occurred to me that he would die so soon. I trained knowing that he would have wanted me to continue after learning his fate. While riding, I glanced down at my rippled calves, thinking of the countless hours he had worked on them to separate the muscle fibers and bring them to their present form. Even though he was gone, I could still see the physical evidence of his influence on me and feel the profound effect he had had on my mind. Thinking about him calmed me, his meditative nature rolling over me like a wave of warm water. If life were half as eventful in the future as it had been in the past, I still doubted I'd ever meet anyone quite like him.

Another week rolled past, the first camp over and the riders arriving for the second, when the thought first entered my mind. Was I infected too? Nobody knew much about AIDS other than that it was transferred by body fluids, which Nick and I had exchanged. It was rumored to live dormant for long periods in its host, like herpes. There wasn't much else known about it. How could he have gotten it in the few months after I'd left and died so quickly? Had he been carrying it dormant all along? Was I carrying it? I hadn't felt sick over the previous year. I had never felt physically better. I was overwhelmed that, on top of everything else, I now had to confront the possibility that I was infected – which made every other concern fall quickly to the wayside. If an illness crept up on me as fast as it had crept up on him, there'd be nothing to worry about in the future anyway. I had already faced the prospect of death, but it would have been immediate and my survival was assured after I'd escaped. This was different. I didn't know whether I was infected, and it was still unclear whether or not the tests could detect a dormant virus. There were rumors that people who had AIDS were living normal healthy lives, even as epidemic numbers in New York City and San Francisco perished.

I found a place in West Hollywood that tested for free. After drawing my blood, the nurse told me to come back in four weeks.

'It takes that long?'

'You should be thankful we even have a test for it.'

'I'll be gone in four weeks.'

'We have counseling available. I know the wait is stressful, but you look healthy, I don't think anything will happen in four weeks' time.'

'I don't mean I'll be dead. I won't be here. I'll be in Colorado. Can I call?'

'I'm sorry. You have to bring your number in. We're a confidential agency. We can't give out results over the phone.'

'Can you mail them to me?'

'You have to come in person.'

'What if it's negative? Can't you just tell me over the phone?'

'We're a confidential agency,' he repeated. 'We don't give out information over the phone.'

'But I can't come back. I can't wait.'

'I advise you to make arrangements. Your result is important to the community.'

'What are you talking about? All I want to find out is if it's positive or negative.'

'We have counseling. I know this is a stressful situation.'

I calmed myself down enough to thank him and took my number printed on the small slip of paper and walked out into the warm noon sun. I can't believe this is happening to me, I thought. I couldn't find out if I had the virus, because I had to get to the camp on time. I had never been left hanging from such a tenuous thread. I knew they wanted me to return for only a single reason – in case I was positive. They wanted somebody to be present in case I broke down on the spot. They wanted to educate me on my duty to act responsibly and not spread the disease. They wanted to be able to track my fate to develop a wider set of statistics. They couldn't break protocol – infected people might not come back. I spent the next two days trying to figure out what to do, then tossed the tiny printed number identifying me off the Santa Monica pier into the ocean. I couldn't sit around waiting to find out if I was going to die and give up all my dreams.

My situation forced me to come to terms with exactly what was important to me. Which goals in life mattered most if I only had another three, four or five months? For the next two days my body hummed with so much tension that the smell of salt in the moist ocean air, the sound of sea gulls swooping down on the pier, the heat of the afternoon sun touching my skin, the taste of the bean and cheese burritos with jalapeños that I purchased from a corner vendor each afternoon and the sight of the waves rolling in from the ocean, surfers waiting for the perfect ride, became heightened until each experience reached such an intensity that tears welled unexpectedly.

It didn't take me long to decide that I had to go forward along the same path I had already set. Even if I were dead in six months, providing I didn't become ill immediately, I could still make the team to Texas and I could still go on to Poland. It was all I'd ever wanted anyway. I had never planned beyond that. Anything else would be gravy. I was fortunate to have a chance to pursue a goal most could only dream about. I didn't need anything more than that. I decided I didn't care what the result was. Even if it were negative, I knew I'd return to get another test to clarify the first. The doctors had admitted that it was possible dormant viruses went undetected. I already knew what I had to do. The end result would make no difference. What followed was a focused intensity unlike anything I had ever known.

Returning to OTC no longer held the same mystery for me. I now knew it was simply an artifact of the military-industrial complex that had been passed down by the government to house elite athletes expected to defend the honor of the United States in international competitions. I had come ready to fight. I was armed with peak fitness and the serenity of knowing I would excel in the coming competition. It was the first time I had ever approached future races without the slightest degree of worry. I had learned enough in my travels and racing experience to know not to overintellectualize what lay ahead. I had discovered that knowledge could defeat you as easily as it could elevate you. Once you had spent enough time acquiring it, you had to learn to keep it out of your mind, for it was intuition that kept a person alive – thinking from the gut.

There had been another scandal and journalists, photographers and news reporters were mobbing the entrance. I didn't bother asking the guard what they were after this time. I didn't care. As I waited for the guard to give me my pass, I saw a group of new athletes in the OTC van behind me that had just shuttled them in from the airport. I could tell they were first-timers by their starry eyes peering into the grounds of the training center as if they were about to receive a pass to the forbidden kingdom – in a way, I suppose they were. Hopefully their numbers would permit them to stay. I understood how Nick, through age and experience, had become jaded about certain subjects and wondered if life weren't more a series of disappointments and disillusionings than accomplishments and successes. But I didn't contemplate it for long. I was here to do business. Jaded or not, I intended to close the deal. I reached out, took my pass and drove in.

I found Alex in a room down the hall from the one I had been assigned to. He was already set up, but it was obvious he had arrived earlier that morning and hadn't been invited to the first two camps either. I still felt a special kinship with him because, while clearly not genetically gifted, he was a fighter. Our numbers were virtually the same. I didn't bother to ask how he had gotten a spot. A large box stuffed with neatly folded T-shirts stood near the door.

'What are those?'

'Some shirts I designed over the winter and had printed up to sell during camp.' He pulled one out and held it up. The illustration showed a small man, little more than a stick figure, with a chain padlocked to his ankle and attached to a large ball near the center of the shirt. In the middle of the ball were the letters: OTC.

He let it sink in for a second or two and then we laughed.

I pulled out my wallet. He pushed it away. 'Take one, dude. On the house. I'll make my money off the juniors. What else can I do? Too old to make a living cycling, right?'

We laughed and slapped hands. It was good seeing him with his humor and optimism intact even though he'd missed the first two camps.

'Man, we got shafted,' he said. 'We rode most of the people here into the ground last year.'

'It's a numbers game. I always knew I wasn't the most gifted person in the world. But you watch. I'm going to Texas. I'm going to Europe. I'm not getting left behind this year.'

'You'll be fighting for my spot,' he joked. But he was serious. We were as good friends as transient racers could be, but he was letting me know that he had arrived with the same intentions.

'I'm ready,' I said.

'We're going to crush these bitches.'

'How did you get into shape in Wisconsin anyway? Isn't that place covered in snow?'

'I've been sitting in my garage on an indoor trainer all winter and going out on the road risking frostbite while these pussies have been training for almost two months down here. But I'll admit it made me meaner and more motivated to prove myself. I think I'm in better shape than if I'd come to the first two camps to train with these guys. I'm not going back to Wisconsin before next winter.'

'Long as you got your game face on.'

'Game face? As far as I'm concerned, I'm already in Belgium racing in Stars and Stripes.'

'At least I won't be competing against you for the Belgium trip. Still the Peace Race or bust for me.'

'You'll be competing against me to make it to Texas.'

'It's us against them. We're both going.'

I also started talking to Craig every few days, calling him in South Carolina from the payphone near the entrance to the cafeteria. I was 'unattached' that season – Cycling Federation parlance for a rider without official sponsorship or team affiliation. He convinced me to name his team on my license and submit it while I was at OTC in case I decided to go back to Columbia after Texas and Poland. By then he knew my plans. For all the things I disliked about Craig, he kept me rooted and forced me to acknowledge that I had to keep a connection to the past, however slight, or the future became utterly meaningless. It felt good to be back in touch with him.

Although Colorado was warmer than Wisconsin, where Alex had spent the winter, compared to Southern California it was still freezing cold, much like last year when our brakes iced up while we were out training. I didn't bother thinking past the first selection race. Its starting line was east of the training center out on the flats but finished atop a short, steep climb, just under a mile long – the distance was perfect for me. The layout presented the best opportunity for me to make a strong impression on the coaches. I didn't want to go into the third race battling other riders for a few points to secure my position on the team. All I needed was one win and I could claim an automatic berth. I had nothing else on my mind entering the race. It wasn't desperation or overconfidence – both of these usually failed – it was do or die. I had no choice. I either climbed the hill in first place, even though I wasn't a natural mountain goat, or I might as well pack my bags. I was determined to make my mark at the beginning. I was still so angry with Tommy K. that we hadn't said a word to each other. Even when we lined up to start the race that morning, the coaches were unwilling to glance at anyone other than a handful of their favorites.

As soon as they shot the starting gun, attacks went off the front, but I stayed tucked into the pack and didn't fret or work too much. I knew it would be decided on the final climb. Even if a group were off the front when we approached it, I was confident that those who emerged from the pack on the climb would pull the leaders back. There were a few dicey moments, including one where I almost went down in a mass pileup on a sharp corner with some gravel, but I stayed upright and eventually arrived at the base of the climb in a large group.

A small group of riders attacked, three slender mountain goats, bobbing up and down on their bikes, dancing on top of their pedals as they stood up and pulled away from the main pack. I didn't attempt

435

to chase them down. I let a gap open, not willing to risk blowing up before the climb started in earnest. I watched the light, nimble riders a short distance ahead, pushing large gears as the gap widened. I kept my heavier, solid frame in the saddle, spinning a smaller gear at a higher cadence to conserve energy.

When the next attack went, I clicked down two cogs and stood up to join the chase group. After a hard effort, I connected to the last man, sat down and began spinning a smaller gear. The large chase group contained nearly fifteen riders. The rest of the field splintered behind us. I was still in the race. As the stronger riders went to the front and set pace, the chase group splintered as well. Instead of responding to each attack, I jumped across small gaps opening between the riders in front of me and the main body of the chase group, which had whittled down to eight riders.

I looked around and noted that three of the eight were pure climbers, mountain goats. The others were breathing heavily and struggling to keep pace. After allowing the initial burst of lactic acid rushing through my veins to subside, I found a strong rhythm and slowly moved up to the front. I was on top of my gear. The numbers didn't matter. I wouldn't let them. All I had right then was my form and it was on.

Cycling was no different from playing the saxophone or buying and selling stocks. There were periods when you were on and periods when you weren't. When you were on, insecurities and lack of confidence fell away. You were simply on. There was no other way to explain it. There was no logic to it, no second-guessing, no ruminating, no psyching yourself up. In these rare periods, your only guide was gut instinct. When not in form, intuition became a dangerous and unreliable resource, but when your form came back – and it always did if you spent enough time at the grindstone – you floated. It worked perfectly every time. These moments were rare, but when they occurred, the number games folded, the tyranny of raw data, number crunching, the odds, the longs and shorts, the calculations, percentiles and clean numerical conclusions went out the window. You split notes, dropped octaves, quartered half-steps, inverted scales, drove your heel into chords, choked time signatures, dropped behind and jumped ahead of the beat, bent notes, squealed, honked, shouted, just didn't give a good goddamn what anyone thought because you were making music – *your* music – as you danced all the rules straight into the ground.

I shifted down another gear, stayed in the saddle and ground away at the front of the chase group. Even with the threat of three pure climbers beside me and three more up the road, I stayed calm. By dictating the pace, instead of letting the lighter riders – who could accelerate easier – do so, I forced them into my rhythm and threw them off their game. I increased the pace until I was near my breaking point, but remained sitting up with a strong posture and breathing steadily, concentrating to stop my upper body swaying so that I appeared relaxed, as if I were still going easily.

From that point on, it became a psychological battle. The selection had already been made. It was mind over body to the finish line. You bluffed. You wiped the sweat from your forehead, before turning to the rider on your right and smiling, as if you were just out having fun, holding back until the real race started. You never revealed that you were close to cracking, because if they sensed it they'd be the first to drop the hammer and send you sputtering out the back door.

Three riders were still ahead, holding onto their lead, but the chase group I now led was closing in and had slimmed from eight riders to five – the three mountain goats, me and another rider. One of the climbers attacked and bridged up to the front group. I didn't respond. I kept setting pace at the front, slowly clawing my way up to them. Another rider snapped, leaving only me and two others in the chase group. One of the four in the first group began to gap out and slowly drift back toward us.

Just before he joined us and attempted to match pace, I bumped it up a notch and cracked him a second time. He drifted off the back. The rule was always to slim the numbers when the opportunity presented itself. Reduce the odds. Dump excess baggage. Drive a nail through the head of any rider foolish enough to expose his weakness.

437

It was a ruthless and beautiful game. You never took pity. There were no charity cases up front, not on the climbs. It was one of those rare moments in life where everyone present pulled his own weight. The gap between us and the leaders was closing.

When the rider who had been sitting on my wheel stood up to jump across the gap, I stood up and matched his pace. We quickly connected with the leaders, now forming a single group, but instead of resting when we made contact, I continued at the pace we had used to bridge the gap, rode straight through the group and off the front, taking the lead for the first time. Two riders broke free and sprinted up to join me.

After establishing a gap over the riders we'd just succeeded in dropping, someone in my group came slowly past me and began setting pace to ensure the other riders now chasing would not make contact again. The climb steepened, forcing all three of us out of our saddles to struggle against the force of gravity and our tiring bodies. I matched the other two riders' rhythm, concentrating on my breathing pattern, exhaling, exhaling, exhaling. You never thought about breathing in. The key was to force all the carbon dioxide – your exhaust fumes – out of your lungs to make room for fresh oxygen. If you didn't concentrate on expelling it, it could accumulate in your lungs decreasing your performance. Lactic acid was rising through my body, burning my quadriceps and moving up into my abdomen. Then I felt a slight tingle in my forearms. My body was becoming overloaded with the lactic acid that would eventually shut me down. I focused solely on exhaling and tried to ignore the excruciating pain that was slowly overtaking me. I saw the summit finish ahead, the flashing yellow lights on top of the OTC station wagon parked on the side of the road, Tommy K. and Boryslaw standing on the shoulder.

The sight of the coaches fueled me to dig deeper. The rider to my left attacked. I hesitated for maybe two seconds, waiting for the other – smaller – rider beside me to respond, before realizing he was spent. I stood up and began to sprint. As I made contact, I felt my form, my pedal stroke, falter. I quickly shifted down one gear and got back on top of the easier gear, finding my form again. The lead rider glanced back, saw me make contact and sat down to find his own rhythm. It was just the two of us now. I was on the verge of exploding. My lungs burned. My legs ached. I felt like falling over and dying. I had overextended myself. There was no more time. No other chance. It was now or never.

Now or never. I came out of the saddle and counterattacked the leader as we came even with one another. He hadn't anticipated the move. When he stood to match my counterattack, he faltered, unaware I was cracking every bit as badly as him. He sat down, readjusted his rhythm and tried to stand. I didn't look back. I didn't look down. I didn't shift gears. I didn't sit down. I mashed one crank-arm, then the other, the left pedal, then the right, back and forth, swaying from side to side, my form going to pieces, staring ahead at the coaches lining the shoulder of the road. I no longer had any form at all. I stopped trying to maintain a circular pedal stroke. I mashed. One stroke at a time. Pushing one pedal downward, then the other, my body swaying maniacally from side to side, heaving from left to right over the handlebars. I felt as though I was about to lose consciousness. I reached one last time for a final thread of strength and crossed the piece of duct tape they had stuck across the road to signify the finish line.

I heard the other rider still close behind me. It was too late for him. It didn't matter how close he was. I had made it over the line first. I didn't look at the coaches' expressions as I crossed the line or raise my hand in victory. I didn't stop to look back at how far behind the rest of the riders were. I didn't loop back around and lean my bike up against the station wagon, as I normally would, to watch the competition straggle in. I shifted into the easiest gear and spun up the road, letting the lactic acid drain from my body. I knew a route back to the training center by going another mile or so straight ahead and then down a different climb. I pedaled slowly away from the coaches. The rider I had beaten came up beside me.

'You surprised the hell out of me. Good climbing, man. I had no idea you were a goat.'

I reached out and grabbed his hand. 'Thanks for dragging me to the top.'

He laughed. 'Nobody dragged your fat ass. That last move caught me by surprise. I thought I'd catch you before the finish.'

'Yeah, I don't think I ever went that deep before.'

'You coming back to the cars to see the rest of the results?' he asked.

'Naw, I'm heading in the back way. Too much commotion. I'm fried.'

'I'm turning back, bro. Gotta go check on my teammates. Good ride.'

We shook hands once more, then split off from each other as he arced back a hundred and eighty degrees to join the pack and I continued riding up the empty road alone.

At the first road race in Texas, which I'd been spat out of the previous year less than ten miles after the start, I stayed with the main group easily up the hardest climb. The air was sticky hot compared to the icy cold I'd just come from at OTC – I was always amazed by how varied the weather could be at the same time of year in different parts of the country. It made me think about America's immensity.

I couldn't go with the leaders when they attacked but I was comfortably in the field on the most difficult part of the course. Last year I'd been dying on the flats before we'd even hit the climb. As always it was intensely competitive, but I slowly chipped away and gathered points by breaking the top twenty in the first three races and finally scoring a top ten in the fourth race of the series. At that level of competition, a top-twenty finish was respectable, a top ten better than victory in a regional race. I continued chipping away at my point count. The coaches knew better than anyone that, as a second-year rider at an international stage race, I was holding my own, and they looked surprised when my name came up repeatedly at team meetings, reading off point totals.

Our group was even bigger than last year with a total of forty

440

riders split between the national A team, the B team and the development team. The A and B squads got automatic berth and first pick to the European races, unless they were sucking wind and having trouble staying with the field. That left the twenty of us on the development team to fight over spots. The numbers were tight right up to the end, but I constantly scored another point or two at almost every race along the way. I was by no means dominant but I was doing as well as the rest and confident of my trajectory. A lot of the guys had picked less competitive races, like the Tour of Chile or Argentina, to make sure they got a spot, but I had picked the Peace Race, the most competitive race that the best riders hoped to compete in. Given my performance at the first selection race and my consistency in Texas, I didn't foresee any problem. But by the end of the month when the Tour of Texas finished and all the points were totaled, I came up two shy.

The coaches wouldn't budge. They said the rider ahead of me had earned his place and there was nothing they could do about it. Tommy K. said he'd list me as an alternate and told me to keep my form in case one of the riders crashed or got sick before they left the country in three months' time. It felt like my life had just ended. I had never given a thought to a secondary goal or put my name on one of the lists for a minor race and now it was too late. All the slots for each trip were filled. Alex made it in by one point above another guy to secure his trip to Belgium. I was happy for him, but it did little to quell the devastation of my failure.

I wanted to go to Poland more than I had ever wanted anything, more than even racing itself. I had no idea how to get a visa to a Communist country, and after everything I had heard about the Eastern Bloc I was scared I might get stuck there as my great-grandfather had. To free myself I had to find the exact place where the carnage had begun, where my father had come from, to break the chains that still mentally bonded me to it. If I did nothing else in my life, I would reach that place. But now it didn't seem possible – and who knew how much time I had?

I saw clearly that my failure lay in putting all my hopes into a

441

single basket. I had built my entire season around making that race, possibly my entire life. Once that dream evaporated in front of me, I was rudderless. I had no idea what to do. I had no other goal. No place to go. No other plan.

Directionless, I had a hard time getting out of bed. The following morning, in a state of agony, I walked over to Tommy K.'s room and knocked on the door. He answered and, seeing my face, said, 'It's only one race, Sam. There'll be others. This isn't the only year we're going.'

'It's not the race,' I said. 'I wanted to tell you . . . I'm not Polish. My father didn't come from Poland – at least it wasn't Poland back then.'

He looked baffled. 'I don't understand,' he said.

'Janek's a friend, that's all.'

'Then what are you?'

'I'm American. Nothing. Just white.'

'Surely you're something.'

'I'm nothing. I never was. If you're asking what my parents are, my father came from Germany, after the war.'

'Germany?'

'Yes, Germany – East Prussia, now split between Russia and Poland.'

He considered the unexpected information that had just been pressed on him.

'I have to admit,' he finally said, 'you have courage to come over here like this. Janek's a good friend. I don't remember exactly what he said, but I guess I did make assumptions.'

'I don't think I helped the matter.'

'I'll tell you this, Sam, the East Germans we competed against in the Peace Race and every other race in the bloc were always strong riders. We come from where we come and we race to win. You can't live embarrassed about who you are or who your parents are. You can't hide it because you're worried what somebody else might think.'

I'm not sure what I had expected him to say, but surely not that. If anything, I had expected him to be angry and have me thrown out for deceiving him. I had come, I guess, to subtly insult him in an attempt to release my pain and he had turned it around and paid me an indirect compliment. When I didn't reply, we fell into an awkward silence, unsure what to say next. At last he said, 'I have to go meet the riders who are leaving for first races in Europe. *Dziękuję*, Sam.'

I felt more depressed after I'd left him than I had before I'd marched to his door with my senseless rebellion only to have him thank me in Polish. No matter how graciously he had treated me, I was sure that if he'd had any respect for me before, he had less now. I guess it didn't matter. We would probably never see each other again. I didn't call Craig. I was too embarrassed to announce my failure. It didn't matter that I had listed myself as attached to his team that season at the Federation office before leaving the training center. As important as it had been to reconnect with the past in Columbia, I couldn't go back there now that Nick was gone. I had sunk so low that I didn't know where to turn. I didn't even want to ride my bike.

I packed my bags and left Austin before sundown, without saying goodbye to any of my former teammates. I had enough money saved from the stipend they gave us for another few months living cheaply in my van. I didn't have the heart to think about making my next dollar from racing bikes.

I struck out north, drove into the night and slept in a rest area somewhere in the Oklahoma panhandle. When I woke the next morning I saw an abandoned windmill in the middle of a field, then miles and miles of empty land, the morning air chillier than it had been in Texas. The landscape reminded me of the old movies about the Depression I had grown up watching on the black and white Zenith television in the corner of our den.

It was there that I decided to go on to Boulder – I was digging through my glovebox for the peanut-butter wrench and found a post-card I had purchased the previous summer when I'd driven there with some fellow racers to climb the Flatirons – five massive rocks that looked like a series of jagged one-sided angular pyramids protruding from the hillside above the city. I decided to go back, climb up on the rocks and look down over Boulder to give me a chance to think. It was as close as I could get to California in a day's drive. The postcard bore a picture of the Flatirons and below, in bold print, the words 'Boulder California.' I suppose the printer had made it as a joke of sorts, aware that persons like myself would feel compelled to buy it. It was the only place I'd ever been east of California that felt similar: it was a place where people didn't seem preoccupied with preserving the past, like cities on the east coast.

As I sat in the driver's seat waking up, watching the sunrise behind the windmill's silhouette, it occurred to me that that was why I had been more attracted to greater Los Angeles than San Francisco. The latter seemed intent on preserving its identity and culture, which were rooted largely in old money and street grids that had more in common with Boston and what I imagined Europe to be than anything I had expected to find on the west coast. My head was still in a tailspin and I began to wonder if California would help this time. I desperately needed to clear my mind but I was no longer sure that the coast would cure me or give me the same sense of freedom I had experienced the first time.

As I drove my VW across the interconnected prairies of the Great Plains in western Oklahoma and eastern Colorado, my mind moved back to Nick. I missed him almost as much as I'd missed my father after he disappeared. The more depressed I was, the darker my thoughts, and soon I was angry that Nick had died. When I'd been to Palm Springs and San Francisco and developed my own perspective, I couldn't agree with his view that gay culture was too self-righteous – but I was bothered by the degree of promiscuity. Cruising was usually laughed off as boys having fun, but for every guy who dismissed it as harmless I saw a hurt partner sitting silently at his side, aware that if he wanted to keep their relationship, he had to tolerate it. I never accepted it – and it was less evident among lesbians. As much as I loved Nick for making me feel safe around men, I couldn't help but wonder if he had lied the night I had asked him if he was sleeping around when he went up to New York City. If I couldn't trust my own partner, then whom could I trust?

There were many forms of pleasure, and for me compulsive sex ranked little higher than drug addiction. I was angry that Nick had gone and died on me for something as small as somebody else's orgasm. I'd never considered being celibate, but I hadn't made love with anyone in over a year and I was certain my life wasn't the lesser for it. I had gone out on the road to find myself, not to see how many people I could sleep with, to seek independence, not the desperate physical coupling of people trying to validate their existence. I had opened up to Nick, I had trusted him, and he had turned around and died. Even if he hadn't been with somebody until after we were apart, he hadn't kept his word about practicing safe sex, and now he had paid the ultimate price, leaving his daughter without a father and me without a loyal friend.

When I eventually reached town and drove up Baseline Road to Chautauqua Park, I left my van in a neighborhood and hiked out across the grass to the base of the rocks. The sun, setting in the western sky, had already hidden itself behind the mountains but I didn't stop: I had to find a release and the only way I knew to free myself at such moments of pain was through physical exhaustion. I worked my way along a narrow dirt path in the woods, then climbed between and over boulders and slabs until I had worked my way around to the front of the tallest rock. Its face was at an angle, allowing me to work my way up through cracks, along lines and following finger and footholds smeared with chalk and other residue from years of climbing. I was lost in thinking about Nick, guilty that I hadn't reached out to him earlier, sad that I couldn't hold him. These thoughts were mixed with my failure to accomplish my goal. Maybe I had aimed too high or not tried hard enough, or simply didn't have the natural talent to compete in such big races. Maybe the coaches had proved themselves right after all – I had not only failed to make it to Poland, but I had failed to smash the tyranny of the numbers that ruled my fate. I had failed in every way.

I continued climbing – the more desperate I felt, the harder and faster I climbed, until I was scaling the rock as recklessly as I had trusted the ride from the man who had raped me in the woods. Surging toward the peak, I no longer cared if I lived or died. Nothing mattered any more.

I had not quite reached the peak when I stopped. The air was freezing now that the sun had disappeared. A crescent moon hung in the sky illuminating the rock face and the forest below just enough that I could see how high I had climbed. Though not vertical, the rock was steep enough that a single mistake would send me sliding down to smash into a group of jagged rocks far below to almost certain death. I had never climbed the rocks even a quarter as high as where I was now perched. There was nobody around, not a single other climber, and the hikers and visitors at the distant park were long gone, tucked into the warm comfort of their homes. I had no rock-climbing skills – I didn't know the name of a single move. I wore no protective gear, not even my cycling helmet. I had no ropes, nobody to scream out to. I was vulnerable and weak. I had exerted too much effort.

Clinging to the rock, it became apparent that climbing upward had been simple compared to the skill and stamina I would need to descend. I looked for a deeper handhold as my legs started shaking uncontrollably. Then my hands began to tremble. I closed my eyes and tried to calm myself. I was a dead man hanging. At once I became consummately aware that, if I did not calm myself, I risked slipping to my death. There was nowhere to fall but down. I focused my mind into the deep inner space Nick had once instructed me to reach through a series of breathing exercises – slow yoga patterns, exhaling with each breath the anxiety that gripped my arms and legs, inhaling the vision of Nick's energy floating somewhere over the rock. As I moved through the exercises, going through the same patterns repeatedly, dispelling tension with each breath, my mother entered my mind.

In my mind's eye I moved from the vision of Nick to her face above me when she lifted me onto a swing. I continued breathing

446

calmly, in and out, as the embodiment of her presence soon wholly replaced Nick's and her soft voice said, 'Don't worry, Sam. I know you can do it. I'm here for you. I love you.' I promised myself that if I could ease myself down off the rock, with her encouragement, I would get into my van and drive north to Montana to find her. I asked God to bring us back together. I prayed for Nick to send me the energy to persevere.

Slowly my arms relaxed. My legs stopped shaking. I stayed in that position, curled like a fetus, on a narrow ledge and remained almost motionless for thirty minutes, maybe an hour, moving just enough to keep blood circulating in my limbs. Finally, without looking directly down, I began to work my way off the rock one handhold at a time. After every few minutes I paused, to gather my strength and think again of my mother, neither looking up to see how far I had progressed nor down to see how far I had to go. I looked only far enough to see if I could continue along the current route. Progress became meaningless. One false move would negate everything I had accomplished. There was no room for satisfaction. There was only flesh and rock. Myself and the earth. Life and death. I moved slowly to each new position, never congratulating myself, aware that a sense of accomplishment could be my undoing. Nothing was certain, other than the fingerholds I clung to and the narrow ledges my toes searched for. More than once I climbed back up, when I reached the point where there was nothing for my dangling foot to rest on.

For what seemed like hours I worked my way across the rock face, clinging, pausing, praying, climbing and descending. There came a moment when I was level with the tops of the tallest trees growing on the steep mountainside and I sensed I was closer, but I still wouldn't look down.

Thirty minutes later, I reached out with my foot and felt nothing but air. I lost my grip, slid off the rock and dropped with a thump onto a patch of dirt some fifteen feet below. I lay on my back looking up through the rocks and the trees into the clear night sky, and at the point, high above, where I had precariously clung earlier. The

447

night air was cold, but the earth against my back felt warm, like a person wrapping their arms around me, welcoming me home. I hadn't conquered the rock: Nick's breathing patterns had saved me. On my own, I could never have made it down. In a moment of recognition, a picture in the stars, I saw the past infused in the present and the present merging into the future, the various currents weaving themselves together, like the challah braids in my father's bakery, to form a single entity, until the future became the past, the past the present, and the present reached infinitely outward in both directions at once.

The following day as I crossed the border into Wyoming my head was itching. I stopped to wash my hair in a sink at a rest area, but the further north I drove, the more it itched and the colder the air became. Soon small patches of snow appeared on the roadside. When I reached Casper I stopped at a barbershop and paid the owner to shave my head. He put some sort of ointment on the smooth skin after he'd shaved it, a cross between moisturizer and aftershave. It burned when he first applied it but soothed the itching. I bought a tube of the ointment and applied it while I was driving whenever the itch came back.

Later that afternoon, I saw myself in a mirror and was horrified at what I had done. I was bald. I still had several days' growth on my chin but that didn't offset my shaven head. I told myself not to think about it. It would grow back. I wanted to make time going north. I had no idea how long my search would take.

I slept that night in the van near the Montana border, shivering in the cold, and drove early the following morning into Billings. There, I flipped through a phonebook hanging by a wire in a payphone. No luck. I drove onward to Bozeman, where I tried again with no success. I followed the interstate west into Butte, pulled off at a gas station, flipped through the phonebook and then moved on. I could see that winter was far longer up here near the Canadian border than in the southern states I had come from and this year's was harder than normal, measured by the banks of snow still piled along the edges of the road, even as April neared.

My mother had often talked about the mountains when I was a child, so I figured if she were still around it would be in the mountainous western part of the state. I stopped at a gas station after entering Missoula – her name wasn't in the phonebook there either. I wondered where to turn next and remembered the shelves of phonebooks for every city in the state I had found in the public library in Columbus, Georgia, when Dr. Neuman had urged me to explore my past. I went into the gas station and asked where the main library was located.

When I got there, the shelf of books was narrower than I had expected, the population of the state smaller than that of most big cities I'd raced in. I finally found her name and address listed in the Granite County directory, in a small town named Philipsburg.

I didn't call. I didn't know how she'd react after not hearing from me in so long. I thought it would be better to show up in person. The librarian indicated a state map on the wall and pointed out the town. I backtracked on the interstate, took an exit an hour east of Missoula and drove up a road that ran alongside a meandering creek through a remote valley surrounded by snowcapped mountains. By the time I neared the town, I was too excited to be nervous. I put a hat on to hide my head and went into a gas station with an adjacent bar to ask for directions. I had scribbled my mother's street address on a slip of paper. The bartender directed me through the center of town and told me to turn left after passing the bank and drive to the top of the short, steep hill.

When I reached the house, it looked to be little more than an old miner's cabin.

I knocked. I heard somebody cross the room. When she opened the door, I didn't say anything. I waited for her to recognize me – I wanted to surprise her. It didn't take long, but shock crossed her face rather than surprise. I waited for her to speak first.

'Look what the cat dragged in,' she said, loud enough for some-body in the room behind her to hear. 'Don't you have impeccable timing showing up out of nowhere?'

'That's how you welcome me? We haven't seen each other—'

She cut me off. 'Who sent you? Your brother?'

'Nobody sent me.'

'Don't play games.'

'I came here to see you.'

'I can see that.'

'You're not going to invite me in?'

'I don't have room for you here, Sam. You can't stay.'

'I didn't ask to stay. We haven't seen each other in years. You want me to turn around and leave?'

'That's just like you, isn't it?'

My younger brother appeared behind her and looked over her shoulder. He glanced at me and disappeared back into the house. I heard him say something inside and then my little sister's voice say, 'Sam? Are you serious?' Then she shouted to my mother, 'Mom, is that Sam?'

My mother opened the door. 'I guess somebody wants to say hello.'

'Where did you come from?' my sister asked enthusiastically, overcompensating for my mother's lack of emotion.

'Texas.'

'You live there?'

'I did, briefly.' Everything I had come to share slipped from of my mind, replaced by a giant knot in my stomach. After all these years I was still unwanted.

'You work there?'

'I was working with bikes for a while.'

'That's so cool!'

My brother still hadn't said anything. He wouldn't make eye contact. My mother went into the kitchen.

'How long have you guys been here?' I asked.

'We haven't been counting the days,' Walt finally said.

'A couple of years at least,' Rebecca said. 'How did you find us?'

'In the phonebook. I saw Carl a while back in Augusta. He said you guys moved out here.'

'Did you come because of Dad?' she asked.

'No. Is he here? I came to see Mom.'

My mother stepped out of the kitchen, with a piece of paper. 'Here.'

I reached out and took it. She had written down a name, Leyna Berman, and a phone number. I recognized the area code. Los Angeles. 'What's this?'

'What you came for.'

'I didn't come for anybody's number.'

'She'll tell you how to find him.'

'Find who?'

'Your father.'

'I don't understand.'

My brother stood up and walked out of the room.

'Whose number is this?'

'Your aunt Leyna's.'

I looked at the note again. For some reason I'd always assumed her last name was the same as mine. 'You've been in touch with her?'

'She calls once a year.'

'How did she find you?'

'We've always talked each December.'

'She knows where Dad is?'

'Of course she knows which hospital her brother's in.'

'Hospital?'

She went back to the kitchen without answering.

I turned to my sister. 'What's going on?'

'He's dying. He has cancer.'

'How do you know?'

'Aunt Leyna told Mom. I think he sent Mom a note when he first got sick, but it's been a while. It didn't seem that serious then.'

'Mom's been in touch with Dad?'

'He sends child support.'

451

'Child support?'

'It's something he and Mom worked out. In court or something. It ends when I turn eighteen next month.'

I went into the kitchen. My mother was standing at the counter rolling out dough.

'You've been in touch with Dad?'

'I don't talk to him.'

'Rebecca said he sends money.'

'He's sent a little through the years. It worked out well for him. He got off smelling like a rose.'

'When did he start sending money?'

'A year or two after we moved to Georgia.'

'Why didn't you tell me?'

'I didn't think I should. You had enough problems.'

'You didn't think it would help if I confronted him?'

'How could you? You couldn't confront yourself. Then you ran off like he did and disappeared.'

'I didn't run off. I got sent away. I didn't think you wanted me to come back. I never belonged in Augusta.'

'You think I belonged there?'

'I didn't say you belonged anywhere. I'm just trying to explain why I didn't come back right away. I tried to find you, but you were gone.'

'I'm sure you did.'

'I did. I found Carl there. That's the only way I knew you'd moved here.'

'I'm sure Carl was helpful. Probably filled your head with all kinds of good ideas.'

'He told me you'd moved here. I would never have known how to find you without him.'

'He's just like your father and you.'

'I'm not like Dad. I'm not like Carl.'

'You got what you came for,' she said. 'You can go find him now and confront him all you want.'

'I didn't come here to find Dad. I came here to find you, Mom. I'm sorry if I hurt you. I'm sorry for not coming back. I'm here now.

I was young. After what we went through with Dad, all I wanted to do was go away. You have to understand that.'

She started to cry. I put my arms around her and held her but she didn't hug me back. She let me hold her, but only briefly. Then she broke away, picked up a paper towel to wipe away her tears and went back to working the dough as if I wasn't there.

I remained beside her. I could reach out and touch her, but a chasm separated us that I wasn't sure could ever be bridged. I remembered praying with her as a child and wanted to cry and hold her, but I could see by the way she concentrated on her work that she wanted to be alone. Never for a second did she open up the possibility of hugging me back. She wouldn't even look at me. I knew what she was doing. She didn't want to be hurt again so she was protecting herself. She had put on an armor that not even her long-lost son could penetrate.

Walt reappeared, carrying a load of wood. He glanced at me with disapproval as he walked through the kitchen and dumped the split logs loudly on the floor in the living room next to the wood stove. I could tell by his demeanor that he didn't want me to hurt her, either. He was protecting her. Without having been in contact with any of them in years, I felt as if I had become the enemy. My mother still wouldn't look at me. I went into the living room and asked my brother if he needed any help.

'We have it taken care of,' he said, as he stacked the wood. Then he turned to me, and asked, 'How long you plan on staying?'

'I haven't thought about it. The night. Two nights would be good. I could rest up before driving on to California.'

'There's not a lot of room here.'

'Two nights. That's all. I'll rest up tonight, then we can spend tomorrow together and I'll leave the following morning.'

'You'll have to ask Mom.'

I went back into the kitchen, aware she had overheard us. 'Can I stay two nights?'

'Nobody's telling you to leave.'

'Can I use the bathroom?'

453

She pointed down the hall.

I locked the door behind me and peered into the mirror. I took off my winter hat. I looked hideous with my shaved head. I tried to ignore it and focused on my face. For the first time I recognized the image of my father from the pictures I had seen of him, years ago, as a young man shortly after he had arrived with his immigration papers – my eyes, my nose, my chin: my young father, the man my mother had met in Santa Monica less than ten years after the war, was looking back at me. After all these years, after all the places I had been, after everything I had been through, I was back where I'd started, looking into the eyes of the man I'd been running from. I realized what my mother had seen when she first opened the door.

I didn't want to stay in the bathroom too long so I went back out, but instead of going to the living room I sat down in the den at the side of the house and looked out at the snow clinging to the branches of the trees in the yard and the ground covered with white. I could see why my mother had come here. It was like Chagrin, but without the hurt that our hometown held. I sat in the den alone for a long time, listening to my mother in the kitchen, the smell of the fresh bread she had put into the oven drifting to me, and the sound of dry wood popping in the stove as flames engulfed it. My sister appeared in the backyard with a dog. When she saw me sitting alone, she waved. I raised my hand.

I heard my mother and brother speaking quietly in the kitchen. I stood up to go out and join my sister, but before I opened the door, my mother came in and asked if I wanted tea. I heard something behind her and saw my brother carrying a tray down the hallway with a teapot and four cups. My sister came in from the cold and we sat at the table and sipped our tea and watched the snow falling outside. We didn't talk much.

To break the silence, I finally said, 'It still snows here in March?'

'It snowed in July last year,' my mother said. 'It didn't stay long, but it snowed.'

We finished the tea in silence, but it was no longer the awkward silence of a stranger having arrived unexpectedly at their door. It was the silence of familial solitude that carried more warmth than empty words could. I hadn't known how early it got dark that far north. I was exhausted and could see that my mother was too. She went into her bedroom a short time later without saying goodnight.

I woke to the sound of my brother splitting wood outside the bedroom window and the scent of quiche baking. Walt had given me the bedroom at the back of the house and slept on the couch. I climbed out of bed and looked outside. During the night nearly a foot of snow had piled up. I heard the once familiar sound of a snowplow coming up the street, scraping snow away from the asphalt – in Chagrin it had been an almost daily occurrence. During my two stays in Colorado Springs there had been a similarly heavy snowfall but we had stayed inside working out in the gym and it had been pushed off the streets by the time we emerged from the training center. The plains east of the Front Range in Colorado weren't as remote as Montana's Flint Creek Valley in which my mother had settled.

My mother's house was on a hill overlooking the aging court-house, with its large dome, from a bygone era when the county seat had held sway over a region burgeoning with mining claims and a larger settlement in the hills above, called Granite, now a ghost town. I understood why my mother had come here – to escape her own past by going to another place whose past had long ago been abandoned. Not even the history of all the marriages, births, deaths, fortunes made and lost was enough to keep a single person rooted in the deserted town in the mountains above her house to which my brother drove me on the back of his snow-mobile after breakfast. It was while standing in deep snow in front of a ruined bank with no door on an empty street once lined with hotels, brothels and bars on both sides that Walt said, 'Mom wants you to go see Dad.'

'Why?'

'Something between you and him when you were young. She

doesn't talk about it. We're not going out. I don't think he wants to see anyone.'

'He probably doesn't want to see me either.'

'Maybe not. But if you have anything you need to do, you need to go now.'

'Is he that sick?'

'He won't let Aunt Leyna come see him.'

'I got here less than twenty-four hours ago. This is more than I can take.'

'Nobody asked you to come.'

'Give me a break. I don't want to cause trouble. I came to see what had happened to my family.'

'You think we can't survive without you?'

'I came here to see you. Can't you get that through your mind? I didn't bring hurt to this family. I didn't destroy us. Why am I being treated like this?'

'Listen, it hasn't been easy.'

'It hasn't been easy on anyone. I'll be gone tomorrow. For one day can't we just put on smiling faces and pretend we love each other?'

'You want me to pretend?'

'Yes, for God's sake. If you don't have it in your heart, then pretend. Don't make me feel guilty for something I haven't done. I've lived with this bullshit my whole life. I didn't come back here to hate myself more. I'm not Dad reincarnate. I'm myself. At least give me that much. I don't care what Mom's said about me since I've disappeared. You don't even know me.'

'I know you well enough. We stayed around. You disappeared and lived your own life. Not everybody is selfish enough to think only of themselves.'

'I haven't lived my own life, brother. You're not inside my head. Don't accuse me of being selfish. I admire you for staying behind with Mom. I'll admit I didn't have the strength to be a good brother or son, but don't make me out to be evil. I'd hoped to come back here with enough accomplishments to make up for everything we've been through. Maybe I was arrogant for thinking

I could. Maybe that's why I failed. But I never set out to hurt anyone. Whatever hurt came to this family was there before I was born.'

'Nobody's accusing you.'

'Then treat me decently. Mom can treat me however she wants. Show some respect for the few hours I'm here. I didn't come here to hurt anyone – and if I did, I apologize. Cut me some slack.'

He turned away and I realized that, like my mother, he had been hurt as well. I was his older brother and I hadn't stayed around long enough to help out after spending my early teenage years inebriated on drugs and breaking into houses, embarrassing my mother and probably confusing him and my little sister. He had built his own wall to protect himself and a deep sadness swelled inside me. I had failed him. I had failed them all. I could have been there to help instead of pretending they didn't exist. Our private pain had isolated us, pushed us apart, instead of bringing us together. I tried to think of something to say to let him know I loved him, but after all these years – and we had never been close – what could I say? We were tied to each other by blood and ancestry but had little more in common than two blue jays with the same parents. Just as he had never been inside my head, I couldn't fathom what he or my sister had been through. We were complete strangers, and my appearing without notice – even if I had carried a gold medal home from the Olympics – had changed nothing.

The only way I knew to connect with him was to tackle him while he wasn't expecting it. I plowed into him from the side and sent him tumbling in the snow. He lurched up, ready to throw a fist in my face. I jumped beyond his range and said, 'Yeah, that's right, hit me with your best shot,' then ducked as he swung and tumbled him a second time. Soon we were wrestling in the snow, rolling on top of each other, ice slipping down the collar of the coat he had lent me and melting against my back, until finally he had me pinned against the ground and drew his fist back, but hesitated before he punched me in the face. I grabbed the fist and pushed him off me, finally getting him into a bear hug, his shoulders pressed tightly

457

against my chest, my arms wrapped around him as he flailed to free himself. I whispered, 'I love you. I didn't come here to hurt you or Mom.' He wriggled out and we carried on trying to pin each other until I fell on top of him and we lay in the snow looking into each other's eyes.

That night we ate dinner together. It wasn't the homecoming I had hoped for. My mother was still reserved. I didn't tell them much about what I had done over the past few years because I felt selfish, focusing on myself. I learned that Rebecca had recently started working as a nurse's assistant at a small hospital in nearby Anaconda. She had finished school a year early. After dinner she showed me her new uniform and a set of books she was studying to become a registered nurse. My brother was a surveyor and worked for the county. When they asked what I did for a living, I said I was between jobs and that I had been working with bikes but had been laid off in Texas.

Later my mother went into her bedroom, while I was sitting near the wood stove talking to Walt and Rebecca, and closed the door, again without saying goodnight. I don't think my brother or sister noticed – they were used to her behavior – but her silence left a tiny hole in my heart, another wound that I couldn't imagine would ever heal. She still hadn't hugged me. I wasn't sure she had hugged anyone since the night my father had disappeared. As far as I knew she had never allowed herself to trust anyone after that, keeping herself reserved from even her children.

The following morning, my sister was already gone when I woke. My brother rose early and shook my hand before he left, saying, 'Drive safely.' For a brief period before I climbed into my van, I was alone with my mother. As we sat together drinking tea, the same awkward silence returned as when I had first appeared at her door the night before last. We hadn't discussed it, but she knew I would drive out to California to find my father. I suppose my doing so probably left a tiny hole in her own heart from which she'd never heal either – all the little wounds between us slowly bleeding away the warmth and love we retained. I was going out to find the person who had rejected both of us years earlier and in doing so it was almost as if I was rejecting her over him in the same way that she had subtly rejected me since my return.

It was the hardest choice I had ever made – it almost seemed that she was waiting to see if I would go to him in California or stay behind with her. But she had made it impossible for me to do the latter. Just as I had been conditioned through the years to relax only when completely alone, I sensed that the only time she felt at peace was when she was locked in the house, secure, by herself. I had no memories of her locking herself away when I was a young child and I felt even worse when I realized my younger siblings probably didn't remember her as carefree and happy, a young, recently married mother, living in her hometown, her family nearby. The legacy of our family was isolation: we shielded ourselves from the hurt of each other and from the world outside. When I stood to leave, she finally let me hug her and put her arms around me. We didn't make any plans. I was frightened she would reject me if I asked to come back to see her and she was probably worried that I wouldn't return if she invited me, so neither of us said anything. When I stepped off the porch, she pushed the door shut behind me. I heard the dead-bolt click as I walked away.

Driving toward the interstate at the end of the long valley, I thought again about praying with her as a child in bed before sleep, our eyes closed, our heads bowed, our foreheads touching, the only time I had ever felt completely secure – the purest form of love, a mother and her child. Memories rushed in. I remembered her pushing me on the swing, high into the sky. When I screamed, she laughed, her voice calling, 'Don't worry.' She swung me higher, until she pushed me so high that the chains attached to the bar above the swing went slack and for a brief second I fell freely through the air, before the chains pulled taut and swung me back past her smiling face and up into the blue sky.

I remembered her taking me to the frozen pond beside the river

459

when I was still too young to skate. She slipped on her white skates and laced them up tightly around her ankles, showing me how to tie the knot, then picked me up and balanced my feet carefully on top of her own. She glided out effortlessly over the frozen pond, propelling herself in a wide circle around people shouting her name, laughing and waving at me.

I remembered her holding me on her lap while she sat at the table building a chocolate layer cake, made from dozens of paper-thin wafers that she carefully pressed down, showing me how to smooth each layer before applying the next coat of chocolate, then handing me the spatula to lick. There had been my first thunderstorm when she came into the room and held me firmly against her each time lightning flashed and thunder shook the house. The following morning she had shown me which doorframes to stand in if a tornado swept through too fast for us to reach the basement.

When I'd asked her what my soul looked like, she had opened her knitting basket and pulled out five different-colored yarns, and when I asked her what happened to it when somebody died, she had said, 'It floats out of your body and up into the sky.' The following week she knitted me a winter hat made from the five yarns she had shown me, surprising me with it after school, pulling it down snugly over my head and telling me it would protect my soul. I wore it every day when I went outside in the winter until I outgrew it.

One day in Indiana she had taken me to where old partially submerged car tires hung from each dock-post to protect the boats from banging against the pier. She reached down inside a tire to show me where the baby turtles often got trapped. We found three, the size of a silver dollar, that we set free in the lake and watched them swim away beneath the water. For the rest of the summer, we freed captive turtles every day after lunch.

At dusk, I had swung in the hammock with her and watched the yard come alive with fireflies. Once it was completely dark, she handed me a jar to run around and catch them, the glass illuminating softly in my hands like a dim bulb that she could see from

460

the distance, keeping track of me and calling out whenever I got too close to the lake. I remembered turning away from her and hiding the jar beneath my shirt and waiting for her to come out into the dark to find me, tickling me when she did, before making me release the fireflies back into the sky as we stood holding hands. Then she had picked me up and carried me upstairs to bed, where we closed our eyes and touched our foreheads together, thanking God for having given us each other.

BOOK VIII

The Lacuna Treaty

They have been to Los Angeles or to San Francisco, have driven through a giant redwood and have seen the Pacific glazed by the afternoon sun off Big Sur, and they naturally tend to believe that they have in fact been to California. They have not been, and they probably never will be, for it is a longer and in many ways a more difficult trip than they might want to undertake, one of those trips on which the destination flickers chimerically on the horizon, ever receding, ever diminishing.

Joan Didion

As much as I feared what lay ahead, I would be forever grateful to my mother for passing me the news of my father's ailing health, along with my aunt Leyna's phone number to help me find him. My mother, more than anyone, knew it was my burden alone to face him. If I could sustain the courage to finish my journey and return to the person who had nearly destroyed me, I was certain I would find the passage to freedom. I did not hurry to California but neither did I crawl. I traveled with a greater sense of purpose than I had ever known.

I stopped in Idaho and called my aunt from a payphone. I had met her only once, but she responded warmly and invited me to spend the night with her on reaching town. I camped on the shore of a lake that afternoon to meditate and gather strength. The following night, lit by a full moon, I crossed the northern California border and drove under the looming presence of Mount Shasta, an enormous volcanic cone that towered over the surrounding plain. There, I pulled off the highway and slept at the end of a dirt road. By dawn, I was driving again, racing against the heat of the Central Valley, leaving the freezing temperatures of Montana far behind. In the evening I crossed the Grapevine and descended into Los Angeles.

Around nine I found my aunt's apartment on Pershing Drive in Playa Del Rey. Passenger jets from Los Angeles International Airport roared into the sky. She lived only a few blocks from the ocean but the neighborhood was old and worn, not what I had expected in the middle of LA. As I walked up to her door, I was apprehensive. I knocked. She welcomed me in as if we had visited months earlier. There were strange scents of food lingering in the air. She showed me to the spare bedroom where I dropped my bag.

We sat up until the early hours of the morning getting to know one another. Her husband had died two years earlier. He had retired as an engineer from Hughes Aircraft a year before his death. She made a point of telling me he was Jewish.

'German-Jewish,' she added.

I asked about my father.

'I haven't seen him in years. He doesn't like to see us. He keeps to himself down in Huntington Beach.'

'You have children?' I asked.

'No – by "us" I meant me and your uncle.'

'Uncle?'

'Don't tell me he never told you he has a brother?' Her voice trailed off in lingering sadness.

'No,' I said. 'I haven't seen him since I was a child.'

She changed the subject. I could tell she was uncomfortable that he had left us. 'He doesn't have much longer, according to his doctor. He won't see us, but he can't refuse you.' Then a hint of insecurity entered her voice: 'Can he?'

'It doesn't matter. I'll go anyway.'

She told me he had lived in an apartment in Huntington Beach for years, but when his condition recently declined, he had been transferred to the hospital, the cancer unit of UCI Medical Center.

She had the phone number. She said that each time she tried to call, he hung up as soon as he recognized her voice. He had done the same to their brother.

'He doesn't want to remember us,' she said softly and started to cry. They had decided against driving down. 'What can we do? We can't force him to see us.'

I lay in bed that night, listening to jets lifting off from LAX. I thought back to the early-morning fishing trips in Indiana and when he used to leave in the fall to go deer-hunting in Maine. I tried to imagine him sleeping in the clinical surroundings of a hospital and decided to call him in the morning. I'd ask only if he wanted me to take him back to his apartment so that he could spend his final days there. Nothing else. I wouldn't ask how he was doing. I wouldn't say anything about not seeing him in years. It was the only way I knew to try to reach him. If he started to say something else, I'd cut him off and tell him he was welcome to die in the hospital. His choice.

The following morning a booming voice in the living room that sounded like my father's woke me. I threw on my shirt, pulled on a pair of pants and crept up the hallway. 'There he is!' my uncle shouted, the moment he saw me. 'You're the spitting image of your father, young man.'

His presence, his warmth, his words were not what I had expected. His voice was similar to my father's but his demeanor was completely different. My façade shattered. Unable to contain myself, I started to cry.

'What did I say?' he asked. 'I said you're the spitting image. I didn't call you a pigheaded, arrogant bastard, did I? To be honest, you don't look like him at all. You look more like a duck. Where did you get that beak?' He turned to his sister. 'He's an ugly son of a bitch, isn't he? This is my nephew?' he said, pointing at me in mock disbelief.

I felt like a child. I wiped away the tears.

'That's my boy,' he said. 'I knew you could do it. Now all we have to do is pretty you up a bit.'

We sat on the back porch built into a steep hillside in the warm morning sun, drinking coffee and watching a flock of wild parakeets land on the electrical cables strung between the buildings.

'They escaped from their cages around town and flocked together,' Leyna said.

'She doesn't know what she's talking about,' my uncle said. 'They flew up from the Amazon.'

'Don't insult me in front of our nephew. My own bird escaped and joined them. The Amazon? Next thing you'll tell him they came over on a ship from Germany.'

'Those ones didn't get citizenship. They shipped out to Argentina.'

'Stop it, now. He doesn't even know what you're talking about.'

I listened to them banter good-naturedly, joking and welcoming me into their world.

'I'll go to the deli and get sandwiches while you boys talk.'

Aunt Leyna still worked in the same deli in Marina Del Rey where my father had helped her get a job a month after her arrival. In all the years that she had lived in the United States she had never altered her routine from driving between Playa Del Rey and Marina Del Rey, a few miles away, other than a rare trip such as her brief visit to Ohio. I tried to imagine following such a narrow routine, but she saw it as productive and stable – and desired nothing more – after what she had been through in the war.

'I need to go do something,' I told my uncle, after she'd left.

I stood up to excuse myself and went inside. I walked to my bedroom and sat down for a few minutes to compose myself, then reached for the phone on the nightstand. I dialed the number my aunt had given me. It took many tries to get through. They transferred me to different units, wings and nurses' stations until finally I heard his voice. It wasn't a 'Hello,' or a 'May I help you?' That would have been too civil. It came out more like a grunt, an angry snort, a simple verbal gesture to let the caller know he was listening: 'Awgh?'

I took a deep breath. Don't sway, I told myself. In as steady and clear a voice as I could muster, I said, 'Do you want to die at home or in the hospital?'

'Who's this?'

'I asked you the question. I won't ask it twice.'

I knew he recognized my voice – his voice.

He paused, but only briefly. 'Home.'

I hung up. It was done. Nothing else needed to be discussed. It was short, but I was shaken. I stayed there for a long time contemplating the exchange that had just taken place. When I finally stood up, my hands were shaking.

I returned to the back porch as another jet lifted off. My uncle was sitting at the table with two shots of ice-chilled vodka already poured and a grin on his face. I could see from his expression that he had listened in from the hallway.

We lifted the shot glasses as he proposed a toast, 'To taking no shit.'

'And stepping in none along the way,' I added.

We clinked the glasses and drained them. He refilled them and we clinked once more without speaking.

My aunt soon returned. 'Rueben on rye?'

The three sandwiches were identical. 'Rueben on rye it is,' I said.

My uncle chimed in, 'Rueben 'n rye.'

He disappeared into my aunt's garage. I heard him rummaging through some bottles. A few minutes later he returned with rye whiskey. 'Don't underestimate me, kid.'

My aunt frowned. 'Don't ruin our nice visit.'

'To the contrary, my dear,' he said, and poured a round into the vodka glasses.

With my uncle's fondness for spirits, I ended up spending another night. My uncle called one of his employees and asked him to handle the run in the morning. He owned a fleet of reefer trucks loaded at sunrise with freshly butchered meat at a distribution center in downtown LA that he delivered to his client base in the Valley – Sherman Oaks, Encino, Tarzana, Reseda, Northridge and Woodland Hills – where he had lived for some twenty-five years: my father had sponsored him, as well as my aunt, to come here.

* * *

The following morning we walked down to my battered VW van parked curbside in front of my aunt's apartment building. The jets continued lifting off. The sun beamed down, forcing us to squint. At quiet intervals between takeoffs, we hugged and said our good-byes. They asked me to join them in a brief prayer on the sidewalk, then sent me off to battle.

I was in no hurry so, instead of taking the interstate and racing straight to his bedside, I followed surface streets – Vista Del Mar down to Rosecrans, Rosecrans across the basin until it dead-ended at Euclid, Euclid south to Chapman and east to the hospital. From my father's guttural response on the phone I already knew I would have to hold my ground.

I was so nervous, I had difficulty parking the car. From somewhere deep within, I summoned enough courage to keep the fear I'd known as a child from overwhelming me. I looked at the clock on the dash – it was already noon. Walking into the building, I practiced greeting him. I was sure we wouldn't recognize each other at first. We were older and my beard hid part of my face. I went to the nurses' station and asked for my father's room number. They directed me to the fourth floor. When the elevator door opened, I took a deep breath and counted the room numbers along the hallway to distract myself. When I reached his, I paused for few seconds, then stepped inside.

There were two beds in the room. One was empty. In the other sat a withered man in an upright position, looking out the window. When he heard my footsteps, he turned. I started to greet him in the formal manner I had practiced in the car, when he interrupted me. 'You look like an idiot,' he said, glancing at my beard and shaved head. 'What are you? An Amish Nazi?'

I started to turn away, then held myself. 'Yeah, yeah,' I said, in a deadpan voice, the English equivalent of 'Ja, ja' already subconsciously falling back into the German-language mannerisms I had learned as a child. 'It's great to see you, too.'

As was his custom, we got down to business. We wasted no time with cordialities. He buzzed for the nurse and told her he was leaving with his son, nodding at me, to return home.

470

'I'm sorry, that won't be possible today,' she said. 'We have you scheduled for treatment this afternoon. Your doctor can review your chart then and let you know.' She fluffed up a pillow that had slid out from behind him and pushed it back into place.

'Treatment for what? I'll be dead this time next week.'

'We have to think positive, Mr. Malessa. You never know.'

'I know, all right – in this hospital you can squeeze blood out of a turnip. I should have gotten into medicine.'

When she left the room, I asked if he was ready.

A mischievous grin appeared on his face – us against them. 'Behind you,' he said. 'My clothes, they're hanging in the closet.'

I pulled the curtain to hide his bed, then helped him lean up and take off his robe. After carefully dressing him in his slacks and shirt, I punched an extra hole in his belt to keep his pants from falling down before helping him stand. He had lost several inches from his waist. I saw a 'Do Not Resuscitate' order taped to the wall above his bed.

'You approved that?' I asked.

'I didn't come here to be a hero,' he said. 'I'm in stage four. I thought that's why you came – to take me home to die.'

I reached out, yanked the DNR order down, folded it and put it in my pocket to post up at his apartment. I helped him pull the robe back on to hide his street clothes. I went out to the hallway, looked back and forth to make sure the nurse wasn't around. From then until we reached the car I felt like an actor in *James Bond Meets the Pink Panther*. I helped him inch along the hallway. He held the handrail with one hand and balanced against me with the other. He seemed to know every nurse in the unit – his old charm fully intact.

'How are you doing today?' one asked.

'Magnificent. Just out taking a stroll with my son,' he said, nodding at me. 'Getting these old bones working again.'

'Your son? You never told me you had a family.'

'I was worried you might not marry me when I healed if you knew.'

I rolled my eyes.

471

'He always makes us laugh,' she said to me. 'We look forward to seeing you around more often.'

After she left we continued shuffling along until we reached the elevator, where I helped him step into the empty box. Descending to the ground floor, I pulled off his robe and tossed it into a corner. When we reached the lobby, another nurse held the door open while I helped him out. Once we were clear of the elevator, she stepped inside and, seeing the robe, said, 'Excuse me, sir. Did you drop this?'

He turned slowly, then without missing a beat, said, 'She's on the second floor. She got off right before us and left it behind. You'd better send somebody after her. She's going to escape.'

The nurse stared at us with puzzlement, unsure whether to laugh or go investigate as the door separating us slid closed.

'Keep shuffling,' I said.

When we reached my van, he looked at it with disgust. 'You drive this?'

I looked at the old VW van that I had been living in, its sun-baked paint peeling off the side, the rear bumper smashed from a collision. A post protruded from where the missing rear-view mirror should have been and a small crack ran across the length of the front window.

'It's home,' I said. 'You're welcome inside.'

Once in the passenger seat, his public charm faded. There was nobody to impress. He directed me east on Highway 22 through Little Saigon and told me to exit on Bolsa Chica. We drove in silence toward the beach, passing aerospace plants on our left and an empty munitions dump owned by the military on our right. A rare, late-afternoon fog hung above the vacant military outpost between Bolsa Chica and the ocean.

'We shouldn't talk at the same time,' I said, trying to lighten the mood.

'I'm not interested in lingering,' he replied.

At his request, we made a pact: no more treatment; no return visits to the hospital, even in panic. He was prepared to accept his fate and asked that I help him reach his goal as quickly as possible. His only

472

desire was to die in a place of comfort and familiarity. Small tumors, like mushrooms sprouting in a dewy meadow, were growing freely on his brain. He had been through chemotherapy. Two small bolts protruded from the top of his head where the doctor had attached a machine to isolate radiation treatments. Nothing had worked. They had even tried Interferon, but nothing had slowed the onslaught of the tumors.

Once we had covered the details, he said, 'I know why you're here. Since you're bringing me home, I'll do what I can. But I hope you don't expect too much.'

His apartment stood near the corner of Warner and Bolsa Chica, less than a mile from the ocean. A farm bordered one side of the complex, near a natural marsh, one of the few agricultural holdings exposed to the ocean that remained in greater LA. After he had settled into his old bed, I called Hospice for assistance. They promised to send a nurse out the following morning: she had the authority to order a hospital bed and anything else we might need. I didn't know how much longer he had, but from his looks and the fact that we were stopping all treatment, I didn't think it would be long.

The first nurse, an assistant, was Filipina. She had a happy disposition and provided a perfect foil to his dour personality. When she appeared, he changed completely, like he had in front of the nurse at the hospital, vying once again for the title of Most Charming Man in the World. She told us her supervisor would come by in a few days to review his case. The minute she departed, he turned off the charm.

We fell into a routine, rising each morning at seven to drink coffee and read the paper. I preferred black; he preferred cream and sugar. This was the source of our first argument each day. I'd place two teaspoons of sugar and a dollop of cream in his cup. Inevitably it was judged too sweet and diluted. On second try the coffee was too bitter. Placing the sugar and cream on the table in front of him created more frustration: his unsteady hands knocked the creamer

473

over, the thick liquid dripping onto the carpet from the table's edge. This agitated him even more than the too-sweet brew, his cheeks reddening and puffing with anger.

I served lunch at noon and dinner at six. He rarely touched either. The only thing he could stomach was an occasional taste of chicken-noodle soup or a spoonful of ice cream. His daily calorie intake was a third of what he needed to survive. The whiskey and cigars he had once relished sat on the mantel untouched, despite my urging. At first I ate voraciously, hoping to entice him to eat by example and stay alive long enough for us to make amends.

'It makes no difference,' he said. 'I'll be dead this time next week.'

'I'm not sure you'll be that lucky. Eat up so you can at least enjoy the days you have.'

'What's to enjoy?'

'Surely not me,' I said sarcastically.

The first week revolved around such interchanges. I tried my best not to snap at him, but locked together, as we were, in the apartment most of the day, it was difficult not to. My only form of meditation was pulling on my Lycra cycling shorts and jersey each morning to prepare for a ride down the coast.

'You look like a girl in those tights,' he said, the first time he saw my cycling clothes.

'It brings out my feminine side so I can tolerate you.'

I walked lightly down the concrete stairs in my cleats and unloaded my racing bike from my van, going through the daily ritual of pumping the tires up to high pressure. I rode down Warner to Pacific Coast Highway, then turned south, shifted into the big ring and mashed the pedals as hard as I could to get my frustration out, sprinting through red lights in Huntington and Newport on my way to do repeats on the hill heading into Laguna.

I had trouble comprehending that, after all our years apart, my escape from him had delivered me to the same stretch of coast where he had lived for years, less than an hour north of where I had slept in my van in San Clemente and Laguna. Spinning back to his apartment I always felt a thousand times better than I had when I'd set out. Endorphins coursed through my system from the hard workout. I ignored my failure to secure a spot on the national team. I had followed cycling to its logical conclusion, given my physical abilities, but I still derived too much pleasure from it to stop. It helped me retain my sanity and provided me with quiet time to think things through. I had no idea what I would do with my future, no career prospects, nothing, but I was sure I would figure it out faster by following a daily training routine and meditating.

On the way home I decided to surprise my father with some bagels. I went to a grocery near his place and bagged a half-dozen from a bulk bin, paid and continued home. He was still sitting at the table where he had been reading the newspaper before I left, but he had nodded off.

'Wake up, old boy, we're having some real food today.'

He sat up in his chair to see what I'd brought home. I looked through the refrigerator for cream cheese, then carried a cutting board and a knife to the table. I produced the bag from behind my back.

'What do you have there?'

I handed him the bag. He opened it, sniffed the onion bagels, reached in and took one out to inspect. He squeezed it between his fingers, looked at it a second time and then slung it across the room. It bounced off the door and landed on the carpet.

'You bring stale, puffed air-cakes home disguised in the shape of a bagel to help my appetite? You can't pick a real bagel after how many trips to the bakery as a child?'

I tried to remain calm but I felt as if I was going to burst and smash his head. '*Achtung*, motherfucker! You tortured me my whole life. Now you expect me to stand here like a grateful son?'

He winced. 'You came to take revenge, like a good German.'

I slapped his face. 'Don't ever call me that again, you piece of shit.'

He was too weak to do anything more than sit there in shock. I immediately regretted my action.

'Have some respect,' he said. 'Don't talk to your father like that. I used to think you were an idiot savant. Now I realize you're just a plain idiot.'

475

'Fuck you and the bed you'll die in.'

'Don't curse at me.' Then, instead of challenging me, he gave in. His voice started to crack when he said, 'Please have some respect.'

I was still so enraged I couldn't stop myself. 'You're looking at yourself, asshole. Don't you realize that? You're looking in a mirror. This is how I learned to behave. You idiot. You bastard. Go fuck yourself, you Nazi piece of shit. Do you hear me? Do you *fuckin'* hear me?'

He started to cry. 'I didn't ask you to come here.'

'Fine. I'll leave.'

He waited until I crossed the room and pulled open the door. 'Don't go.'

His words hit me, like his hand clapping against the side of my head. I started to cry, then stopped myself, unwilling to let him win. I drew air into my lungs, exhaled and turned back. 'Why?'

'You came here for a reason.'

'I came here to free myself from you.'

'I'm not holding you prisoner.'

'Maybe not physically. I never wanted anything more than to be like every other kid. You took that from me. I don't care what your childhood was like. I don't care what you went through. You had no right to steal mine. You have no idea what my life was like after you disappeared.'

He remained silent. After all those years we still knew each other beyond language. It occurred to me that I had spent much of my teens as a frightened child, trying to prove to his ghost that my child- hood was just as rough as his. That regardless of whether I had grown up in the wealthiest country on earth, regardless of whether I had never seen a single bomb explode or been forced into the military as a child and exiled from my abolished homeland as an adult, I had made myself suffer to prove my self-worth. In my distorted state I had raged against a world that assumed I couldn't know true suffering because I had grown up in a village where nobody was murdered, went hungry or was oppressed.

I have no idea how long it was before we spoke again, but I do know it wasn't a minute or two. The sun had shifted its course from high overhead, its light passing through the window. Neither of us rushed to fill the void. We were like two spiders sitting in opposite corners of a web. I felt like I was back in my old bedroom crying, but this time no tears rolled down my cheeks and there was no crisp air or scent of autumn leaves to run out into. I'm still not sure what would have happened if he hadn't spoken first and picked his words carefully. I avoided latching on to the dark thoughts that passed through my mind as we sat in silence, waiting.

'You're a good son,' he said. 'I won't deny you that.'

I turned to him, nodding like a patient in a mental institution. I stared straight through him. He knew exactly when to give, like he used to with my mother during their fights.

'I never went to see my dying father,' he continued, 'even though he died slowly from an untreated ulcer in a room just blocks from the bakery I worked at in Goslar. Germans didn't get medical treatment straight after the war and many didn't get food. My grandfather starved to death, my father died slowly from a simple ulcer and my mother, my mother . . .'

The war. It had happened ten, twenty, thirty – more than forty years earlier and I still lived inside it every single day. I hadn't even been there, wasn't even born. The same war I knew would rage inside his cancer-ridden brain until the second he died.

He started to cry again. It caught me off guard this time. I was too rigid to empathize with anything he was saying, but the sound of my father crying in the otherwise silent room broke something within me and I started crying too.

That night, after he'd fallen asleep, I climbed over the wall surrounding his apartment complex and walked out through the asparagus field. At the edge closest to the apartments somebody had taken a thick rope from a ship and strung it from a high limb on the only tree – an enormous oak – and tied an old tire to it. To decompress, I slipped my legs though the tire and swung as hard as I could, leaning back on the downswing and staring up at the night sky. I imagined that each star was a different thought and that all of them connected to form the sum of human knowledge, no person or place exempt from sharing thoughts, no private space to claim as your own that nobody else could access.

I let the momentum of the swing run itself out, then walked between the long rows of asparagus to the furthest edge of the field, where it fell away to wetlands below, sealed in by the sandy beach on the other side of the marsh. I could see the ocean from there, separated only by the narrow wetlands and a diminishing trail of car lights passing on Pacific Coast Highway and the beach beyond. I could smell the ocean air: a breeze blew directly into my face, carrying with it the faint sounds of surf. I fixed my eyes on the oil platforms out at sea and a passing freighter departing Long Beach harbor for some destination on the other side of the world. I thought about my father sailing to America.

All these years later I could still remember the details, like other kids memorized baseball stats: October 30, 1954, Port of Hamburg, Home Lines Steamship Agency, vessel *Italia*, destination New York City.

Out in the hills of Catalina Island on the remote northern tip I saw a house light flickering. I pictured an old man sitting on his porch, breathing in the scent of the water surrounding him, as he stared out at the infinite series of lights on the mainland, a glowing, convoluted sea, illuminating the shoreline from Tijuana in the south all the way north to Santa Barbara.

If only I could have changed places with him, free from the past, from tension, duty and the future, free to absorb the world around me. If only I had the power to reclaim my mind from when I was five or six and everything was new.

I climbed the stairs to my father's apartment and tuned into Long Beach State University's jazz station as a Bill Evans song began. During my years on the road cycling I'd rarely listened to jazz. I stepped out onto the balcony and listened to the radio at low volume, thinking about all the other people across LA listening to the same song at the same moment, connected through music.

The following morning when I helped my father to the table, he seemed mellower than usual. He didn't complain about the coffee or the fresh scones I had picked up at the bakery. He looked at me wearily as he sipped his coffee. 'What do you remember?' he asked.

'I remember everything,' I said. 'I remember it all.'

'You were just a little kid. How could you remember everything?'

'I was small but old enough. I think maybe you remember more when you're a child,' I said. 'It's the later years you forget. I wish it were the other way around.'

'I know what you mean,' he said. After a pause, he repeated it: 'I know what you mean.'

'White man's burden.' That was how my father described his disease. He knew the details. Statistically, Caucasian males were most frequently affected. 'Nature's revenge against the pale skins. Even God is frowning on us now.' He sighed. Melanoma. Malignant. Metastasized. Cancer had colonized his body. Each day tumors invaded new territory, set up outposts, assigned sentries and moved onward to explore, conquer and claim new land to settle. Despite the blood-brain barrier's resistant nature, the cancer had penetrated it, like water squeezed through cheesecloth, and settled in for the ride. It would soon claim ultimate control, squeezing off his vitals until his dying breath. He had accepted his fate. He held nobody to blame, though perhaps he should have considered himself. His nurse, Malaya, had left a prescription for dexamethasone, the steroid he had used at the hospital. It acted as an anti-inflammatory, in this case to counteract edema and prevent the tumors from pressing against the areas of his brain that controlled motor function, speech and memory. He had decided to continue the medication for a couple more weeks to give him time to tie up a few loose ends.

Later that morning, while he was sleeping, Malaya handed me a box of morphine patches. 'In case he feels pain near the end,' she said. 'By the way, my supervisor is supposed to come by this afternoon to check up on him, if that's okay.'

479

'Yeah, of course. Thanks for helping out.'

'It's God's work,' she said. 'I work for him.'

When my father woke, I gave him the patches.

'Morphine?'

'Yeah, that's what Malaya said.'

'You weren't supposed to give them to me, idiot. She gave them to you. They're yours,' he said.

'Why me?'

'You agreed to help. It's only right for you to administer the final blow.'

'You're going to die no matter what.'

'I'll die quicker with your help.'

Morphine relaxes the diaphragm, he explained. When one becomes too weak and no longer seeks to fight, morphine is dispensed to relax, to soothe pain and to slow the breathing until it stops, a passive form of euthanasia.

'Let's discuss it later when we reach that bridge,' I said.

'Let's not.' He pushed the box back into my hands.

I carried the patches across the room and set them on the fireplace mantel.

He might have overcome the disease if he had had any faith in humanity. He didn't trust doctors. He had no use for them. All they did was take your money and give faulty diagnosis. They might as well have been car mechanics. He didn't care how long they had been in school. He didn't want to contribute to the insurance racket, either. Doctors could charge whatever they wanted. They might be clever enough to get money from everybody else, but they weren't going to get it from him. At least, not until it was too late.

When eventually a doctor examined the asymmetrical black mole growing on his back – it had been bleeding when he turned over at night, spoiling his sheets – the cancer was already at stage four. Colonization was well underway before he was even aware the invaders had moved in. Those attracted to spongy brain tissue had proved most resistant. Not even direct radiation had driven them off. He had no choice but to see the humor in it now. When I helped

480

him balance in the bathroom so he could brush his teeth, he glanced up at his reflection in the mirror and the bolts protruding from his head.

'I look like Frankenstein,' he said. 'I guess the doctors were finally able to reveal my true nature.'

A knock at the front door interrupted him. He set his toothbrush down and I took his elbow as he shuffled down the short flight of steps to the main room where I had moved his bed. There was more rapping at the door, this time louder, impatient. When I had positioned my father on a chair at the table, I went to answer it.

A tall man wearing a white medical uniform stood at attention – the supervising nurse Malaya had mentioned. I invited him inside. He had a thick accent and introduced himself as Oleg.

'Russian?' my father asked.

'Yes, of course,' he said. 'I just arrived last year.' He explained that he had been a doctor in Russia, but that the U.S. didn't recognize his medical degree so he was forced to become a nurse while he returned to school.

My father's eyes had narrowed. He looked more furious than he had on the day we'd fought. He stared at the nurse who was only a few years younger than himself, pointed at the door and yelled, 'Out!'

The nurse looked at me, then at my father.

'Dad—'

'I said *out*! O-U-T! Which letter don't you understand?'

I motioned toward the door, opened it and asked Oleg to step outside. 'Forgive me,' I said. 'I'll get straight to the point. The Russians entered my father's village in East Prussia at the end of the war. It was never returned.'

'I see,' he said. 'I've had similar problems with other patients here.'

His reply struck me as absurd. 'You're serious?'

'I assure you I'm serious.'

I laughed. He shook his head in resignation.

'So many years,' I said. 'Halfway around the world. What can I say? Welcome to America.'

'Many years,' he agreed.

481

'Can you wait?'

'Yes, of course.'

I stepped inside and began negotiating a peace treaty. 'Dad, you wanted to come home to die. I can't do it without Hospice. I've never taken care of somebody before. We at least need their advice. It will take him fifteen minutes max to take your pulse and write down some information.'

He stared at the wall, like a child.

'You do this or you go back to the hospital,' I said.

'No questions,' he demanded.

'Fine, no questions. I'll answer the questions. He can talk to me.'

I opened the door and waved Oleg in.

'Let's do this quickly,' I said.

He took my father's blood pressure and recorded his pulse. 'Have you eaten today?' he asked.

My father ignored him.

'He hasn't.'

'Liquids?'

'Some coffee this morning.'

'We should get him an IV.'

'No, we don't want an IV. We already discussed it. That's why I called Hospice.'

'Yes, but comfort. His illness is terminal. That will not change.'

'Thank you, but no IV,' I said, pointing to the order I had taped to the wall: Do Not Resuscitate.

My father looked at me and smiled for the first time since we had reunited. I knew the smile. It translated as: 'Serves you right, you Russian bastard. You'll play no part in comforting or saving me.'

I assumed Oleg knew enough about German black humor without need for interpretation. When we'd finished, I walked him to his car. 'I appreciate Hospice's help. Malaya said you guys would drop off a wheelchair tomorrow.'

He looked at his clipboard. 'Yes. At one in the afternoon.' He paused. 'I'll let the girl handle this one. It will be easier on everyone.'

'Hey, listen. I don't know what to say. I'm sorry you have to put up with this when you're out here helping people.'

'It comes with the territory,' he said matter-of-factly.

My father wanted to make one last trip while he could still walk. Hospice had delivered the wheelchair, in which he now spent most of the day. He was able to stand briefly at the counter in the kitchen and walk across the room with my assistance.

'I want to go see some of the old places in LA and visit my sponsors.'

'What about your brother and sister?'

'What about them?'

'You don't want to see them?'

'What for?'

'To say hi . . . to say goodbye.'

'I said goodbye to them long ago. I'm sure they're doing just fine without me.'

'Yeah, but—'

'I said no. When you die you can decide who to see and not to see. Get my fishing cap to cover these damn bolts.'

I didn't argue. If he had treated them anything like he treated me, they probably wouldn't want to see him either. Besides, they hadn't requested that I arrange a visit. They'd seemed relieved that I had arrived to take care of him. He told me to pack a change of clothes and to bring the dexamethasone. 'You're going to see some of the past,' he said.

I loaded him into his car, which had been stored down in the parking garage, and we drove up the 405 and took the 10 West into Santa Monica. He had the area mapped out in his mind as if he had been there last weekend – in fact, he'd had the entire grid of Los Angeles memorized since he'd been driving between the bakeries he had worked in and the chain he had supervised. We drove by an apartment building near the corner of 16th and Arizona that he had lived in with a couple of buddies when he got out of the army.

'Go check if that apartment is still number 107,' he said, pointing to a door near the stairwell.

'Still 107,' I said, returning to the car. 'Where next?'

'Let's take a look if there's still at bakery in Marcel's building on Pico, then over to Culver City.'

We spent the morning weaving around the Westside in no particular order, looking at apartment buildings and storefronts where bakeries had once been. We went by the Santa Monica hospital, where Carl had been born before they moved to Ohio and had me. He showed me a small apartment near the corner of Venice and Sawtelle where he and my mother had once lived. He asked about my mother, brothers and sister for the first time. I told him they were doing well. I wasn't sure what to say. He didn't push the issue so I let it drop.

Next we drove to Beverly Hills. He had worked at several bakeries there. At that time he had specialized in pastries and wedding cakes. We had planned to find a parking space on Wilshire to walk past some of the old storefronts, but the traffic was so heavy he decided against it. 'Go on to Fairfax,' he said. 'We'll find a space over there.'

I continued east on Wilshire until we reached Fairfax where I turned left and drove north to the Farmer's Market at the corner of 3rd Street. We drove through the parking lot while he squinted out of the window, trying to find the bakery he had worked in the day he was granted citizenship. After a fruitless search, he told me to drive a few blocks farther north to the deli he had eaten lunch in every day back then and where he celebrated getting his papers. I found a parking space close enough to the front door that I was able to help him hobble inside without the wheelchair. We found a table near the back and he ordered pickled herring and chicken livers with sautéed onions.

'Maybe we should order something else that will mix a little better,' I said. 'Maybe fish *or* liver – I'm not sure about fish *and* liver.'

'Maybe you should shut the hell up and eat. We stopped here to have what I wanted. You're not the one who's dying. If you wanted a hamburger, you should have stopped at McDonald's.'

484

Okay, asshole, I thought. I'm not falling for your bullshit in public. But, like him, I couldn't bite my tongue for long. 'You didn't bring those morphine patches by any chance, did you?'

'Funny. Very funny.'

'I thought they'd go good with the herring.'

When the waitress brought the food to the table, he said, 'I'll take the livers, he's having herring.'

Then, in his roundabout way of apologizing, he ordered a pastrami sandwich to split.

'At least you're eating for a change,' I said. It was the first time I'd seen him with an appetite.

'If you'd learn to cook like this I'd eat every meal.'

On the way out we bought poppy-seed strudel at the bakery near the front door and had them pack it carefully for the drive to his sponsors. I turned the car around and headed south on Fairfax, until we reached Interstate 10. They lived out in Monrovia in the foothills of the San Gabriel Mountains. Once we'd cleared downtown, he directed me to Glendale and then the 210, an interstate that hugged the foothills. We drove in heavy traffic for nearly an hour. If he hadn't been keeping an eye out, I would have missed the exit completely. After we pulled off the interstate, he directed me through the surface streets of a neighborhood that had a quaint feel. Older craftsman houses, neatly kept lawns, trees shading every street. His sponsors owned a small split-level, the garage built into the hillside.

They were friendly but not warm. While we'd been driving my father had sworn – and I had no reason to disbelieve him, regardless of his own past – that the old man had done nothing more during the war than fight the Russians after being drafted while his wife kept house in East Prussia.

Even though they had sponsored my father and brought him here, I could tell on meeting them that they didn't trust me. I could feel it in my gut. Even if they had nothing to hide, they were still suspicious that someone might turn them in on a rumor. I hated them instantly for their paranoia, but it was more self-revulsion at the trace elements of shame and guilt that I carried.

485

The sponsors must have been in their eighties. They knew my father was ill, so after they'd set me up with a soft drink in front of the television, they switched to German and I phased them out. Later that night the old man came over, sat down at my side and asked me if I had ever heard of Stalingrad.

'The largest and bloodiest battle in human history,' I said, to prove myself a good student.

'Please forgive my behavior,' he said. 'I was there. I fought. Between the things I saw before I escaped and the things I saw fleeing back to East Prussia, I shouldn't be here.'

He looked up at the ceiling as if communicating directly with God. Out of respect, I bent my head in prayer.

'Bring your father downstairs with you so he can see his old bedroom one last time, then help him up to the guest room over there,' he said, pointing to an open door near the television. 'You can sleep on the bed down there tonight. We'll wake you in time to beat the traffic home. We rise early.'

I helped my father across the room and down the stairs into the garage. A door near the stairs opened into a small room. I smelled damp earth and switched on the light. A small steel bed with a tightly pulled woolen blanket was pushed against the far wall. On small shelves against the wall nearest me stood rows of canned food, batteries, two flashlights, a stack of candles, matches, a couple of books and several large containers of water. The room had been carved into the hillside. My father remained silent, taking it in. I helped him to the bed to sit for a moment and rest. Then I realized what it was.

A bomb shelter. Stocked. Ready to use.

'Will you be okay down here?' my father asked.

I looked around the room again without answering.

'I slept in here for the first three months after I arrived,' he said. 'I thought everybody had bomb shelters in their homes in America. Hell, after what we'd been through it seemed like the wisest idea ever. At least I slept soundly. Their two children were in the other room upstairs.'

He said his sponsor had dug the room into the hillside when he had purchased the house soon after immigrating: he hadn't wanted to leave anything to chance again, even if he lived in the most powerful country on earth. 'You never know when things will turn upside-down,' my father said.

I stood near the shelf, turning cans of food over, looking for dates, when he asked, again, 'Are you sure you'll be okay down here?'

'Yeah. We leave early in the morning anyway.'

I spent most of the night lying awake, trying to imagine what it had been like to arrive in America and move straight into a bomb shelter on your first night in LA after crossing the country from New York City. When I finally fell asleep, I dreamed I was in a cellar some-where back in East Prussia. There were dried herring strung along the wall and mushrooms stored in a large basket in the corner. Leaning up against the far wall was a stack of dried turf used to fuel the stove.

In the distance I heard somebody calling my name, but each time I yelled, 'I'm down here!' the earth absorbed the sound of my voice. There was a trampling sound, like horses galloping, then a deep rumble as earth broke free from the wall and fell to the floor. I couldn't see anything. It was pitch black. I stood up to feel my way around the room. Then I heard the voices again, but I couldn't under-stand what they were saying.

Somebody rapped on the door. I opened my eyes.

'Wake up. Wake up. Come upstairs and help your father out of bed.'

A few hours later when we reached Huntington Beach again, instead of helping my father back up to the apartment, I urged him to walk with me around the complex. His motor skills were declining. It was only a matter of days, I worried, before he'd be unable to walk. At first he resisted the idea.

'You'd better do it while we can.'

He glanced out at the bright sun hitting the ground outside the carport.

'Just one lap,' I said. 'It's not very far.'

Once we reached the parking lot and started making our way slowly around the complex on the asphalt, my father said, 'I never thought I'd spend the last days of my life enjoying parking spaces so much.'

'There is something exhilarating about them,' I agreed. At least we weren't fighting. 'Especially when you see an empty one.'

'The smell, too. Nothing like the stench of hot tar melting beneath your feet.'

A car pulled into a space ahead of us. A young woman climbed out, clutching a large bag of new clothes from the mall. She turned toward us and said hello.

My father straightened up, a flirtatious grin on his face. He reached up to make sure he was still wearing his fishing cap to hide the bolts. 'I was just saying what a nice day it is to go to the beach,' he said.

'Perfect,' she said. 'If only I didn't have to work later.'

'You can always call in sick,' he said. 'Or you can just call me.'

She laughed and glanced at me. I was too embarrassed to speak.

As she turned to walk to her apartment, my father began singing, in his best Charlie Rich imitation, about the most beautiful girl in the world.

Even near death, desire didn't diminish.

She turned back. 'You'd better teach him to behave,' she said to me.

'I'm trying. Believe me, I'm trying.'

My father shot her a corny *Gotcha!* look.

When she finally passed out of view, I said, 'You're pathetic.'

'At least there's a few of us left in the world. Besides, what are you complaining about? She thinks you're cute. Didn't you see the way she looked at you? You got your father to thank for that. I think I'll spend the rest of the afternoon sitting on the balcony in my underwear smoking a cigar.'

'Pick up the pace, Don Juan.'

Back at the apartment, I helped him into bed. The apartment was primarily one large room. After you entered the front door, the kitchen was to the left. Directly ahead, a small nook that doubled as the dining room was located near a set of stairs that climbed to the

488

bathroom and then to a balcony bedroom that overlooked the room below. The main section of the room was part living room – in which a couch, which I had replaced with the hospital bed, that had once stood near the fireplace – and part study, where an antique desk and bookshelf were pushed against the wall near the sliding glass door that led onto a porch that overlooked the parking lot and the farm. My father began fiddling with a control attached to a cord so he could put the bed in an upright position.

I walked over to his bookshelf to turn on the jazz station. Horace Silver's standard 'Song for My Father' was playing. I didn't place much weight in coincidence – it was one of those old Blue Note records that they always overplayed anyway since it seemed to fit just about any mood, but a good tune nonetheless. I remembered Tyrone playing it for me, walking me through the solos and telling me Steely Dan had borrowed the opening refrain for 'Rickie Don't Lose that Number.'

I was standing in front of the stereo, thinking about Tyrone, when I glanced down and saw the original handwritten manuscript of which he had left me a copy on a shelf bursting with books. I had noticed it the first day I arrived at his apartment but had avoided mentioning it. The mood was light enough that afternoon that I slid it off the shelf and held it out for him to see.

'Why didn't you let me read it or tell me the story back when I pestered you about your past in Chagrin?'

He let out a sigh. 'Did you read the copy I left?'

'Not until years later. It made me angry. I felt like all your talk about German-Americans was to cover up a lie.'

'I've never lied to anyone. I've done some regrettable things – unforgivable. But I never lied. I never denied anything.'

'I thought you were the one who said there can be no regrets in life.'

'What was I supposed to say to my son? It was an insinuation – that there should be no regrets in your own life. I already carry enough for both of us.'

'Then why did you leave?'

489

'Here we go.' He sighed deeper this time. 'Do we have to start this after such a good day?'

I hesitated. He was exhausted from the trip and the walk that morning around the complex. I knew it was cruel to force him into a subject he'd probably hoped I'd never raise, but he must have known I'd bring it up sooner or later. We were too much alike. Maybe I should hold off and give him a break. But what if he died in his sleep that night? I couldn't predict the future.

'Yes,' I said calmly. 'We do.'

He looked resigned and shrugged his shoulders. 'Get me a cigar.'

I walked to the small humidor on his desk and opened it. There were two Cohibas and several different kinds of Fuentes. I recognized the Cohiba as a famous Cuban cigar, pulled one out and used his trimmer to cut off the end. When he saw the yellow wrapper, he said, 'Throw that garbage away. They're fake. Give me one of those Dominicans and get me a drink of vodka out of the freezer while you're at it.'

It was a small price to pay if this was what it took for him to open up. I could have used a shot of vodka myself, except I knew he'd say something smart-assed if I joined him in a midday drink. I carried the bottle and a shot glass to the small table Hospice had left at his bedside for meals.

When he saw only one glass, he said, 'Too much of a prude to join your old man for a drink?'

I would never figure him out. I went back to the kitchen to get a second glass, while he sat in bed rolling the cigar back and forth in the flame of a match until the end was burning like a torch. He pulled it out of his mouth and blew out the flame. A thick plume of smoke curled up into the air.

'Fuck the Cubans,' he said. 'The Dominicans kick their ass at half the price.' He held up his cigar. 'If only they'd had Castro sucking on their cigars all these years maybe they'd be half as fashionable.'

I opened the sliding glass door enough to let in some fresh air to disperse the smoke. 'So why didn't you tell me about your past?'

'You were too young.' He reached for the bottle and poured a shot.

490

'What was I suppose to do? Teach you about the Nazis? I wanted to teach you about the past, but I wanted to teach you something honorable. I wrote out my past to honor my mother, but it felt like something that could get me arrested or deported or at the very least ostracized. I came here for freedom, not to be saddled with an unforgivable past. At the time you started prodding me I had no past I could speak of. I'm dying now so I can admit it. The only hero I knew as a child was Hitler. There were no football players to look up to, only Hitler. From the time I was born in 'thirty-three until I became a teenager, he was the only reality I knew.' He paused to let me take it in. 'As an adult, I hate Hitler. He destroyed me. His influence made me hate everything, including myself.'

'You hated your own family?'

'I didn't love myself, so in a way it was impossible to love you.'

I didn't know what I'd expected from him, but the last thing was for him to tell me he didn't love me. Even if I hated him, I was unable to comprehend a parent not loving their own child. 'Then why the fuck did you beat me? Why didn't you just ignore me?'

'I did ignore you. You wouldn't let me alone. All these years later it's the same. You're the only person who shows up at my doorstep. In my own way I do love you. I love all of you. You were the only person who ever gave me purpose after the delusion I was forced to follow as a child. But I never learned to express love. I didn't have the tools to show it. It came out twisted. I fucked everything up I ever touched in life. It's too late now to fix.'

'It doesn't have to be—'

'It is. I wish to God I could go back and change things. But I can't.'

He pushed my shot glass forward beside his own. I picked it up and downed it. I stood up to get a glass of water from the kitchen. When I came back he had poured another round.

'Why did you leave?'

This time he didn't look up. A tear ran down his cheek, the same way it had on our trip to Columbus, Ohio, years ago. I took a deep breath and held it. I didn't want to be drawn in. It was his pain. His guilt. His sorrow. Not mine. I had already paid.

491

'I woke up hours before sunrise after that night we sat up watching TV until it went off the air. I didn't plan it. I had never considered leaving your mother or you kids. But as I lay in bed it became crystal clear to me what I was doing to you in the basement. I'd already started grooming you without even knowing it. After all those years of keeping my mouth shut, you were the only one ever interested in hearing about Germany during the war, hearing what happened to us on the inside. It thrust me back into childhood. I could feel myself becoming full of the same resentments, prejudices and hate that I thought were out of my system. How can you completely wipe out what you were brainwashed as a child to believe? I didn't trust myself. I wasn't sure what I might teach you next.'

Sweat dripped down his forehead. He reached up to wipe it dry with his sheet. His once broad, muscular body had withered to a sack of skin and bones. His once thick jowls had sunk into his face; his cheekbones protruded from beneath his eyes. His enormous, porous nose was exactly the same. I remember reading that, no matter how much one's body shrinks with age, the cartilage in one's nose remains. He looked scared. He glanced at the door as though he were half expecting somebody to barge through it and take him away.

'I sat straight up in bed,' he continued. 'It's probably the only time in my life that I didn't second-guess myself. I knew what had to be done. I knew I had to do it right then before I changed my mind. I climbed out of bed and slipped on my baker's clothes in case your mother woke up. I grabbed some of the money we kept hidden under a floorboard in our bedroom – something I'd learned to do in the war. I crept out of the bedroom onto the landing. The house was silent. I wanted to come in and kiss you goodbye, but I was frightened I'd wake you. If there had been a moon that night I would have run from my own shadow. I knew I could make a living anywhere as a baker. I went to the kitchen, grabbed the vodka bottle out of the freezer and swallowed nearly a half-pint so I wouldn't lose my courage. Then I looked at that stupid electric stove I bought that you burned your hand on. I went into the basement and grabbed some books and left that one copy behind for you. Then I went out to the driveway, put the car in neutral and rolled it out into the street. I let it roll half a block so I wouldn't wake anyone before I popped the clutch and drove away.

'I went straight to Cincinnati. There was a baker there I had worked with a long time ago in Cleveland. He hired me. After saving a couple of weeks' wages, I headed west. He gave me a reference to another bakery two blocks up from the first one that had hired me when I arrived in LA, in 'fifty-four. He knew I was running from something. But he didn't ask what. I have to give him that. When I got back to LA, I settled for a couple years in a place on Pico, then I found a job as supervisor of a cookie plant over in the Valley and started leap-frogging my way up, until I was running a chain of bakeries from LA, to San Diego. I cried for years after I left you guys. I know your mother would never believe me, but there wasn't a day that I didn't think of you all. But all those years of living in this country in total silence – it eats at you. I kept a lid on it for twenty years, but once you got me started talking, I didn't think I could stop. It wasn't your fault. You just wanted to know who we were. I wanted to give you that. You deserved that. But I couldn't trust myself. I didn't want to fill your head with all the hate they made us swallow back there when I was your age. I left to save you, son, not to hurt you.'

I stood up from the edge of his bed and walked to the sliding glass door to breathe in the stream of fresh air blowing in from the coast. A light blue haze of cigar smoke hung in the small room. I carried his hand-stitched book back to the shelf to put it away and stood for a few minutes, my back to him, the tension of my child-hood rising in my exhausted mind. Maybe it was true what my uncles on my mother's side had said – perhaps he was a child in a man's body, maybe he hadn't matured as a result of childhood trauma. I was an adult myself now. I couldn't remain focused on the anger and sadness of my own childhood – or fixated on trying to make sense of his past in an attempt to understand my own – out of fear it would destroy me in the end, through violence, self-hate or both.

Standing there, I recognized that a point comes when you must cross the threshold to focus on the present and the future. The past

493

can never die and the journey forward can only be negotiated by first acknowledging and understanding it, but when the past looms in the present it risks overshadowing and confusing more than clarifying. A few titles away from his manuscript – which I had returned to the shelf, pushing its spine back far enough to hide it so I wouldn't have to look at it again – was a copy of Martin Buber's *I and Thou* and beside it a copy of the German original *Ich und Du*. It was the same copy that had been in the basement. I thought back to Relativity when Dr. Neuman had let me read his copy.

In my understanding, Buber forwarded the idea of an I-Thou encounter as one in which two individuals come into contact without preconceptions and communicate in an empathetic manner, as a mother does with her child or a nature lover might with trees – a peaceful interaction and understanding that cannot be forced, a union between two mutually respectful entities. The I-It relationship was its opposite, in which the two interacting individuals never truly meet, their interchange guided by preconceptions that block any meaningful, empathetic or spiritual understanding. They analyze and dissect in an attempt to make sense of the other and in doing so confuse the interaction further, pushing the other away instead of coming together. I faced my father.

'Why didn't you share your story with others, if you couldn't share it with me?'

'You're joking, right?' he asked, in the stern tone I hated. 'Americans can't even look straight in the eye of the vast German influence on their own culture, arguably larger than any other single element. Who wants to hear about the expulsion of millions of Germans in Eastern Europe? Who cares how many were raped, murdered and starved trudging westward? It's just a fantasy we invented to get sympathy, a coworker once told me. We deserved it, right? Maybe we did. I certainly didn't deserve to come out of the war alive. Hardly anybody here has even heard of East Prussia, and if they have they think it's some ancient part of the Russian Empire. I gave up any hope a long time ago of sharing what went on in the mind of the other side, how a Nazi became a Nazi. I know this better than anyone on this planet. I wasn't born a Nazi, but by the time I was a teenager I was as proud a Nazi as any. But nobody's interested in penetrating the psyche that took us into the Holocaust. They're only interested in the end result. Let me tell you something. An endless stream of pictures of atrocities won't by itself prevent history repeating itself – in many ways it just makes the hardened ones more resentful and perpetuates their hate. Kind of like being white. You're always guilty of something, no matter how many hundreds of years before you were born it happened. That's the beauty of not being white in America today. You can always blame your problems on whites, just like the Germans were convinced the Jews were the root of all evil. But let me tell you this as well – the millions of Germans after the war who claimed they never knew Jews were being murdered, I spit on those lying bastards. Where did they think those trains and trucks were taking them? On vacation? We knew what was going on just like the settlers here knew the Indians were being slaughtered. Six million is too large a number to keep secret.'

'So that's it? You're going to die a bitter old man?'

He looked at me as if I were insane. 'No. I'm going to hire a marching band and sing at the top of my lungs while I toss candy to the children lining the sidewalks, thanking everybody for a wonderful life! Did you hear a single word I just said? My dream was to share the nightmare I lived through as a child, not out of glory but atonement, to help future generations avoid murdering their own brothers.'

He paused. I didn't say anything. I didn't want to push him any farther. I couldn't take it any more than he could. It didn't seem like there was anywhere else we could go. I stood up to walk out onto the balcony to stand alone in the fresh air. Before I reached the door, I heard him clinking his shot glass on the table to get my attention.

'My wish never came true,' he said. 'But, like every deluded parent for thousands of years before me, my hope now lies in you.'

'How so?'

'Over there,' he said. 'In the corner.'

I looked around and saw an old gun.

'The rifle?' I asked.

'Move the damn gun.'

I leaned it against the bed.

'Under the carpet,' he said. 'Pull it up. It's already loose.'

I slid my fingers under the edge and peeled it back, exposing the wood floor.

'Farther.'

I hauled it back until I had exposed a seam in the plywood.

'There,' he said. 'Pull it up.'

I slipped my fingertips between two sheets of plywood. One had been cut into a piece twice the size of the lid of a shoebox. I pried up the board.

Four wooden cigar boxes lay in the narrow space.

'Go ahead. Take them out.'

I carefully worked them free of their snug hiding place and set them on the ledge of the fireplace to my right.

'That one with the mark on top. Open it first.'

I lifted the top and saw a neatly folded handkerchief and below it a bunch of old letters and documents in German.

'Take out the hankie and look inside.'

I lifted it out and unfolded its corners. Lying inside was the black and silver Parker pen I had given him years earlier for his birthday on our trip to Columbus.

'I saved it,' he said. 'For you. I wanted you to have it in case you ever decided to write anything. You listened to me for so many years, I figured one day you would have your own ideas about things. You know too much about me now as it is. There will come a time when you'll have to look back at your own life and make sense of it.'

The sight of the pen so many years later, and everything it conjured up from my childhood, our final trip together in Ohio and him disappearing a week later, was more than I could hold. I knelt on the floor and remained there as long as it took me to steady my breathing. My father was too weak to risk falling out by leaning down to touch me. I didn't expect his comfort.

After a period of silence, he said, 'Open the others.'

I looked at the three cigar boxes sitting on the ledge. I picked one up and opened it. Several rows of neatly placed one-hundred-dollar bills were packed tightly together.

'Open the other two,' he said.

They were similarly packed with stacks of mint bills.

'Thirty-seven thousand dollars,' he said.

'For what?'

'You can go,' he said. 'All those questions you used to ask about your grandmother and grandfather. Go see and find out for yourself. Go to Europe. Go to school. Whatever it is you need to do, do it and don't say I never helped you.'

I looked at the stacks of bills. In my entire life I had never seen more than a few hundred dollars at a single time. Down in Albany I had lived on a little over three hundred dollars a month, working full-time washing laundry for two dollars an hour under the table. I had lived most of my life on handouts, prize money and sponsorships that, in a sport as small as cycling, got you a free apartment with a refrigerator full of food during the good years and free tires and gas for the van you lived in during the bad ones. I didn't know what to say. I had never given thought to money having the power to free me, but staring at those stacks of hundred-dollar bills I began to sense their power. The recognition was frightening. Could something as inanimate as money help me find the path to freedom I had chased since I was a young teenager?

'You better seal them up in the floor,' he said. 'You can get them later.'

I placed the Parker pen back in the handkerchief and carefully wrapped it, refastened the boxes and put them back in the hiding place, one by one, slid the plywood over the top and returned the carpet to its original position.

'Do you still have the Iron Cross?'

I'd known sooner or later he would ask. I walked over to the bag I kept behind the sofa and dug through it until I found the small pouch in which I had stored it. I pulled it out and carried it to him.

'I didn't think you'd lose it,' he said. He turned the medal over in his hand, studying both sides. 'Do you mind if I keep it?' he asked. 'Put it up there on the mantel so I can look at it when I'm tired.'

I was exhausted. I lay down on the carpet in the middle of the room. I fell asleep shortly after sunset and slept through the entire night without waking.

It was almost nine the following morning when I heard my father say something. I rolled over on my back and saw him looking down at me. I noticed something dripping off the edge of his bed onto the carpet. I jumped up and pulled the covers back. 'Did you piss in bed?'

My first reaction was anger – as he had reacted whenever I had done anything wrong. Quickly I acknowledged that he hadn't done anything wrong: it had been an accident. He hadn't even interrupted my long sleep to get me to help him to the bathroom. 'It's okay,' I said. 'It's not a big deal. Let's get you to the bathroom.'

I tried to be calm, but I was in a state of panic, trying to figure out how to deal with this new development: he could no longer hold his bladder. His weight was such that it was impossible to carry him easily to the bathroom. He kept slipping from my grip. I couldn't put him in the wheelchair because the toilet was up a short flight of stairs.

'Put your foot down. Come on, help me balance, keep your leg straight,' I said.

Each time he did so, it flopped out from beneath him. I laid him back in the bed.

'Move your leg,' I said. He moved his left leg but the right – the strong one he favored to balance – remained motionless. I picked it up and dropped it onto the mattress. 'Can you feel that?'

He didn't answer.

I looked at his arms. 'Lift your arms up.'

It was the same. He lifted the left one into the air, but the right remained supine. Malaya had told me that as the tumor grew and pressed into sensitive areas of his brain his motor functions would decline, but I had never interpreted it to mean that he'd become paralyzed on the right side of his body. I was in a complete panic when I realized he was looking at me silently. I stepped away from him, walked over to the sliding glass door and gazed out at the workers gathered at the far end of the asparagus field. I knew I had to maintain my strength.

'Okay,' I said. 'Let's get you to the bathroom and then have some coffee.'

I walked back to his bed, slid my arms under his back and legs and in one fluid motion picked him up, as if he were an outboard motor balanced precariously over the water, and carried him directly to the bathroom where I set him gently into the tub as my strength waned. He still hadn't said a word, but he was looking up at me. It occurred to me that this was what it was like to be powerless, to rely on another for everything – an unsettling thought that I pushed from my mind.

'Here, let me fill the bath so you can soak and relax. I'll run to the corner store and get some doughnuts and fresh coffee.'

He still didn't say anything. I filled the tub halfway so he wouldn't slip under the water.

'I'll be back in a minute.'

I didn't want him to overhear me calling Hospice. It was still early enough in the morning to catch Malaya at the center while she loaded up her car before going out on calls for the day. I stopped at the payphone around the corner and dialed.

'Is Malaya there?'

'One moment, please.'

I counted cars passing on Warner to distract me from what seemed an endless wait. Finally somebody came on the line. I held my breath.

'This is Malaya speaking. May I help you?'

'Thank God you're there. This is Sam, Karl's son. The old man in the apartment on Bolsa Chica in Huntington.'

'Hello, Sam. How's your father doing?'

'Not so good. He can't move his right arm or leg. I think he's paralyzed. He pissed in bed last night. I barely got him to the bathroom.'

'Calm down,' she said. 'It's natural, God's way of helping him along. We've been waiting for this, haven't we?'

'Well, I'm not sure I was.'

'It's why you came to stay with your father, Sam. Isn't it? You wanted to take care of him. Now he finally needs your help. This is your gift.'

Her voice was so calming, so assured, that I wished I could reach out and hold her.

'This is what we've been waiting for, Sam. He needs you now. I'll come by this afternoon with a catheter so he doesn't wet his bed again. I'll show you what to do. I can't come until around three, but everything will be fine. I promise you.'

'How can you say that? How can you promise?'

'I promise, Sam.'

I didn't know whether she was being sweet, naïve or if she knew exactly what would happen, but the tone of her voice had a soothing effect – I had to remain calm and let everything happen as it would. I had to accept each new event with as much grace as she did.

'Thanks, Malaya.'

'You're welcome, Sam. See you soon. God bless.'

From the moment I placed the phone back in its cradle everything changed. The world took on a different hue, a different mood. In hindsight, I suppose it was the shade of looming death, the process of waiting at one's parent's bedside for the end. The altering and compression of time. The intense focus on the present while countless memories forming the sum total of one's existence flittered in and out of the periphery. A calm that bordered on serenity, an emphasis on scents, acceptance.

I re-entered the apartment with the *LA Times*, a box of glazed doughnuts and two large cups of coffee that I set on the table and ran up to make sure he was okay, then ran back to the bed, pulled the urine-soaked blankets and sheets off, stuffed them into a large trash bag and carried them down to the laundry room. I went back to the bathroom and helped him out of the tub and down the stairs to the table, where I figured he could spend the morning.

'I think your girlfriend's coming over today,' I said. 'Didn't she tell us the other day she'd be back this afternoon?'

He looked at me suspiciously. I put cream and sugar in his coffee. 'What are you so chipper about?' he asked.

'Bagels,' I said, opening the box and holding up a glazed doughnut. 'Firm skin, moist center, perfectly boiled, not overbaked. Here, try one.'

I laid one on his plate.

'Now I've got a comedian in the house. Did you get into my funny pills?'

I was a little giddy – it was easier to be silly than to focus on the gloom of death. He picked up the doughnut with his left hand and took a bite.

I grabbed the *LA Times* and unfolded it in front of him to read the news. I carefully set his coffee on his left so he wouldn't have to reach for it and maybe knock it over. I put the newspaper directly in front of him.

When I came back upstairs later with folded sheets and blankets, I noticed he had the newspaper spread across the table and was staring intently at it. 'What are you reading?'

He looked up with a half-grin. 'The health section. "Ten Tips to Longevity."'

After lunch I put him back to bed, but he stayed awake anticipating Malaya's arrival. He was still vain enough to ask me to get his rechargeable shaver an hour before she arrived to shave the stubble off his chin. She eventually showed up with a catheter as promised and a bag of diapers.

My father looked crestfallen. 'Now the love of my life is going to dress me in diapers?'

'It'll make things easier,' she said. 'They're comfortable.'

I imagined she must have terminally ill suitors up and down the coast.

'That's one comfort I could live without,' my father said. 'We can't have all the luxuries in life, can we?'

501

She held up a catheter sealed in a plastic bag. 'This one you have to have. It'll hurt only a little, but your son can't take care of you without it. I want you to lean back in the bed, close your eyes and relax. It will only take me a minute.'

She readied the tip by applying lubricant. My father twitched but he had a high resistance to pain so he didn't protest. Once it was in place she took out a small pump, inflated it slightly in his bladder and gave the tube a gentle tug to seal it. I squirmed in my chair. 'All done,' she said. 'Now, that wasn't so bad, was it?'

My father reserved comment. She hooked a bag to the bottom of the bed and showed me how to empty it. She asked if we wanted her to bring an IV tomorrow for nutrients. My father thought about it, then said, 'We'll do this the old-fashioned way. No reason to go out with all the bells and whistles.'

I laughed, but Malaya retained her professional demeanor. I could tell that my father had expected a giggle out of her or at least a grin, neither of which he had got.

'You're a tough one, Malaya. You mean business, don't you?' he said.

'We all have our duty in life. This is mine.'

'Yes, we do. You're right about that. Do you mind if I ask you a serious question?'

'You can ask me whatever you want. I'm here to help you.'

'This is a difficult thing for me to discuss at this point in life. As you know, my health is faltering. I don't know how long I have, so I need an honest answer.'

'I wouldn't answer any other way.'

'Will you accept me as your lawfully wedded husband?'

She held up her wedding ring and this time she smiled. 'I think it's a little late for that.' She packed her bags and told us to call if we needed anything else.

Pulling that little smile out of her had a greater effect on my father than wrapping his entire body in morphine patches. For the rest of the day he sat up in bed as though she had not only accepted but was still in the room attending to him. 'You gotta take chances in life, son.'

'What are you talking about? She said no.'

'She didn't say no. She said, "It's a little late for that." That's not a no where I come from.'

To change the subject, I said, 'I didn't want to embarrass you in front of her, but you're going to wear those diapers. I'm not strong enough to carry you to the bathroom every day.'

He shrugged his shoulders. 'I knew you'd spoil the party.'

Each morning I slid him out of bed into the wheelchair and pushed him to the table to drink his morning coffee and nibble on some food. His energy came in waves. Occasionally he'd wake up and want to engage in conversation to help pass the time. After coffee I'd put him back in bed before eleven so he could nap. I did my daily ride around noon to clear my head.

In the evenings I sat around and read. Neither of us cared much for television. The radio played continuously in the background. Sometimes he'd get tired of jazz and tell me to switch to the classical station. He could still read but he tired easily, so I'd prop whatever book he wanted on the table with a towel behind it and paperclip the page he was on. He read slowly. I had started picking my way through the books on his shelf. He had hundreds, including a small library of German-American history, printed by small Midwestern presses, along with a few popular Nazi titles like *The Rise and Fall of the Third Reich*. There was a Churchill biography, Solzhenitsyn's *The Gulag Archipelago* and James Michener's *Poland*, which he said best retold the conflicts he had grown up listening to his grandfather talk about. On the top shelf I found a small collection of novels by a writer named Herman Broch, *The Sleepwalkers*, *The Unknown Quantity* and *The Spell* – a book he claimed gave the best insight of any novel he'd read on how otherwise normal people were drawn to a figure like Hitler.

The only books he still read at night were on German-American history. He'd have me carry over his magnifying glass to read parts of an old copy of *The German Element in the United States*. As much as he subtly tried to interest me in them, I mostly avoided those titles. Out of curiosity, I did start reading *The Spell*.

The following day when I returned from my ride, he was drumming his fingers on the Hospice table, whose wheels rolled beneath the bed giving him a surface on which to read. He was agitated. I had been gone longer than usual.

'Is something wrong?'

'It still gets me,' he said. 'All these years later.'

I looked around to see if anyone had been there, but I saw only the books he had asked me to bring to his bed that morning. I didn't want to engage him and ruin the elation I felt from my training ride, but my presence was enough to urge him on. He didn't have anyone else to talk to.

'I can understand people dismissing the Germans. They elected Hitler to power in a democratic election. He had already spelled out his program in his autobiography. You can't argue with that. There's nothing to sympathize with. But Germans in this country remain invisible outside New York, Milwaukee and Cincinnati compared to the Mexicans, Irish, Italians, even Chinese, and that's wrong. I guess after having your culture bashed through two world wars it's easier to do the jig on St. Patrick's Day and celebrate Cinco de Mayo by drinking margaritas.'

'Dad, can we take a break? We've been through this already.'

'You had your time,' he said, raising his finger. 'No, we can't. I gave you what you needed. I listened to you. I answered your questions. I'll be dead soon. The least you can do is let me rant one last time. It's not going to kill you.'

At that moment I regretted coming back. He was drilling into my skull. 'Give me a break,' I said forcefully. 'I just got in. Let me clean up and have lunch.'

I walked up to the bathroom, slammed the door and looked into the mirror. Why had I come back? Nothing had changed. He was the same person who'd left me as a child. I filled the bathtub and soaked, concentrating on exhaling, breathing out all the negative energy. *It's almost over. He'll never bother me about this again. I'll never have to think about my roots, never have to think about where my people came from, who they are, what they did.*

I tried to convince myself that I had the stamina to withstand him – that one last lecture wouldn't hurt me. I didn't care about the accomplishments of any culture, race or religion: I wanted only to be my own master. If I had to submit for one more day to achieve that goal, so be it. I wasn't proud. Resistant and persistent, maybe, but not proud. In my small way of thinking, pride resulted in a sense of superiority. Ethnic, national and religious pride repelled me. I kept telling myself it wouldn't hurt to let him get it off his chest one last time. I convinced myself to go back downstairs and enter into a Buber I-It relationship with him and listen without being emotionally engaged. All he wanted was for me to listen. I would have my freedom soon enough. If this was what it took for him to find release, I'd give it to him. I wouldn't agree with it, but I'd give it to him.

I finished my bath, dressed and walked calmly downstairs. 'I want to eat first,' I said. 'Then we can talk, but you have to promise me one thing.' He waited for me to continue. 'That after today we won't discuss the past any more or any remote connection to it.'

'That's it?'

'Yes, that's all.'

He didn't respond.

'Why is this so important to you?' I asked.

'What else do I have? I don't have many good memories of growing up. Learning obscure German-American facts gives me a way to have pride without hurting anyone. That's not so hard to understand, is it? Probably like racing bicycles for you.'

I looked at my bike, leaning against the wall. 'Do you want something to eat?' I asked. 'More coffee?'

'I'll take a piece of stollen.'

I went into the kitchen, sliced some, carried it to his bedside and sat down. 'You still haven't promised me.'

'I'm not promising you anything. My death is my promise.' He glanced at the books resting on his lap.

I looked at the clock. His life was ticking by. I knew I wasn't accomplishing anything by shutting him down, any more than I had through the years of trying to forget he existed. 'I thought you had something you wanted to tell me.'

His face brightened. 'You really interested?'

'I wouldn't be sitting here otherwise.'

'I'll try not to bore you by carrying on about our national fixation with hot dogs, hamburgers and beer. You know anything about the military?'

'Only what I've seen on TV.' I knew he had something up his sleeve. I felt like I was back in the basement in Chagrin. I tried not to let him see me shift uncomfortably in my chair.

'Germans not only defeated Germany, they brought the Second World War to a close.'

I didn't bother stopping him. I no longer cared how distorted his views. I wanted it to end as quickly as possible and I knew arguing with him would only prolong it.

'They had a more central role in defeating the Nazis than any other group and then went on to defeat the Japanese.'

It was too much. I couldn't stay silent.

'You've lost your mind!'

'I thought you were going to let me talk!'

'If you want to make sense, I'll listen. I can't listen to nonsense.'

'Then shut up and let me finish!' A look of disgust flashed across his face. 'German-Americans returned to their ancestral homeland by the millions to defeat their own people without ever receiving the credit they deserve, but so that I can get to the point, I'll forget about the German-American grunts for now who went to kill their ancestors in the name of freedom.'

I had heard him carry on about endless minutiae regarding German influences, but this was new. He ignored my raised eyebrows.

'The highest ranking military officer in Europe during the Second World War, the Supreme Commander of the European Allied Forces, was Dwight Eisenhower – a German descendant who went to Europe to defeat his ancestral homeland. It's called fighting fire with fire. The Americans used the Germans to defeat the Germans. Eisenhower wasn't the only German in high command. Carl Spaatz ran the U.S. Airforce in Europe. Spaatz and the other Allies under Eisenhower's command dropped more bombs on Germany than any country has ever experienced in war. I was there. I saw the bombs falling. Those bombs killed more people than the atomic bombs, but I'll get to that. When Germany finally surrendered, Spaatz became Commander of the Airforce in the Pacific, where he joined Admiral Nimitz, the Commander-in-Chief of the U.S. Pacific Forces and the grandson of a German merchant marine. Nimitz won two of the biggest naval battles in history, before mounting amphibious assaults on Iwo Jima and Okinawa. Spaatz then directed the atom bombs – that another German-American, Oppenheimer, helped build – dropped on Hiroshima and Nagasaki, defeating the Japanese. The Germans ended the Second World War – the German-Americans,' he announced defiantly to stop me interrupting him.

'And then there's Wernher von Braun, the man behind the Nazis' rocket program. The U.S. snatched him up after the war and put him to work creating the U.S. missile program. He even helped launch NASA and put a man on the moon ahead of the U.S.S.R. But all of that is just recent history. Back in the Revolutionary War, Germans helped create the U.S. Army. Baron von Steuben immigrated here and trained the American troops to beat the British. George Washington named him Inspector General. Von Steuben also wrote the first *U.S. Army Manual*. Later on, General Pershing, a German born in Missouri, led the American Expeditionary Force in the First World War and became the role model for Patton, Bradley, Eisenhower, Marshall – all the generals who helped defeat the Nazis.'

He glanced at his shelf of books, then back at the ones resting on his lap that he had been reading before I returned from my ride. He looked exhausted. I knew then that he didn't have much longer. I started to speak, but he raised his hand, silencing me, caught his breath, and said, 'Few people know these facts, nobody wants to know them. Germans are evil – Nazis. That may be true, but Germans also helped America become a superpower. If schools want to teach that the Chinese built the railroad out west, that a black fired the first shot in the Civil War, that California was a Mexican territory, then give credit where credit is due. Outside a few Midwestern cities most people have no clue about the Germans' contributions.'

'Let me see that,' I said, grabbing one of the books off his lap and flipping through it, stopping on the pages he had dog-eared. The details I found matched what he'd told me. Unless the books were blatantly lying, the information appeared to be true. I had never thought about it that way, but there was no denying history. Maybe he wasn't crazy. The anger and frustration I'd felt when I first returned from my ride started to fade. I looked at my father, staring out of the window at the setting sun. The burst of energy that had propelled him, that he had used to force me to listen, had subsided. He sat there quietly lost in thought. I didn't say anything.

I knew he had pored over that information. I still didn't like hearing it, but it was better than him reverting to the dark interior of his youth – the distorted history he had once been forced to study as a child during the years he had been brainwashed at the Adolf Hitler School. How could I hold against him his interest in Germans here? I could have argued with him that it was exactly what Hitler had wanted – trumpeting German accomplishments around the world. But hadn't these Germans he now championed returned to Germany to defeat Hitler like he said? Were they not honorable even if it was unfashionable to celebrate them? He was right. Nobody wanted to hear about Germans in America.

I can't say I was proud of my father, but I was impressed – not so much with what he had told me but with him. He had found something positive in which to channel his frustration. I wondered if all of America's vast German population experienced the pain of silence as he had. Perhaps it was only those who had come here from Nazi Germany, like my father, who had never again identified publicly with a particular group, who most felt the sting of silence and fear of reprisal – and, no matter how much it might have been distorted or inflated in their minds, it was still real.

Germans had arrived by the millions as hard workers, laborers, just as the Mexicans who would soon replace them as the nation's largest ethnic group. They had come to tend farms, grow wheat and corn, run hotels, work construction, build bridges and be soldiers – dirty work. Sitting in that darkening room with my father, I realized he was right too about Midwesterners being pigeonholed as WASPs, when most whites didn't have an Anglo-Saxon bone in their body. Even Mexicans called them Anglos without grasping how much Germans had in common with them, right down to the Tejano music played on accordions: the musical scale's root and fifth repeated infinitely – oompah, oompah – and constantly across the Los Angeles Basin.

My father had wandered around like a ghost, living in different neighborhoods and never finding a home in any. I suppose it was just as well that the 'white man's burden' had come to save him. He could spend his last days reading his books, looking out of the window at the rows of asparagus being tended by laborers playing music that reminded him of home while the scent of salt air blew in from the ocean, reminiscent of the Baltic. In a way I guess he had found his home in that anonymous rundown corner of Huntington Beach whose farmlands would likely be paved after his death to make way for more ocean-view subdivisions. People would live there who probably wouldn't know or care where their ancestors had come from and would probably be better for it. At least they wouldn't have to spend their lives chasing ghosts, as I had. They would be saved from the past.

My father could see I was deep in thought and his mind appeared to be clicking along on another tangent as well. He had used his energy to articulate his thoughts. Nobody besides me was interested in what he had spent his adult life learning under the false assumption that one day he would share with the world what he had discovered on his journey through life.

We spent the next few days carrying on the routine we had become accustomed to, but his demeanor went through a profound transformation. He was more relaxed. His body showed signs of shutting down. One evening we had a pleasant conversation about European bike racing. The following morning he had difficulty telling me what he wanted from the kitchen. He formed each word perfectly in his mouth, but his voice cracked and refused to participate. A few hours later he was able to talk again, but we both knew that soon his voice, like his right side, would fall out of use. Aware of this, he made what little use he could of his final words. He told me to stop the dexamethasone.

That marked the turning point.

'The tumor's already pushing on my brain,' he said, acknowledging his partial paralysis for the first time. 'No reason to hold it back now.'

I placed a cup of coffee on his table in the morning loaded with sugar and cream since it provided most of his calorie intake for the day. He didn't complain about the sweetness. He asked me to help him out of bed to the balcony so that he could sit in the blazing sun. He wanted to feel the heat on his skin. I carried him out and started to put some lotion on his arms and forehead to keep them from burning. He stopped me.

'Let me burn. It's one of the few things left I can feel.'

Sitting at his bedside that evening, spoon-feeding him as if he were my own child, I realized we had been the fiercest of competitors – even during the long period that he wasn't in my life. I looked at my hand that held the next bite of mashed beans for him to eat and saw dirt under my fingernails. I smelled it – dried feces from wiping his ass.

'Where's the nail scrubber?' I asked.

Our roles had been reversed. He was withdrawing into childhood, to infancy, and soon wouldn't exist. I no longer had the urge to lash out at him. He spoke less and less until almost everything he said was in German and even though I didn't speak the language it wasn't difficult to understand what he wanted. He was done with English.

At night I sat at the desk near the foot of his bed and turned occasionally to make sure he was okay. His feet stuck out of the blanket. I noticed that his aging toenails appeared rotten, slowly melting away; the cloudy white nails weren't liquid or even soft, yet somehow with age they had drooped from their original shape. I spent most nights reading passages from different books on his shelf to try to understand his perspective, his interests. He had an old Saul Bellow novel, *Herzog*, that I stayed awake all night reading. The next morning when I went to put it back on the shelf, I pulled down another book – a thin volume by Christopher Isherwood called *Goodbye to Berlin*. I stayed up late the following night reading it. Out of habit, whenever I read, I'd run my fingers down the long scar on the left side of my head that I still carried like a battle wound. All these years later it still acted up, itching and occasionally oozing trace amounts of a thick clear fluid that had the viscosity of motor oil. A doctor at OTC had once told me it was brain or spinal fluid and that some wounds never healed completely. It's strange, I thought, as I dropped my hand back to my side, how a scar can carry in its raised skin the memory and pain of an injury it tries to hide.

Two days later I noticed blood in my father's urine and called Malaya to come check his catheter. After a brief examination, she said nothing was wrong with the catheter. 'His kidneys are probably beginning to shut down.'

'How long does he have?' I asked her quietly, near the kitchen so he wouldn't overhear us.

'It's hard to say. It might only be a couple of days, but I've seen people carry on for a couple of weeks in his condition. It really depends on him. I think we should give him an IV for comfort.'

My father was looking at us from across the room but no longer trying to charm Malaya. We walked back to his bedside.

'She wants to give you an IV.'

He didn't say anything, communicating only through a barely perceptible facial expression.

'He doesn't want it,' I said, turning back to her.

'Well, it's his decision.'

He started to say something, but his voice went out halfway through. With effort, he took a deep breath and tried again. This time his voice worked. '*Auf Wiedersehen.*'

She looked at me.

511

'He says goodbye.'

I waited for one of Malaya's soothing replies, but for the first time his words caught her off guard. If he had said it in English, I imagine she would have said something to comfort him, but the foreign language had created a disconnect for her and the weight of the translation seemed to throw her even farther off kilter. It sent a wave of sadness over me that she immediately sensed. Like my father, I had come to rely on the security she brought into the house whenever she visited and never imagined she would falter.

She turned to him, looked directly into his eyes and said, '*Paálam.*'

She collected her bags and departed. By chance, years later, I learned she had said goodbye in Tagalog, her own language. But somehow I think he understood its meaning, for after she walked out of the door, a tear rolled down his cheek. I didn't interpret it as a tear for her – it was a tear for himself. He never cried or said another word.

I started monitoring his vital signs much as I monitored my own leading up to major competitions. I took his pulse each morning and recorded it in a ledger, along with his body temperature and blood pressure with a device I purchased at the local drugstore. I recorded them on waking, at noon, at six and again at midnight. I then recorded my own so that I could run my eyes down the page, comparing us and watching his decline. I'm not exactly sure why I did it. I knew he would die soon. In one way it helped prepare me for the end and in another it allowed me to communicate with him by watching how our bodies worked side by side. At the very least I hoped that by monitoring him I would be calmly prepared so that nothing came as a surprise.

He could still hear everything I said and I could understand most of what he wanted to communicate to me from his facial expressions. Each day he ate and drank a little less. Whereas before I had eaten voraciously to encourage him, more recently I had unconsciously followed his lead until I noticed that I had hardly had a bite during an entire day.

One morning I woke up with the sun flooding through the sliding glass door, illuminating the apartment like an operating room. At a few minutes to noon, I walked over to record his vital signs and noticed it was shining directly into his face. As I sat down at his bedside I made a mental note to close the blind. When I took his pulse, he lurched in a brief spasm, his face contorted, frightened – eyes wide open, breathing short and erratic. I thumped his chest with my palm to get his diaphragm to relax enough to pull in oxygen, glanced down and noticed that the tips of his fingers had turned bone white. I grabbed his hand and shook it lightly to increase circulation.

The room was so bright that I wanted to slam the blind shut and make it go dark, but I was too scared to leave him. Even with the sun illuminating every surface I sensed an element present in the room that hadn't been there before, too vague to confirm, but too insistent to deny. It bounced around me so swiftly and with such force that there was no way to harness or even fully recognize it, yet I knew that our separate realities were converging and being torn apart at the same time.

'Don't die, you bastard!'

I thumped him on the chest harder, this time with my hand clenched in a tight fist. I realized there was nothing I could do. I was stunned into submission. I stood for perhaps five seconds in silence as life drained from him, listening to his erratic breaths. I took his hand and spread his cool fingers across my palm, watching the skin turn limpid. I inhaled deeply as tears surfaced.

As the first left my eyes, his breathing evened out. He took a single deep breath. I began to massage his chest and within seconds he was breathing regularly again. Less than a minute later the color returned to his fingertips, the erratic gasping now as remote as if it had happened in a dream.

With death fluttering away as abruptly as a dragonfly leaving a maple leaf floating on a pond, our breathing patterns joined and color returned to our faces. Once I was certain he was stable, I moved slowly toward the sliding glass door to escape the cocoon of the room and stepped out onto the balcony where a woman was unloading groceries in the parking lot below. She saw me and waved.

I contemplated the face of death that had just shown itself and vanished as my emotions shuffled between relief, frustration and grief: I was relieved that we had succeeded in chasing death from him, frustrated when it would have been so much easier for him to die, and I grieved at the thought of the pain that would remain when he finally surrendered.

By nine that night he was fully conscious and aware of what had happened that afternoon. Considering the circumstances, he was almost energetic, proud that he had whacked that bastard in the face and sent him away without his soul. His expression communicated that he was still ready to die, but that he wanted to do it on his terms, not to be thrown into convulsions, slapped and punched in the chest. He would go, but either he'd go peacefully or drag it out, his eyes seemed to say. He was almost smirking.

'Okay, Wiseguy, we'll do it your way.'

That seemed to satisfy him, because after I'd said it, he closed his eyes and went back to sleep.

At midnight, I took his vital signs again. His resting pulse had risen from 75 to just over 100 during the last day, his temperature from 97.6 to 99.7 degrees and his blood pressure had dropped from 137/80 to 90/60.

I went searching for the morphine patches.

I stuck two on his chest. He didn't wake up the following morning. His breathing pattern was regular, his vital signs remained elevated but stabilized as his body settled into a new equilibrium. He didn't wake that afternoon or evening, either, and therefore neither ate nor, more importantly, drank. His lips were starting to dry out. I drove to the pharmacy, bought some glycerin swabs, came home and brushed them over his lips to keep them from cracking. I took a washrag, soaked it under the kitchen faucet, then held it above his lips and squeezed lightly so that drops of water would rain into his mouth. He seemed to like it. I continued until I squeezed it a little too hard and almost choked him to death.

Although he was taking in hardly any moisture, he sweated profusely, as if he was running a marathon. I mopped it up with a bath towel. Soon his skin became cold and he started shivering. I turned on the heater and covered him with thick blankets.

The following morning the blankets and sheets were soaked and I had to remake the entire bed, but at least he had stopped sweating and shivering. Around noon he opened his eyes as if he had woken from a bad dream.

'I'm still here,' I whispered. 'Guarding the door.'

Dehydration was affecting him: his eyes were looking in different directions, never straight ahead at the same time. That can't be good, I thought. Since he was conscious I returned to the washrag routine, dripping water into his mouth. We sat like two soldiers in a foxhole rationing the last of the water before the onslaught. I held the rag above his mouth for nearly thirty minutes, until my arms ached, then went to the kitchen and got a cup, but only succeeded in choking him again so I went back to the rag.

'The cavalry's coming. Hold tight, old boy.'

Even in his discombobulated state, he knew where he was. He knew what was going on. He was appreciative. I could see it by the way he nodded at me. When I'd first brought him home, he'd joked a couple of times with an obscure German saying that translated approximately as 'Old man, no fast train.' Back then he was still getting around okay, so I'd ignored it, but he was certainly no fast train now. I doubted it would be another day or two before he retired from the tracks for good.

That evening his resting pulse rose to 148 and his core temperature to 103.6 degrees.

By midnight he had the crackles: a horrific, gurgling sound – like somebody drowning in their own body fluid. I raised the head of the bed so high that he was almost in a sitting position. I affixed the rest of the morphine patches to his chest and arms. I pulled out a partially filled bottle of bootleg garlic vodka he had hidden in the closet and dipped large cotton swabs into it to moisturize his mouth. He wasn't awake, at least as far as I could tell, but he closed his lips around the first two and nearly sucked them dry.

515

I did several shots in his honor, before standing up to turn the lights down and walking over to the humidor. I pulled out his most expensive cigar, a Fuentes Opus X. To his last day he was frugal and would have never indulged in such a cigar, but an old client, a bakery-supply company he had bought goods from for years, had delivered a handful by courier when they heard he was dying. I trimmed the end, lit a match and rolled the cigar around in the flame, like I had seen him do. Then I put it into my mouth and slowly drew on it until the entire tip was engulfed in flame. I crossed the room to his bedside. With one powerful puff, I blew out the flame, put the cigar back into my mouth and softly drew until my mouth filled with smoke. I exhaled the cloud gently across his face. His whole body seemed to relax. I gave him a cotton swab of garlic vodka and poured myself another shot. I drew in a fresh mouthful of smoke and blew the dense leathery white cloud across his nose so he could take in the subtle hints of flavor. After we'd finished the cigar, I joined him in a silent toast, then stood up and walked to the stereo where I put *Kind of Blue* on the turntable. I fell asleep on the carpet listening to Miles's muted trumpet bleed out into the room, thick with smoke, as the moon rising over the ocean came into view through the sliding glass door.

I opened my eyes at sunrise, disoriented and groggy. I saw the empty vodka bottle on the floor beside me. I jumped up, angry with myself for getting drunk and passing out, knowing he had died as I'd slept. His face was pale. The disturbing sounds emerging from his throat were gone. The auto-return mechanism on the turntable had failed to pick up the arm holding the stylus and the recurring noise of the needle hitting its end point near the record label and bouncing backward filled the room. I rushed over, pulled it off and went back to my father. I lowered my ear to his mouth.

He was still breathing, shallow but regular. I sat on the edge of the bed, closed my eyes and held my breath. With the stereo off, I could hear him now, his breath as delicate as a newborn baby's. I didn't bother to take his vital signs. I left the bedside only to open the glass door a crack to let the morning fog that had drifted in from the ocean enter the room to dilute the scents of smoke, vodka, urine and sweat. I went to the front door and picked up the *LA Times* the delivery boy had thrown on the doorstep before dawn, then back to his bedside.

I worked my way slowly through the newspaper over the next couple of hours, listening to his breathing slow and become shallower. At one point he stopped breathing; I set the paper on my lap and listened for a few seconds, but as I did so he inhaled a tiny breath, then went back to the same light pattern. Dark purplish blotches appeared on his hands and feet as they lost circulation. The bluish tint of his skin then receded, replaced by the whiteness of drifting clouds. I stood up and placed my hand, fingers splayed, flat on the center of his stomach to feel his temperature. His body was cool. When I lifted my hand, its imprint remained.

Five minutes later, he inhaled, held his breath momentarily, exhaled and stopped breathing. I placed the tip of my finger on his neck and found a fleeting pulse in his jugular, like the distant thumping of a helicopter's blades passing over a mountain ridge and moving into the valley beyond.

Unlike the previous time when I had watched life drain from his body in a state of panic, I was calm now, present yet queerly detached. I sat back in the chair and stared at the wall. About an hour after he died, I called Hospice to send a doctor out to file a death certificate.

'We're a little busy right now. Is it okay if somebody comes in another hour or so? Are you okay there with him?'

'Yes, everything's fine. No hurry.'

I walked over to my father and began stripping him down to wash him. I can't really explain why, other than to say perhaps it was German intuition – instinct to prepare him for his journey. Hygiene, cleanliness, sanitation. He kept the sink in his kitchen so thoroughly scrubbed that it appeared sterilized, even though it was probably fifteen years old. I knew he wanted to be clean for the doctor when he arrived. I also wanted to peel the morphine patches off his body. Once he was naked, I carried a pail of warm water with a rag and soap from the

517

bathroom and spent the next hour scrubbing him. I removed his false teeth and took them up to the bathroom, where I gave them their final brushing, then reinserted them in his mouth. I dressed him in a clean, ironed suit that I found in the closet so he'd be presentable.

Noticing stubble on his chin, I went upstairs, retrieved his cordless electric razor and shaved him, running the shaver gently back and forth along his chin and neck. I combed his hair with my fingers. As I stepped back to see how he looked, I heard a quiet knock on the front door.

I laid the shaver on the desk, looked down at my father one last time and placed my hand on his forehead, then patted him gently on his chin. 'You're on your way, old man. It's finally over.'

I took a breath to control myself and walked calmly to the door, where I found Oleg and a doctor standing patiently on the other side. I let them in and cleared out of their way while they handled their business. As the doctor was filling out his report, I saw him glance at the small trash container beside the bed that I had forgotten to dump out after bathing my father. The top layer was filled with the morphine patches that I'd torn off his chest. He glanced at Oleg and nodded at the trash basket. After gazing at it for a moment in contemplation, they turned away.

They told me they'd have the death certificate ready that afternoon.

'Would you like me to stay until your father is transported?' Oleg asked.

'No, I'm fine here by myself. I need to make some phone calls anyway.'

Out of courtesy, they asked where the funeral would be held.

'I think we'll skip that part,' I said. 'Cremation should cover it.' I asked if they'd like a cup of coffee. To my surprise, they both accepted. We sat around for the next forty-five minutes, chatting, while they went over their notes for appointments that afternoon and made a couple of phone calls. I pulled a kielbasa sausage out of the refrigerator, sliced it and carried it to the table.

'We really shouldn't,' Oleg said, before we all dug in.

When they stood up to go, I said, 'I'll be leaving here soon and all this stuff will go to the Salvation Army. If there's anything you see that you'd like, please take it.'

I said this because throughout lunch Oleg had stared at a tiny sculpture resting on the fireplace mantel of an intricately detailed and painted Polish-Lithuanian hussar on horseback with enormous wings mounted on his back and a long lance pointed straight ahead. I would never be able to fit my father's belongings into my van and didn't have the heart to keep his possessions anyway.

'We really can't.'

'In that case, I insist.'

I walked over to the mantel, picked up the small pewter sculpture, carried it to Oleg and deposited it in his hands. I noticed the doctor glance at the humidor on the desk. I opened it, took out the last few cigars and held them up, saying, 'For tonight.' I set the cigars on the table and carried the humidor to the doctor. They told me that some-body would be by within a couple hours to pick up the body. I thanked them for dedicating themselves to Hospice. 'I'm sure there's much better paying work out there,' I said.

I pulled out the phone book and called across the entire Los Angeles Basin, from the San Joaquin Hills bordering Irvine down south to Hollywood nestled against the beginning of the Santa Monica Mountains to the north, to find the least expensive crematory. It was what my father would have wanted. It didn't matter how many cigar boxes stuffed with crisp bills he had left, I knew he didn't want some-body overcharging for tossing him into a furnace. We had discussed it. He didn't want a gravestone: he didn't want to leave his mark on earth any more than he already had. He wanted to fade.

I called some twenty places that afternoon, getting wildly varying prices. Everything on the coast in Orange and LA Counties was ex-orbitant, but when I started moving inland to Santa Ana things dropped considerably, and the farther north I moved in LA the more I noticed that intense competition pushed the prices lower. Several were even willing to let me haggle over the price. I didn't have anything else to do, so I figured I could spend my time finding the lowest prices in town. Eventually I ended up on the line with two Armenian brothers who had just opened up in Glendale right over the hill from Hollywood. They were ambitious. One would put me on hold to take more calls, while the other came back on the line to start negotiating anew. We went through several rounds. Once we reached a price, he asked when I wanted my father picked up.

'Hospice has already sent someone to bring him to the morgue. You'll have to call them. What's the earliest you can arrange the cremation?'

'The day after tomorrow at ten in the morning.'

'I want to come up. Is that okay?'

'Yeah, sure. We get people in here sometimes, but most people prefer to leave it to us.'

'I just want to make sure the body gets there.'

'Yeah, of course. We'll see you at ten, then. If we need anything else, I'll call you.'

A white van with no markings on the side arrived. They put my father on a stretcher, covered him with a clean sheet and carried him away.

The next person I called was my uncle.

'We've been waiting to hear from you.'

'He passed this morning.'

He was silent for a short time. Then we made small talk for a few minutes, and I said, 'I'd like to come up there tonight, if you don't mind. I have to be over in Glendale the day after tomorrow. I was hoping we could visit again.'

'Yeah, yeah, I'll call Leyna. Why don't you come over to my place in the Valley this time? I'll pull some cuts out of one of the trucks and we can grill steaks if you're hungry.'

'I could use a good dinner and company.'

He gave me directions. I told him I'd be up after the traffic eased.

I had already been thinking about what to do after my father died. I had decided to return to Chagrin for a couple of days so that I could clear everything out of my system. I wanted it finished completely. I didn't want to see anybody back there. I didn't want to visit, but I needed to go back and walk through the village and get my bearings.

I planned to spend a few days in LA with my father's siblings, drive back down to Huntington to make sure the Salvation Army had cleaned up the apartment, then return to my uncle's place to store my van while I took a plane to Cleveland. I didn't want to spend a week driving across the country and I didn't want to get stuck in Chagrin in case relatives saw me there. If I left my van in LA, I'd have to return. It would give me an excuse to come back and move on to the next rock in the river.

I didn't want to spend the rest of the afternoon sitting in the empty apartment waiting for traffic to subside, so I loaded my bags into the van and drove down to Crystal Cove, twenty minutes south, one of the few beaches in the basin that didn't have houses hanging above the cliffs overlooking the water. I wanted to be alone. I didn't think I'd see many people down there on a weekday.

The parking lot was nearly empty – only three other cars. A small park, a tiny undeveloped wilderness, stood on the mesa above the ocean and stairs built from railroad ties led down the face of a tall sand cliff that hid the beach from view. I took my shoes off, left them in the van and ran across the hot pavement until I reached the steps, filled with sand between each tie. I stood above the ocean for a few minutes, staring out at Catalina, then descended to the beach. A woman was playing with her children at the bottom of the steps.

I walked south. The beach was desolate from there to Laguna, five or six miles away, cliffs rising above the ocean to my left blocking civilization, and surf breaking to my right on the sand. I waited until I had walked a couple of coves from the steps and sat down. I didn't want to cry and didn't think I had to, but the tears came anyway. I didn't try to hold them back. Nobody was around. No one could hear me.

* * *

I spent that night in Reseda listening to stories about their child-hood in East Prussia and the trek across Poland, stories I vaguely recalled from my father's writings. I fell asleep while my aunt was telling me about living on a farm in the mountains somewhere in East Germany. I felt bad when my uncle woke me at dawn: she had left while I was asleep so she could drive back over the hill and sleep at her house to go to work that morning.

My uncle asked if I wanted to make a run with him into down-town. We spent the morning helping his crews load the trucks with meat and then the entire afternoon driving from one restaur-ant to the next – Mexican, Guatemalan, Cuban, Chinese, Korean, Vietnamese, Armenian, Lebanese, Persian, Indian, Italian, Hungarian, hamburger stands, a BBQ joint, a couple of delis and I don't know what all else. My head was spinning from trying to absorb the cornu-copia of different cultures my uncle did business with each day. He told me he had never taken a single day off work since finding his first job in America. I looked at him suspiciously.

'Don't believe me, then. Means nothing to me. I went enough years without work in Germany. What's the point of staying home if you have work?'

It wasn't until later that night while eating dinner that I realized we hadn't dropped anything off at a single German restaurant. When I asked why that was, he replied matter-of-factly, 'There are none.'

'There's no German food in LA? We just toured half the globe this afternoon.'

'There's burger and hot-dog joints, but the only real German place I know of is in Silverlake. Otherwise, good luck.' He got up and pulled a container of homemade kraut out of the refrigerator and set it at the center of the table. 'You remind me of your father,' he said. 'Anybody ever tell you that?'

We ate in silence. A while later, he said, 'We left that place behind.'

Neither my aunt nor my uncle was interested in accompanying me to the crematory the following morning. They both seemed a little taken aback when I asked them. I took Sherman Way across the Valley to the Hollywood Freeway and followed it south to the

134, then drove on until I found my exit. The place was set back from the road in a quiet section of town. I pulled through the gates of a large cemetery and parked in front of the administrative building beside another van with a young man sitting in the driver's seat. I went in and asked if it was the place where my father would be cremated. One of the guys I had talked with on the phone shook my hand and pointed to a small building surrounded by trees near the center of the graveyard, perhaps an eighth of a mile away, whose windows were boarded shut with plywood.

'The crematory's over there,' he said. 'My guy's waiting outside in the van for you. Follow him on over.'

I went back outside, waved to the driver, then fell in line and followed him slowly along the narrow road winding among gravestones. When we reached the building, he pulled over and parked. I drove around him and parked a little way up the road and walked back. The driver was waiting for me near the rear door. A young Latino who apparently operated the furnace stepped outside. The driver and crematory attendant exchanged a few words in Spanish and the attendant went back into the building.

'Help me slide this out,' the driver said. 'Grab the other side.'

I looked in the back of the van at my father's coffin, a rectangular plywood box. We carried it a short distance across the grass and set it down on an industrial cart the attendant had brought out to roll the coffin into the building.

Once inside the driver and the attendant began talking again. I asked if there was a restroom. The attendant pointed to the side of the building. The door was stuck open – clearly not many people came out here to see off their loved ones. The floor was covered with the attendant's muddy footprints tracked in from outside. A cockroach was trying fruitlessly to ascend the side of the urinal it had fallen into. I might have been in a gas station along a desolate stretch of Georgia highway.

When I returned, I noticed the attendant was wearing worn blue jeans, a torn T-shirt and tennis shoes with holes in them – not exactly a welcoming committee. I felt foolish in slacks and the button-up shirt my uncle had made me put on that morning. It seemed clear from the surroundings and his worn shoes that the attendant was paid little more than minimum wage for inserting bodies into furnaces. It was also clear that only employees were expected to be here, but it put me more at ease than if the building had been superficially decorated. I felt at home in the present setting, as though I had returned to my job in the laundry room down in Albany after a long absence.

The driver asked if I wanted to see the body.

'Yes, please. If it's not a problem.'

It was. The request was clearly unusual, for the attendant had to step into another room and search for a hammer to pry the lid off the box. He returned a couple of minutes later and inserted the claw end of the hammer between lid and box – a loud screeching noise filled the room as the nails slid from the wood.

My father was lying inside, his head rolled to the side, his cheeks sunken. A bunched-up sheet was pushed haphazardly between his body and the sides of the box so he wouldn't roll around during the drive.

I nodded.

The attendant pushed the cart into an adjacent room, perhaps thirty by thirty feet in diameter, composed of cinder-block walls in which sat four large furnaces: two on one side of the room, two opposite. The dull roar of burning natural gas rumbled from within the furnace closest to us. They resembled large kilns, set slightly off the ground on concrete foundations; the walls were composed of large bricks. A thick steel door operated by the large chain on a pulley faced the center of the room. The room itself was relatively clean in comparison with the restroom and entry room, in that it had been swept, but since the building and furnaces looked as if they had been manufactured in the 1930s everything was shopworn, giving the impression that we were inside an artist's ceramic studio in an industrial area of the city.

The attendant explained that the body would burn for four or five hours at high heat – he pointed at a switch to my right used to fire up the furnace – and then cool inside the furnace with the door still closed for another two or three hours. He'd open the door and take a heavy tool – which he picked up from its leaning position against the furnace – and crush any bones that had not disintegrated so that nothing larger than a medium-sized pebble remained. Except for troublesome bones, the hips usually, the rest would have already been reduced to smooth ash.

Once the process was complete he'd take a small hoe-like tool and push all the ash toward a square hole at the center of the furnace, clearly visible from where we stood. The ash would fall into an iron drawer below. He pointed to a stack of drawers leaning against the furnace that was in use a few feet to my left. Beneath the large iron door through which the body entered the furnace was another, much smaller, iron door built into the foundation, almost exactly like the small iron doors at the foot of coal-burning fireplaces in which you cleaned the ash that had fallen from above. It was through this smaller door that my father would re-emerge.

Comfortable that I understood the entire process the driver and attendant slid the cart toward the furnace, while I remained in my present position, a few feet back. Before pushing the coffin into the furnace the attendant placed two small hardened-cardboard tubes a few feet apart at the entrance, then nodded to the driver that he could leave and waved me over. We lifted the coffin and slid it onto the tubes. It rolled in with little effort until the head smacked the far side and bounced back slightly. He apologized, then pushed it gently back in, making sure it cleared the heavy iron door.

He turned to me and pointed to the switch.

'Fire it up.'

His order caught me off guard. He wasn't asking me if I wanted to participate, his voice was stern. I had only come to make sure that my father's body had been delivered. He glanced at his watch. I had not come to fire up the furnace and slide my father inside. He looked at me impatiently.

I obeyed.

I reached down and lifted the cover of an industrial switch attached to the side of the furnace and flipped it on. Almost instantaneously a huge orange flame exploded inside, propelled by a blower. I flinched. The attendant smiled. Flames were blasting from the wall of the interior, dancing off the edges of the thin coffin that had already began to brown under the intense heat, before the end nearest my father's head burst into flames. The attendant grabbed a thick chain and slowly lowered the iron door until the fire disappeared from view, leaving only the sound of dull rumbling flames.

Rain was dripping off my uncle's roof when I awoke the next morning. I called a courier and asked him to go to the crematory that afternoon to pick up the ashes and deliver them to my uncle's warehouse in Canoga Park. I didn't want to drive back there.

That afternoon the clouds pulled back. The rain had dispersed most of the smog that usually hung over the city and a breeze coming in from the ocean blew away the little that remained. I drove over to Encino and up into the Santa Monica Mountains to spend the afternoon alone. When I reached Mulholland Drive I followed it west until it turned to dirt and continued until I reached San Vicente Peak where I found the remains of a decommissioned missile silo that had been built during the height of the Cold War.

I was astonished at how remote and vast the wilderness was, given that I'd left my uncle's house less than thirty minutes earlier. A coyote yapped in one of the ravines below me. I followed the uninhabited canyons with my eyes westward to where they fell into the ocean. Each time I'd participated in bicycle races in the city, I was focused on competition, and in Huntington, other than occasional walks through the farmland next to my father's apartment complex, I'd rarely had a chance to explore the surroundings.

I thought back to the exodus to California during the Dust Bowl and the waves of immigrants who had come as a result of the war before the city was overcome with the cars that created much of the pollution. Standing deep in the wilderness, I absorbed the same view that immigrants had seen when they first arrived in Los Angeles a half-century earlier – the only global city split in two by a mountain chain, containing more wilderness than any other city in America. It was one of the most startling and unexpected views I'd ever seen.

Palos Verdes rose from South Bay. Further out, the cliffs of Catalina shimmered in the sun, and beyond that, I glimpsed San Clemente Island. I could see clearly all the way down past Huntington Beach. From above there were no divisions between the areas that everyone had marked out below – gang members often defending one block over the next with their life: it was all the same geological formation, the same coast, a single basin, a single place, the same people all locked in private wars convinced that their block, school, town, city or county was better than the next. The Santa Monica Bay spread out in a perfect arch between Palos Verdes and Malibu.

Behind me the San Fernando Valley, containing dozens of towns and the most diverse ethnic community I'd ever wandered through, abutted a series of hills and mountains that rose to the north. In the other direction the skyscrapers downtown rose from where the mountain chain I stood on crumbled into the city's center. Beyond downtown several snowcapped peaks stood a mile high, forming an arch of mountain ranges that encircled the entire metropolis. I understood for the first time why my mother had once come here from her small village in Ohio and why my father had traveled halfway around the world. Standing by myself atop the abandoned missile tower, I felt a sense of optimism and freedom that I had never truly experienced in my entire life. My father was gone. I was free.

I stored my VW van behind my uncle's warehouse and collected the belongings I needed for the trip to Ohio. That evening he drove me over the hill to LAX to catch a midnight flight. I was apprehensive but excited. I had never flown before. Walking through the airport, approaching my terminal, entering the plane, finding my seat and waiting for takeoff, I sensed a transformation taking place within me. It was like watching a movie when the character on the screen senses something profound has happened – but now it wasn't somebody else experiencing that epiphany, it was me. I relaxed and closed my eyes as the forward thrust of the plane pressed me back in my seat. I fell into a deep sleep somewhere over Nevada and didn't wake until the flight attendant told us to fasten our seatbelts for landing.

I had no real memories of Cleveland other than the insides of bakeries – and one afternoon when my mother had driven us there to see President Nixon passing in a black limousine, the top half of his body protruding through a sunroof as he waved at people crowding the sidewalks while dozens of secret service agents in black suits jogged ahead and alongside his car, peering intently at us. I couldn't tell whether anything had changed or not. It was the one city I had always avoided during my cycling career. I had never wanted to go back to Chagrin.

I rented a car and drove through town on Highway 422. I passed three cyclists riding in a paceline dressed in racing gear. I thought about my old team back in South Carolina. I knew Craig was wondering what had happened to me. As much as he irritated me sometimes, I missed him. I decided to give him a call later so I didn't feel compelled to look up lost relatives in Chagrin.

When I reached the village I turned onto Main Street and drove across the falls. Everything was identical to what it had been when I'd left, right down to the colors of paint on the Popcorn Shop standing at the edge of the bridge, the triangle park forming a plaza with the hand-wrought gazebo built from large grapevines at its center where I'd sung carols at Christmas each year. Even the stores looked the same, including Fireside Books, one of the first businesses I remembered entering, following my father in search of some title he undoubtedly couldn't find – he'd probably yelled at them for not stocking it.

I turned right on Maple Street and rolled slowly past the house where I was born. It was as we'd left it, no new additions, no new shrubbery, same large trees, same gravel driveway. My eyes dropped to the narrow basement windows. I turned right on Church Street and rolled slowly past my cousin's house on the corner. Nobody was about. I breathed a sigh of relief. I didn't know whether they still lived there or not. I then drove over to the funeral home to look up at the hill I had first learned to race a bike down. I pulled into the entrance, drove slowly past the building and into the rear parking lot where I had collided with the car. A hearse was parked in the same spot. The ancient buckeye grove still stood at the bottom of the hill.

I turned around and pulled out into the street leading toward the center of the village. I rolled a short distance before I became nervous and pulled over to the curb. I had planned on spending the night and waiting until around noon the next day but I was worried I'd lose courage unless I did it right then. The village was even smaller than I'd remembered it as a child. Within a few minutes I had already covered the places that had loomed so large in my life. I was no longer certain it would help to stay overnight and immerse myself as I had planned.

I reached down to the floor of the passenger seat and picked up the plastic box. Each time I had touched it I was surprised by its weight, its density – it was heavy, like an iron brick. On the sidewalk, I cradled the urn in the crook of my left arm and strode along. I stepped gingerly over the tree roots that had raised the slabs and opened cracks just as I had done many times before to keep from tripping – the exact same stones I had walked along in my youth.

I went past the stores lining the street, the shoe store where my mother had bought my first pair of shoes, the hardware store where I had picked up my first hammer, the drugstore where I had bought the pen my father had recently given back to me, but I tried not to look too deeply into any of them. I didn't want to pause or absorb the past any more than I'd already done. I reached the bridge, crossed to the center of the span and stopped above the river. Traffic whooshed back and forth in each direction behind me. Only a single other person was crossing on my side, a businesswoman carrying a briefcase, walking briskly. I nodded as she passed.

I looked across the traffic at the upper falls, with its even lip of water spilling into the flat section of river that passed beneath the bridge before reaching the second set of falls. I turned and looked at the lower falls. Its jagged lip fell sharply into the wide river below, creating a thunderous roar as a light mist brushed my face.

I opened the lid of the container, peered at the ash and bone

529

fragments of my father, then slowly poured them into the river. Small chunks of bones fell quickly, plopping into the water before being carried over the falls, followed by the ash – the finest caught the wind and disappeared into the air before reaching the water below. When I finished I was about to drop the plastic urn but stopped myself and looked around for a trash can. A group of tourists were standing near the only one in sight beside the Popcorn Shop. I didn't want to interact with anyone. I didn't want to smile or talk and I didn't feel right tossing the container into the trash anyway since it still contained the residue of my father. I looked back at the rushing current and let the plastic urn tumble into the river. I didn't care what anyone thought. This was my hometown. The place in which I had entered the world.

I then reached into the bottom of my pocket and grabbed it firmly, letting my hand warm its metal surface before pulling it slowly out of my pocket, clenched tightly in my fist, which I held out in front of me, over the railing. I thought momentarily about my mother. In the back of my mind, as childish as it seemed, I still clung to the hope that one day she would be proud of me or of something I did. I held my hand like that until it began to tire, then opened my clenched fist and released it, just as my grandfather had released it into my father's hand and my father had released it into mine. I watched the small, tarnished Iron Cross my grandfather had been awarded after losing his leg at the battle of Tannenberg tumble downward until it, too, made a tiny splash and disappeared over the falls as the Chagrin River carried it away.

I walked across the street and up through the park and sat there for a couple of hours. Across the river I saw a window of the office where the dentist had filled my teeth. Even the area where I sat was full of memories – I recalled running through the park during Blossom Time Festival. I turned and looked at the pond I had skated across with my mother. It was impossible to silence my mind completely.

Eventually I walked back into town to call my old sponsor. I didn't want to let my mind linger in Chagrin. I went into a store and asked to exchange a ten-dollar bill for a roll of quarters, hoping nobody would recognize me. It seemed absurd that anyone would, but you never knew, especially when you'd spent the first part of your life in a place that they had never left. In some ways I wished I could have changed places with them, although I couldn't fathom what such stability might feel like.

I found a payphone on Main Street. At least the phone itself was no longer the rotary dial that I remembered. I filled it with quarters and dialed the number to the bike shop that I'd memorized long ago. As always, Craig answered and, also as always, once he'd recognized my voice, his reply wasn't exactly Southern Genteel: 'Where the fuck you been?'

'Don't ask.'

'They just called four days ago.'

'Who?'

'OTC.'

'About what?'

'They've got an empty slot on the short team heading for the Peace Race in a few weeks. Their first pick got popped for doping. He's out. They want to put you in his place to see what you can do in international competition.'

'You shitting me?'

'More like you're shitting yourself. They wanted to know how your form was.'

'What'd you tell them?'

'That you're flying – I've never seen you stronger.'

'We haven't spoken in a couple of months.'

'So what? I knew you'd call once you stopped crying about not making the cut. You'd better not have made a liar out of me. You been riding?'

'A little. Doing some time-trials down the coast and a few hill repeats.'

'Where are you?'

'I'll explain later.'

531

'You need to get your ass back here so we can do some back-to-back hundred-milers pronto to get you ready. How long will it take you to get here?'

'I'm not sure. I left my bike in California.'

'I thought you just said you're on the coast?'

'I was, but—'

'Man, when are you going to drop someplace and call it home? I got another bike you can use. Get down here ASAP.'

'But my van—'

'I don't want to hear your whining. I got work to do. See you tomorrow or the next day at the latest. I'll be waiting.'

He hung up without even letting me thank him. I had no idea what to do. Fly back to California and get my van? Drive the rental car south that night? Try to find a flight to South Carolina in the morning? It was the sort of problem I had been waiting my entire life for. I felt like laughing and crying at the same time. I stood there for a moment holding the phone in my hand like an idiot. I slammed it back down and yelled out, 'I'm going to Poland.'

Everyone in the vicinity stopped to see what the commotion was about. I clapped my hands and broke into a run up Franklin Street to get my car, which was still near the funeral home. I came back through town trying to obey the speed limit as much as possible. I was heading home. So much for escaping the South. That old southern capitol was about to deliver me to Warsaw. I crossed the bridge and glanced at the spot where I had been standing earlier. When I reached the left-hand turn to take me out of town, I punched the gas so hard the tires squealed and the car fishtailed slightly through the intersection. I was on my way to Europe. I was on my way home.

Epilogue

Almost twenty years later I was in the South traveling on business. I had some meetings in Charlotte, North Carolina that turned out to be less productive than I had hoped. On the last day of meetings, I slipped out early, rented a car and drove down to Augusta. Many of those memories still haunted me. I traveled there on back roads and entered town on the old highway I used to train on. The road had been widened. The tight shoulders that trucks used to brush past me on, the dips and rises in its surface, the ravines along the roadside and sharp curves around old farms and houses were gone. It had been transformed into a smooth, flat highway. When I reached Fire Tower Road I turned off. The road was still rough but the fire tower had been dismantled and carried away. Back on the highway, the hill descending to the bridge crossing the Savannah River wasn't as steep a climb as I remembered.

I parked the car before entering Georgia and walked into the woods and eventually found what little remained of the old two-lane blacktop of the original highway. Time had eroded it, the pavement was cracked – weeds, bushes and trees had sprouted up through the surface on which I had once raced. So little of the original road remained that unless you knew exactly where to look it was difficult to find beneath the overgrowth.

I drove west to Washington Road and turned off on the side street to see the area where the old farmhouse had stood in which I had lived with my brother. I descended the hill to the stop sign at the railroad tracks. The narrow road that once turned left just over the tracks and the dirt lane that had climbed to the farmhouse were gone. In front of me stood a massive four-lane expressway connecting traffic from the booming suburbs out in Martinez to downtown Augusta. Where the stables and house had stood at the top of the hill, giant earth-movers – graders – were passing back and forth, leveling the rolling hills and meadows that my brother and I used to walk across to reach the canal and river. Down near where we once entered the woods in the lower meadow stood a manufacturing plant or warehouse of some sort. I didn't bother to get out of the car to investigate further. Instead, I continued across town to Augusta College.

All those years later I had finally been admitted – ironically, in the year that the American General Schwarzkopf had led the Coalition Forces into Kuwait to defeat Iraq – to a university in California and later another in Europe. I wanted to take a look at the place my college career had started. Its name had been changed to Augusta State University. The old brick buildings that once stood in rows throughout the campus had been torn down and replaced with modern steel structures. I hardly recognized the place. New buildings blocked the road that had passed through the center. I finally made my way around them to where the old quadrangle – the arsenal that General Sherman had once stayed in – still housed the administrative buildings. I walked inside the old fort, along its loop-hole fortification walls, and peered through the slots for the soldiers to slide their muskets through, then looked back at the buildings I used to clean – the first stable job I ever held. Students swarmed out of a classroom to their cars in an adjacent parking lot. All that time later I still saw only a handful of black students in the crowd. I guess you can't expect everything to change. In recent years I had become less inclined myself to reach out to others.

While completing my undergraduate degree, I took every ethnic studies class I could find – Chicano Studies, Asian-American Studies, African-American Studies – and, with few exceptions, every time I raised my hand in class to talk about my own ethnic conflicts in relation to their struggles, I was shut down by a barrage of verbal

534

assaults by students a year or two out of high school who were far more articulate than I could ever hope to be.

'Whites aren't ethnic!'

'You'll never understand what it truly means to struggle!'

'You were raised in the dominant paradigm!'

I remember one time in casual conversation after class I had asked a Chinese-American woman, who had given a presentation about arriving in America when she was fourteen, if she had come by ship. She had exploded, 'You think all Asians are Boat People?' and threatened to file a formal complaint against me for making a racially insensitive statement. At first I thought she was joking, but the look on her face told me she wasn't so I apologized. The only thing I had been thinking about when I asked her was my father's journey to America by ship.

I didn't stop enrolling in ethnic-studies classes, but by my second year in college I had stopped contributing to class discussions. I listened to lectures with genuine interest and respect and wrote papers mimicking the young professors' lectures. I was usually one of three or four whites who sat silently through those large classes. I was still struggling to understand myself, but there wasn't a single class that studied German-Americans, either on campus or anywhere else within the state's public college system, which encompassed 110 community colleges, twenty-three state universities and ten research universities – the largest three-tier feeder system of higher education in the world and the reason I had returned to California. But make no mistake: I was less interested in making known or sharing facts about German-Americans than curious as to how many other subjects – in a nation with some of the most prestigious universities on earth whose campuses championed free speech – went unspoken.

I had long ago come to understand that the world would carry on with or without whatever knowledge we held individually as quintessential to our separate identities. At the university I observed that by clinging to that knowledge we were often pushed farther from one another, instead of bonding, connecting and finding the

535

empathy we had hoped for. After graduating, I continued moving from one place to the next. I added every kind of job imaginable to my resumé.

By the time I was in my mid-forties I had lived in sixty different places, slept in well over a thousand different beds, wandered across thirty countries and called three different continents home – through birth, descent and marriage. I never did learn why, to be considered authentic, you had to belong to a state, nation, religion, ethnicity or sexual orientation. Who I was and what I had seen no longer mattered, but I wanted my children to grow up in a world not blinded by preconceptions of identity, not enslaved to histories they were burdened to uphold by their parents, cultures and nations.

As for myself I simply tried to blend as best I could, no matter where we lived – clean cut, wearing anonymous business suits, smiling cordially. In those later years I never did return to my place of birth and I supposed that I never would go back to Chagrin.

Dublin, Ireland – Philipsburg, Montana: 2000–2009

Acknowledgements

Jane Lavonne Keal, Clare Reihill, Hazel Orme, Vernon Felton and Leonard Michaels (1933–2003), under whom I studied writing.